The Engine
Ferrari 365GT/4 BB

Ray Ichiro Fukuno : Text

Yoshifumi Ogawa : Photograph

Hajime Saburi : Translation

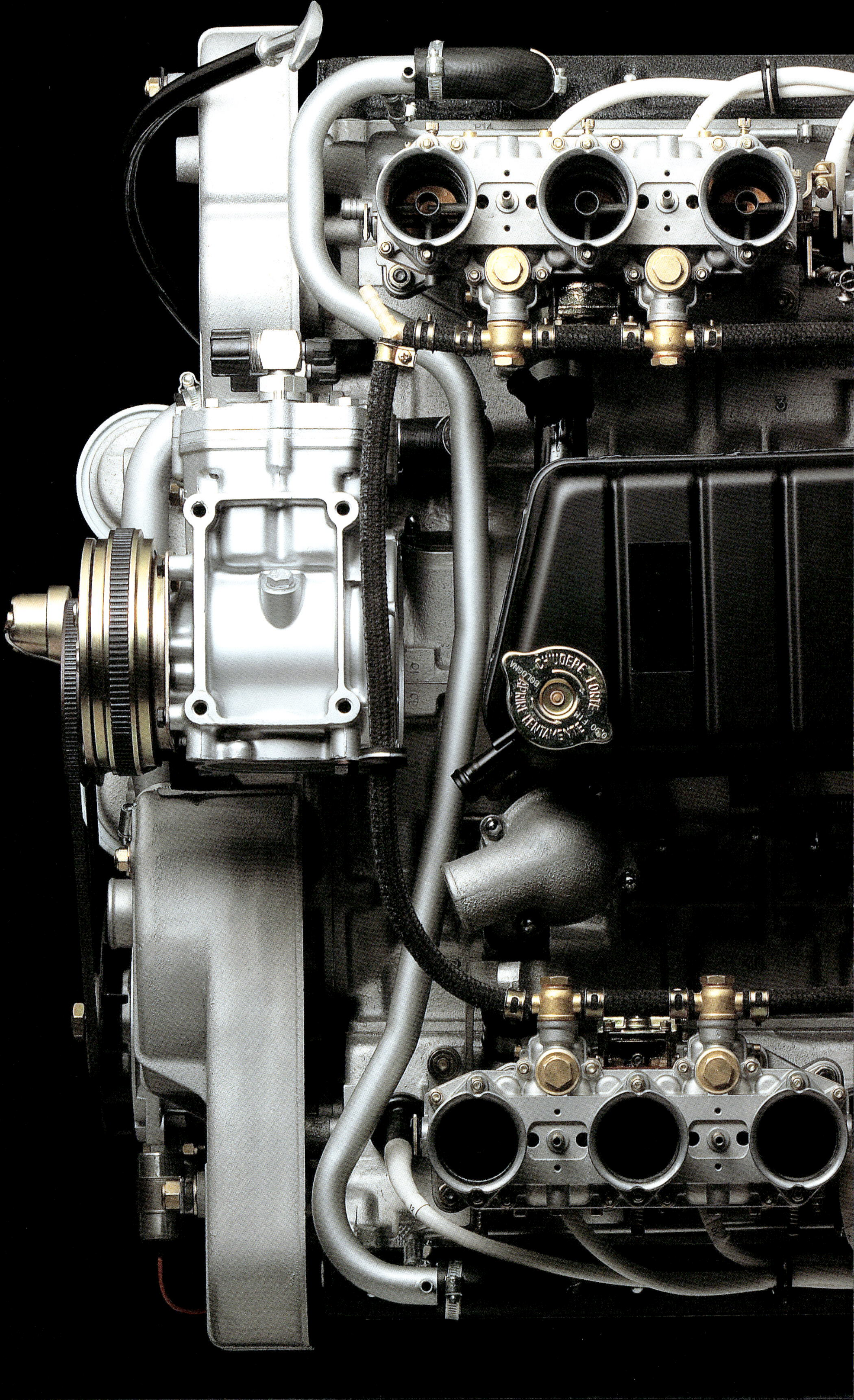
CHIUDERE FORTE
APRIRE LENTAMENTE

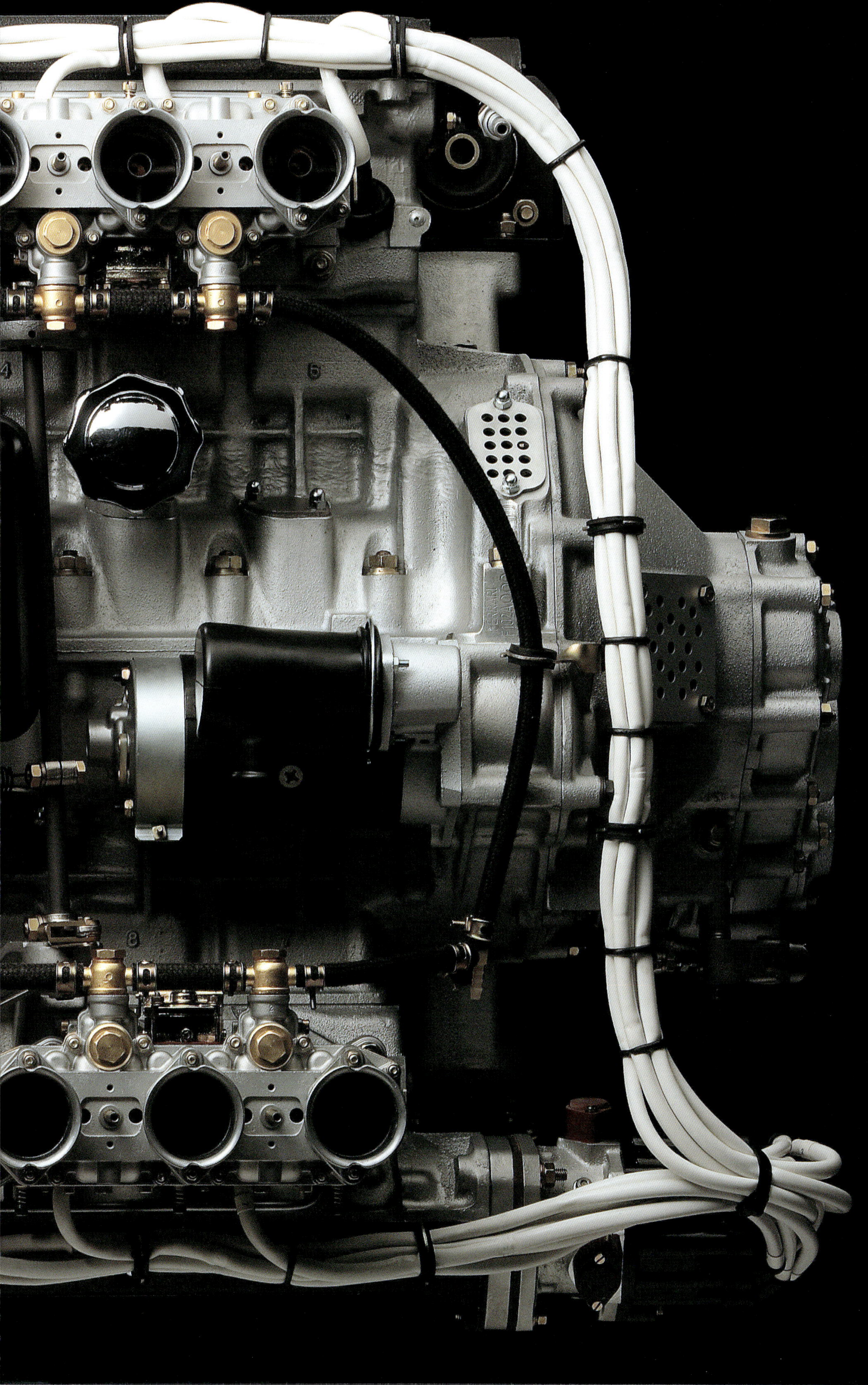

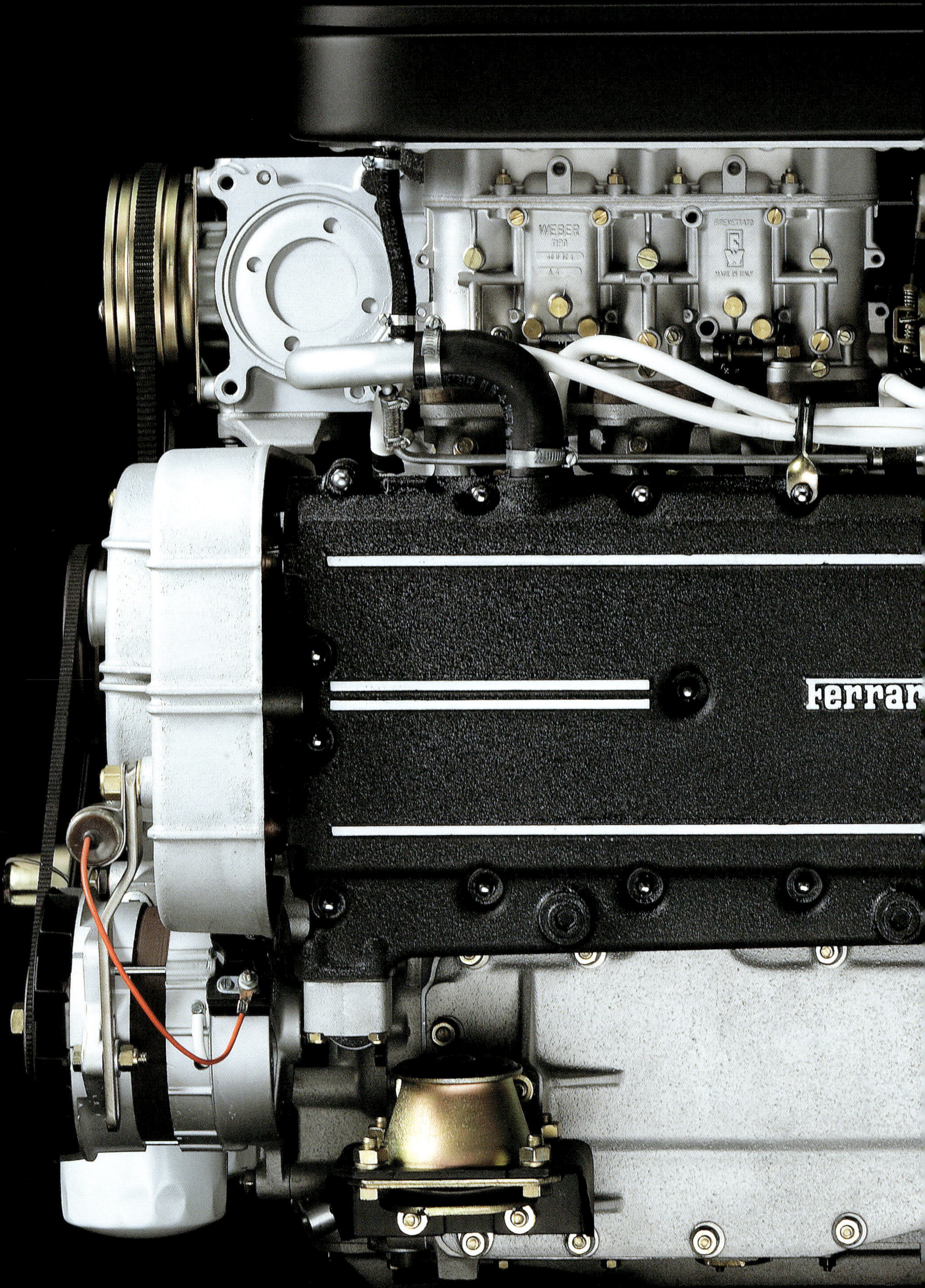
WEBER

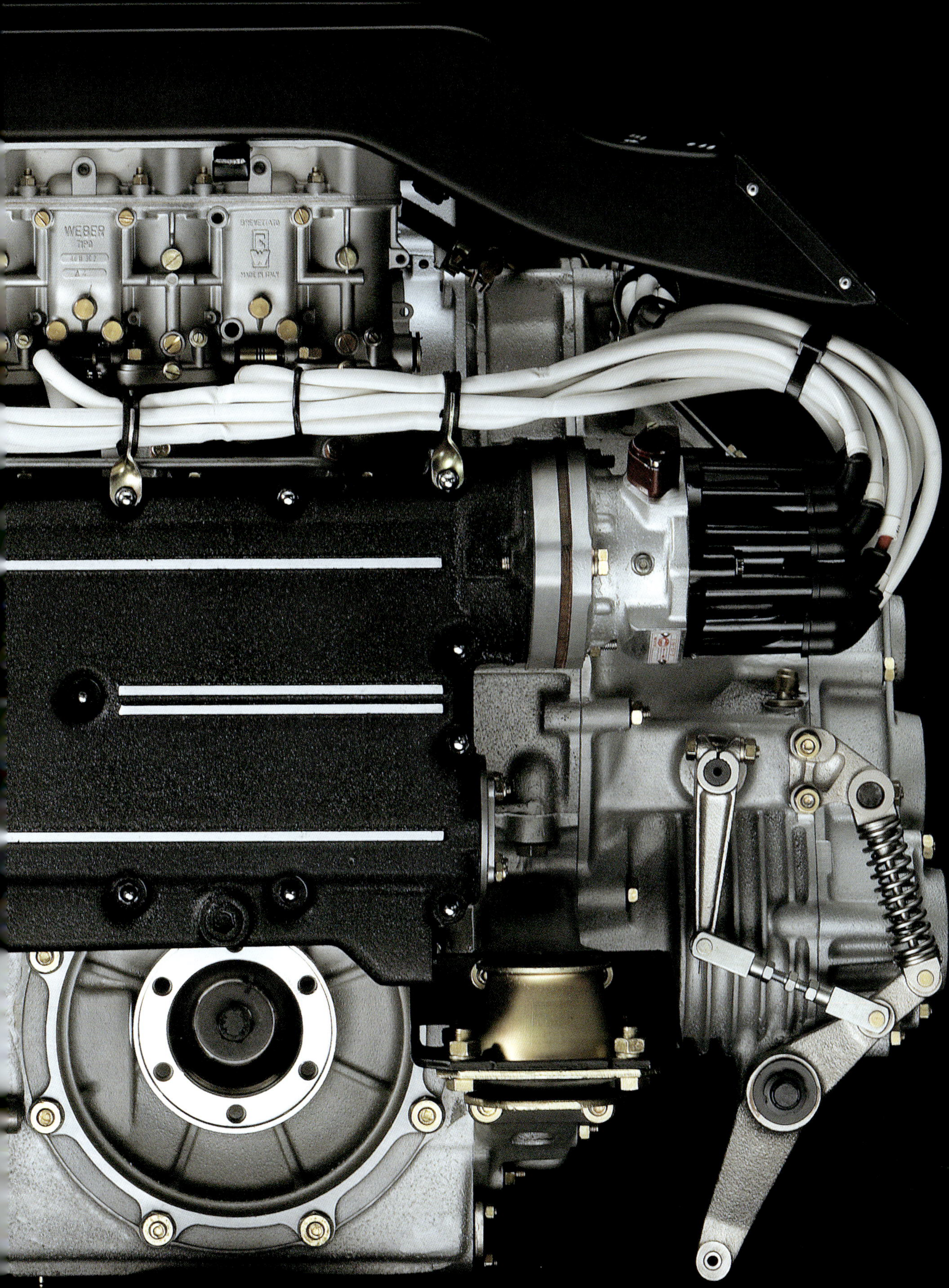
WEBER
TIPO
MADE IN ITALY

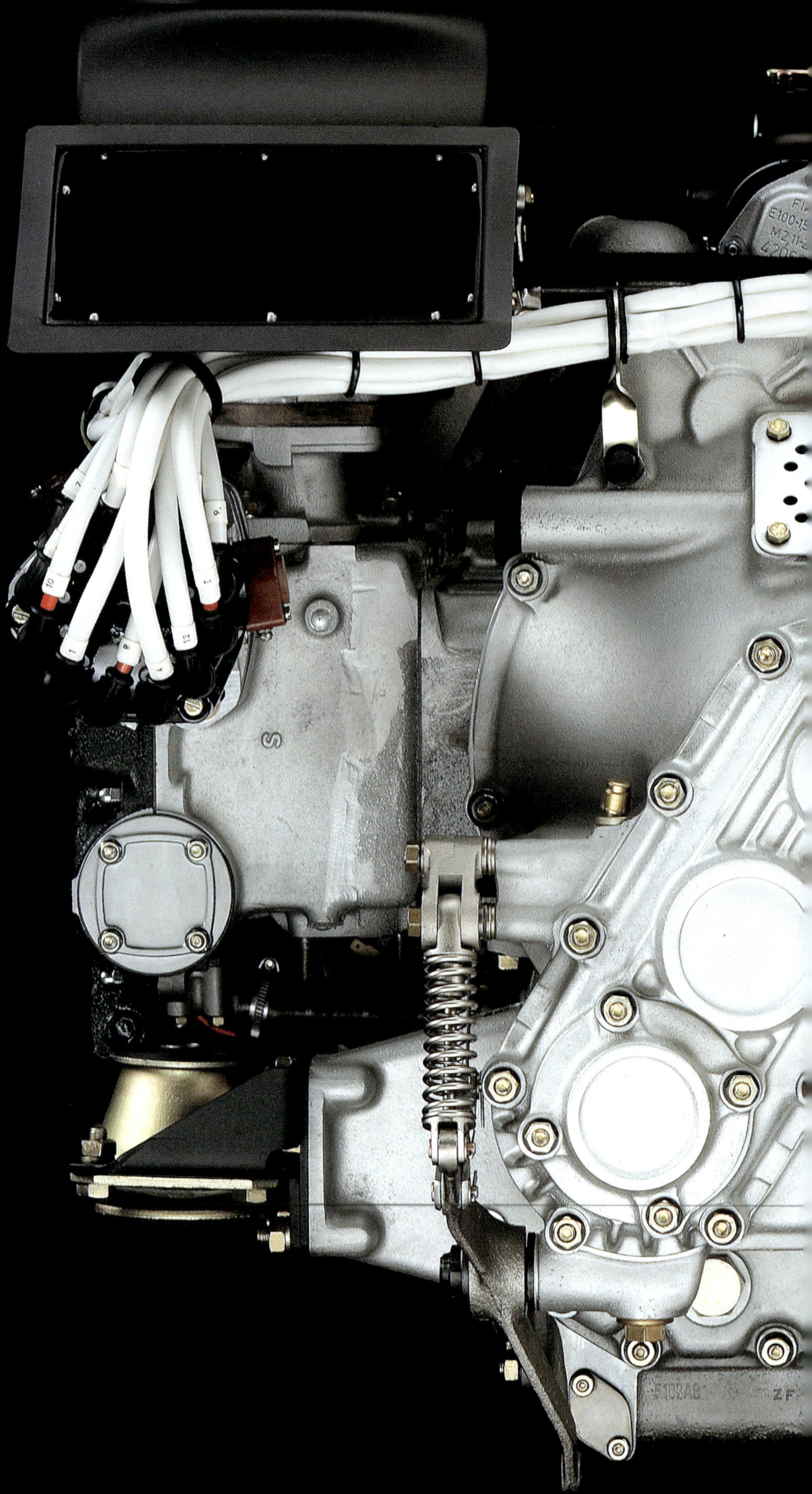

7

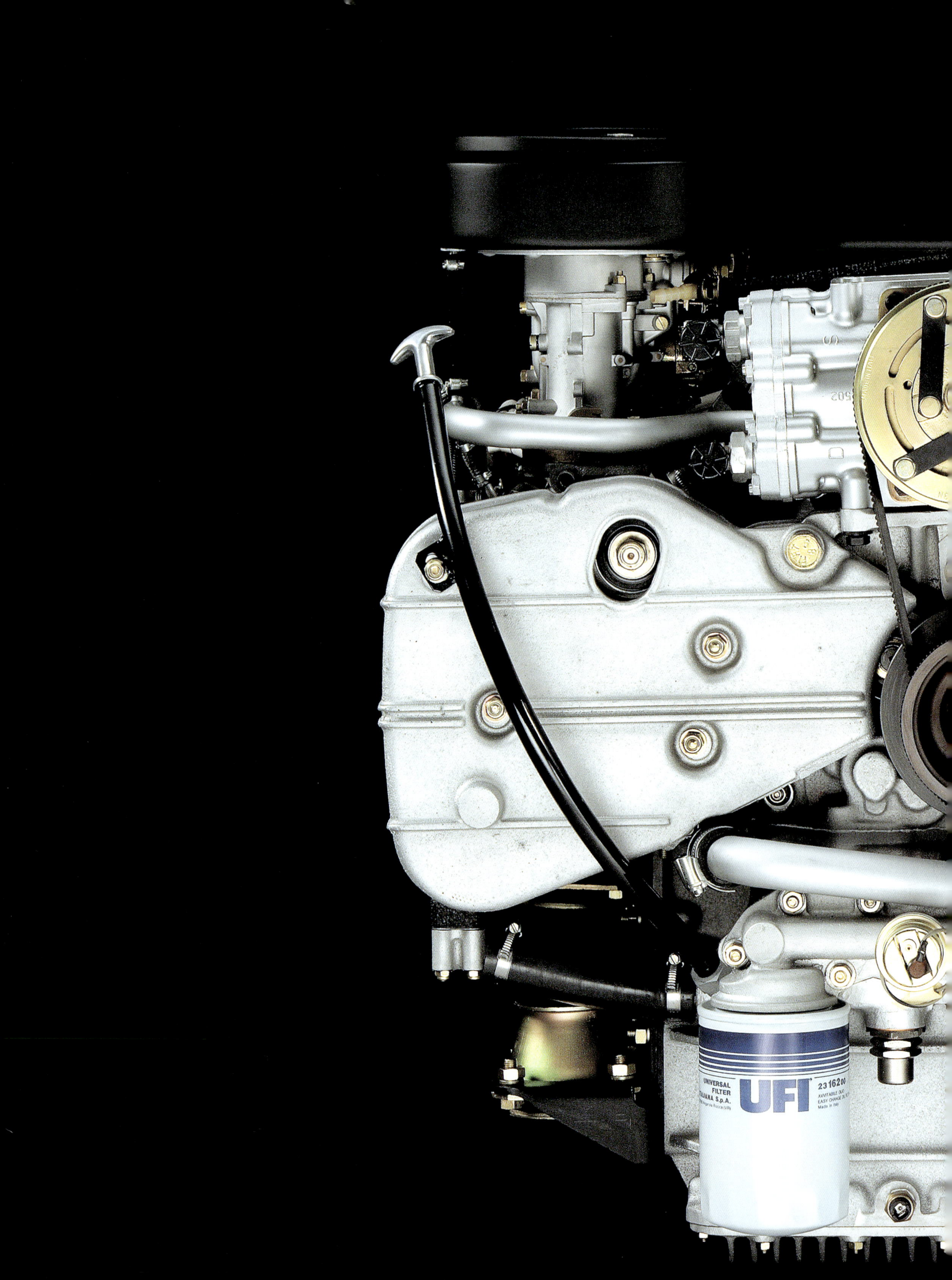
UNIVERSAL
FILTER
UFI

9

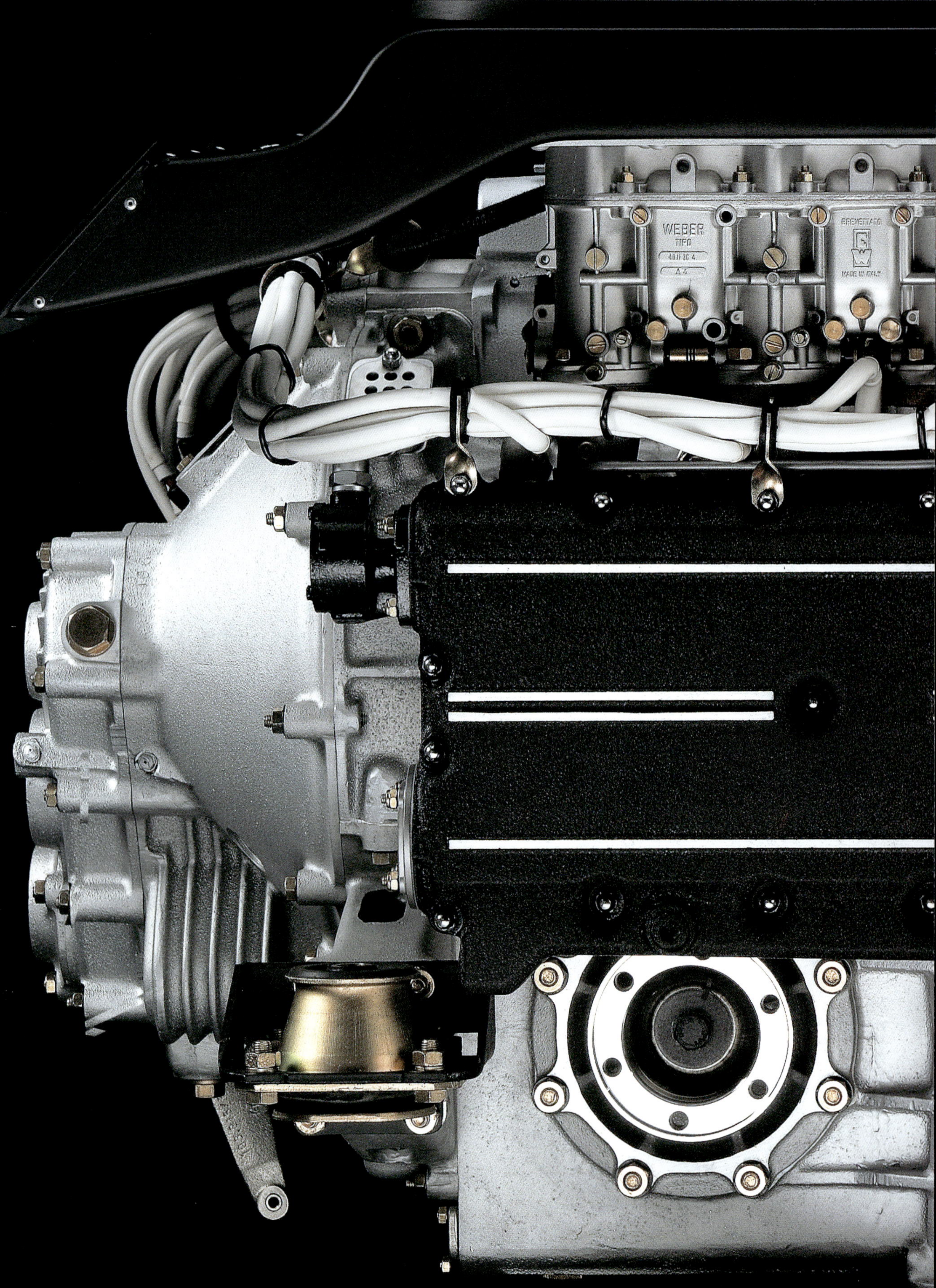
WEBER
TIPO
BREVETTATO

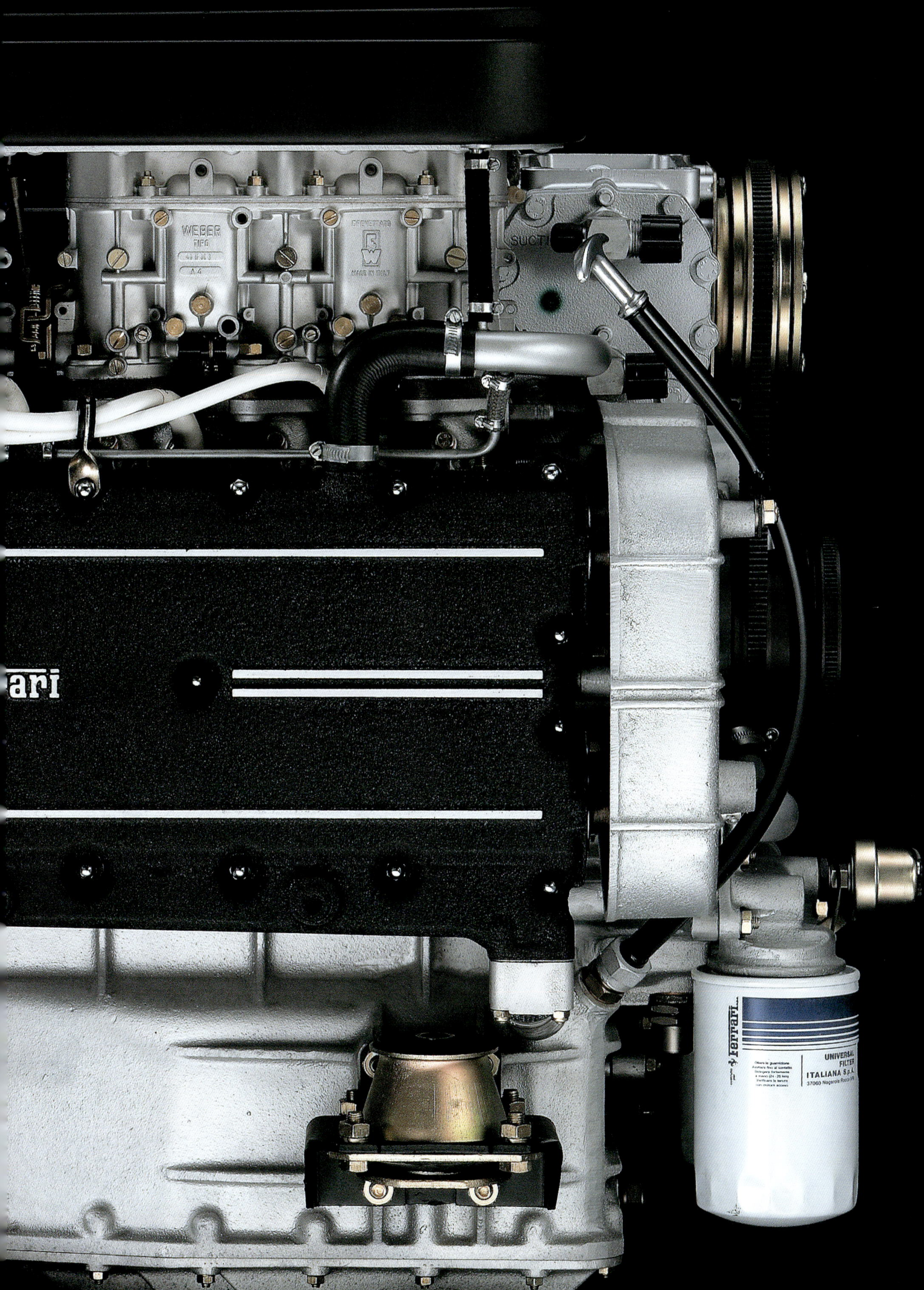
WEBER
ari
UNIVERSAL
FILTER
ITALIANA S.p.A.

The Engine
Ferrari 365GT/4 BB

©2005 Ray Ichiro Fukuno/©2005 Yoshifumi Ogawa

All right reserved. No portion of this book may be reproduced
-mechanically, electronically, or by any means including photocopying-
without prior written permission of the publisher.
October 27th, 2005 First Printing

Text : Ray Ichiro Fukuno
Photographs : Yoshifumi Ogawa
Translation : Hajime Saburi

Editor : Shintaro Watanabe/MPI Corp.
Designer : Toshikazu Sasagawa/Kotobuki Design Co., Ltd.
Graphic Editor : Junpei Fujiwara/Yoshifumi Ogawa Photo Office Co., Ltd.
Contributing Photographer : Ray Ichiro Fukuno, Masayuki Arakawa,Yukio Shirai/Little Garage Corp.,Shouji Nishiyama/MPI Corp.
Special thanks : Kouichiro Furuya/SONNY'S FERRARI, CANON Co., Ltd., PHOTOM Co., Ltd.,
　　　　　　　　Sanwa Plating Industry Co.,Ltd., Katsunao Arai/Stickshift Corp., Trueman S. Fukuno

Publications Director : Takao Watanabe
Publisher : Nigensha Publishing Co., Ltd.
　　　　　　2-2 Kandajimbocho Chiyoda-ku Tokyo 101-8419 Japan
Phone:+81-3-5395-0511

Printed in Japan

2005年10月27日発行

写真：小川義文
解説：福野礼一郎
翻訳：佐分利一

編集：渡辺慎太郎/有限会社エム・ピー・アイ
デザイン：笹川壽一/株式会社 寿デザイン事務所
画像編集：藤原潤平/株式会社 小川義文写真事務所
現場資料写真一部カット写真：福野礼一郎、荒川正幸、白井幸夫/株式会社リトルガレージ、
　　　　　　　　　　　　　　西山昭智/有限会社エム・ピー・アイ
協力：古谷康一郎/有限会社ソニーズ フェラーリ、荒井克尚/有限会社スティックシフト
　　　キャノン株式会社、株式会社フォトム、三和メッキ工業株式会社

発行人：渡邊隆男
発行所：株式会社 二玄社
　　　　〒101-8419東京都千代田区神田神保町2-2
　　　　営業部　東京都文京区本駒込6-2-1
　　　　TEL.03-5395-0511

印刷：共同印刷株式会社

ISBN4-544-40002-3
©2005小川義文/©2005福野礼一郎
無断転載を禁ず

JCLS　（株）日本著作出版権管理システム委託出版物
複写許諾連絡先：Tel.03-3817-5670　Fax.03-3815-8199

CONTENTS 目次

14 写真：個体F102A00000117エンジンおよび同F102AB/ZF/N.85トランスアクスル
Photographs: The Engine #F102A00000117 and The Transaxle #F102AB/ZF/N.85

小川義文
Yoshifumi Ogawa

69 解説：個体F102A00000117エンジンおよび同F102AB/ZF/N.85トランスアクスル
Comments: The Engine #F102A00000117 and The Transaxle #F102AB/ZF/N.85

福野礼一郎
Ray Ichiro Fukuno

- **70** エンジン#F102A00000117搭載車 フェラーリ365GT/4 BB #17903（個体）について
About the Ferrari365GT/4 BB #17903 mounted with the Engine #F102A00000117
- **72** エンジンの分解
Disassembly of the Engine
- **74** アルミ砂型鋳物の生産技術的考察
Study on Production Technology for Aluminum Components made by Sand Castings
- **76** タイプF102A型およびその改良版パワートレーンのF102AB型の設計
Design of Type F102A and its improved Type F102AB Power-Train
- **78** クランクケースの設計仕様
Design Specifications of the Crankcase
- **79** クランクケースの製造仕様
Production Specifications of the Crankcase
- **80** シリンダースリーブのガタつきとクランクシャフトのわん曲
Clattering of Cylinder Sleeve and Curved Crankshaft
- **81** メカニカルレストア
Mechanical Restoration
- **82** コスメティックレストア
Cosmetic Restoration
- **84** クランクシャフトの設計・生産仕様
Design and Production Specifications of the Crankshaft
- **85** クランクシャフトのレストア
Restoration of the Crankshaft
- **86** ピストンおよびコンロッド
Pistons and Conrods
- **90** ヘッドおよびバルブトレーン
Heads and Valve-Train
- **94** カムドライブ
Cam Drive System
- **96** キャブレター
Carburetors
- **100** 冷却系
Cooling System
- **102** 点火系
Ignition System
- **104** スタータモータ
Starter Motor
- **105** オルタネータ
Alternator
- **106** ACコンプレッサ
Air Conditioner
- **108** クラッチ
Clutch
- **110** トランスアクスルおよびギアトレーン
Transaxle and Gear-Train
- **114** ディファレンシャルおよびドライブシャフト
Differential and Driveshaft
- **116** 排気系
Exhaust System
- **118** 小部品および消耗部品
Small Parts and Consumption Parts
- **120** トランスアクスルの組み立て
Assembly of the Transaxle
- **122** エンジンの組み立て
Assembly of the Engine
- **124** スペック
Specifications
- **126** あとがき
Afterword

写真：個体Ｆ102Ａ00000117エンジン および
同Ｆ102AB/ZF/N.85トランスアクスル
Photographs : The Engine #F102A00000117 and The Transaxle #F102AB/ZF/N.85

小川義文
Yoshifumi Ogawa

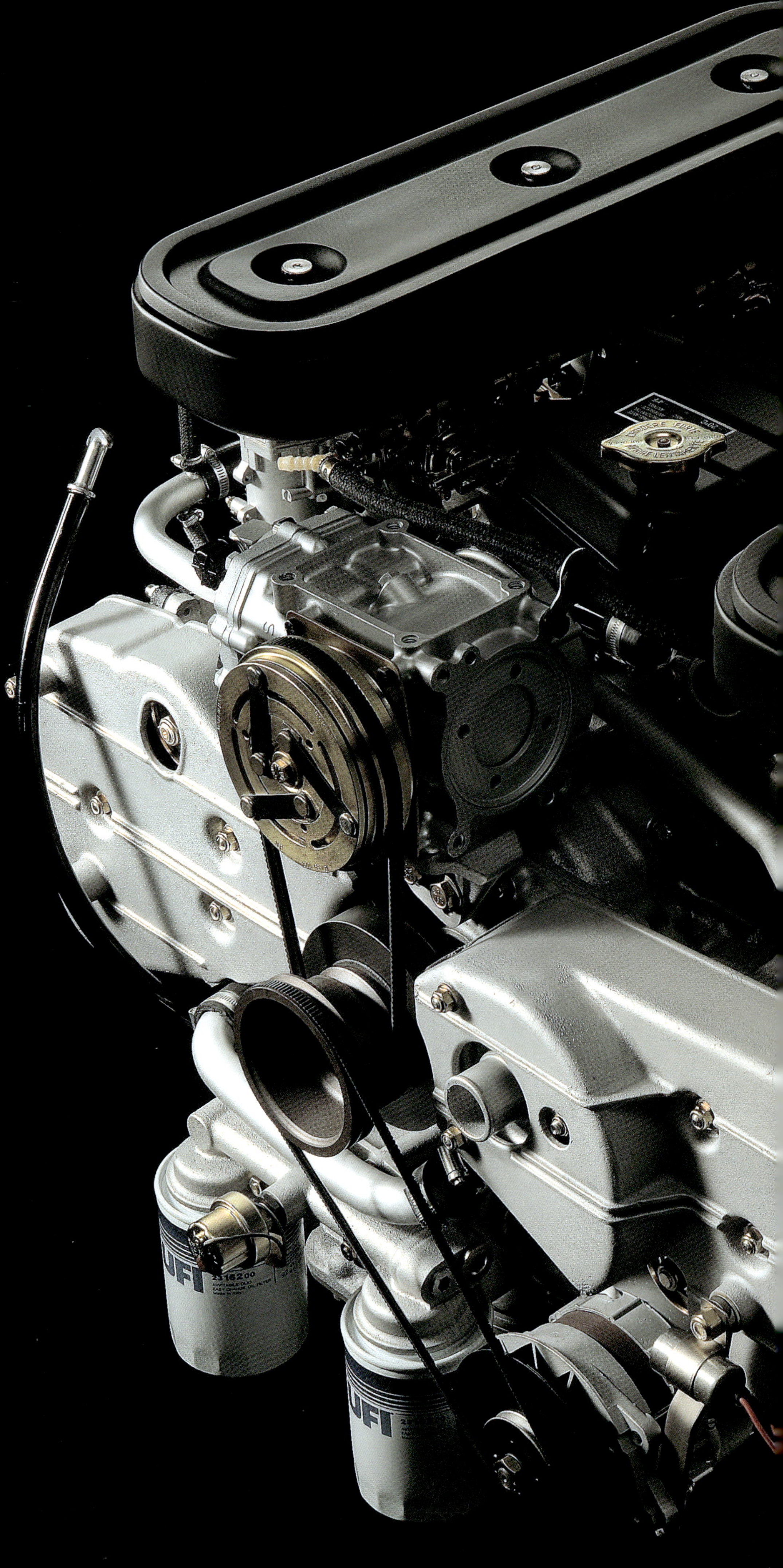
UFI

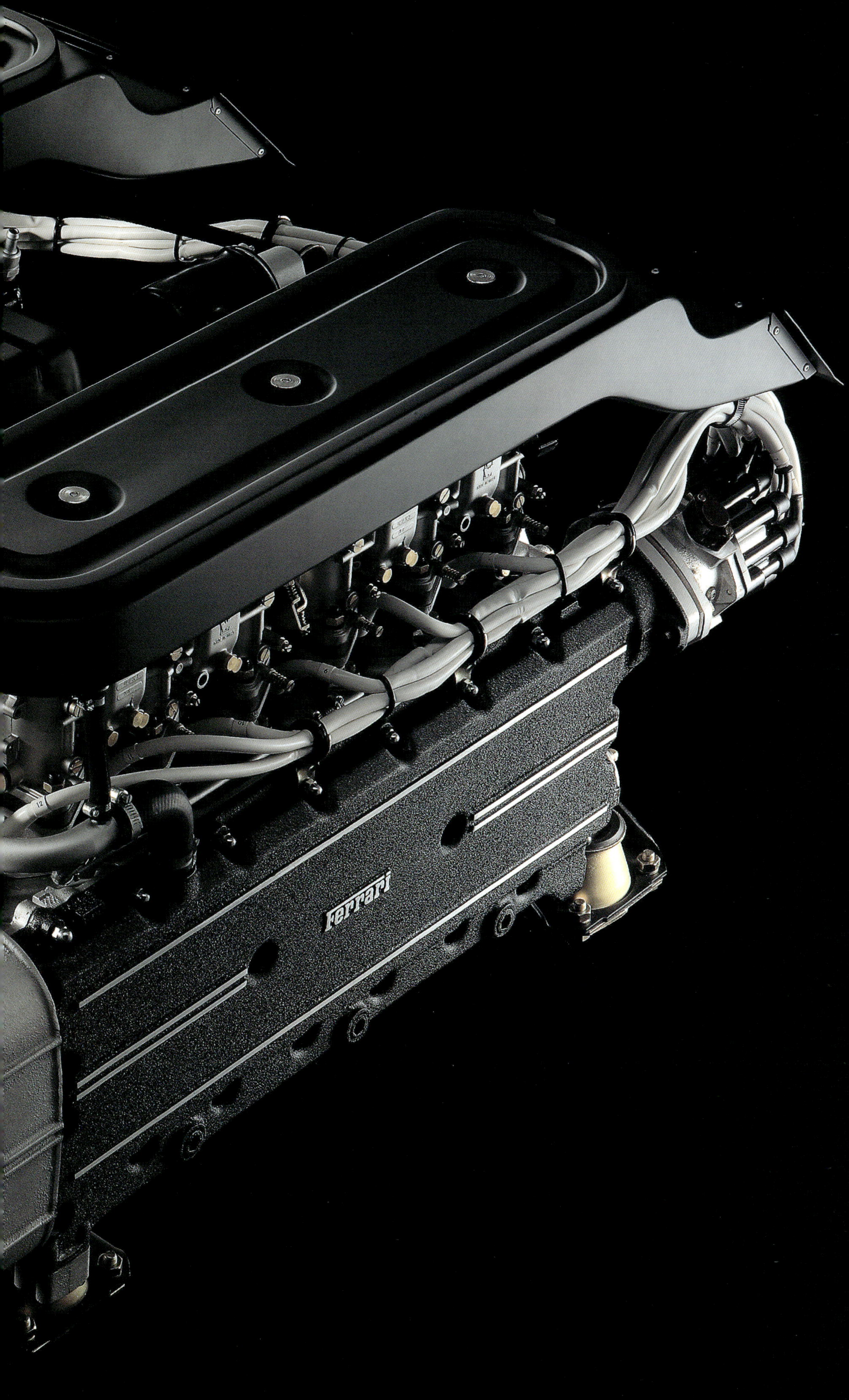
Ferrari

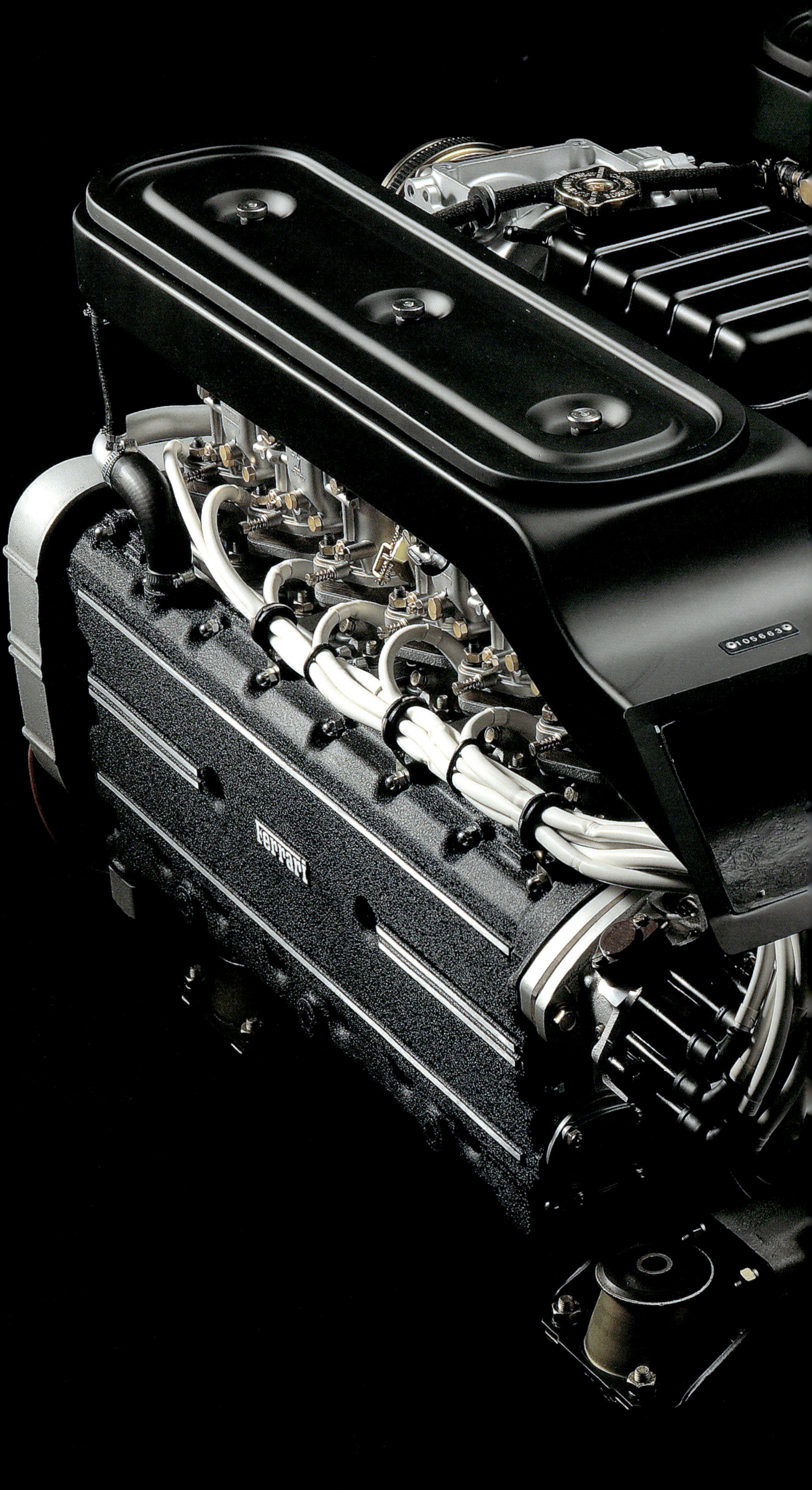
Ferrari

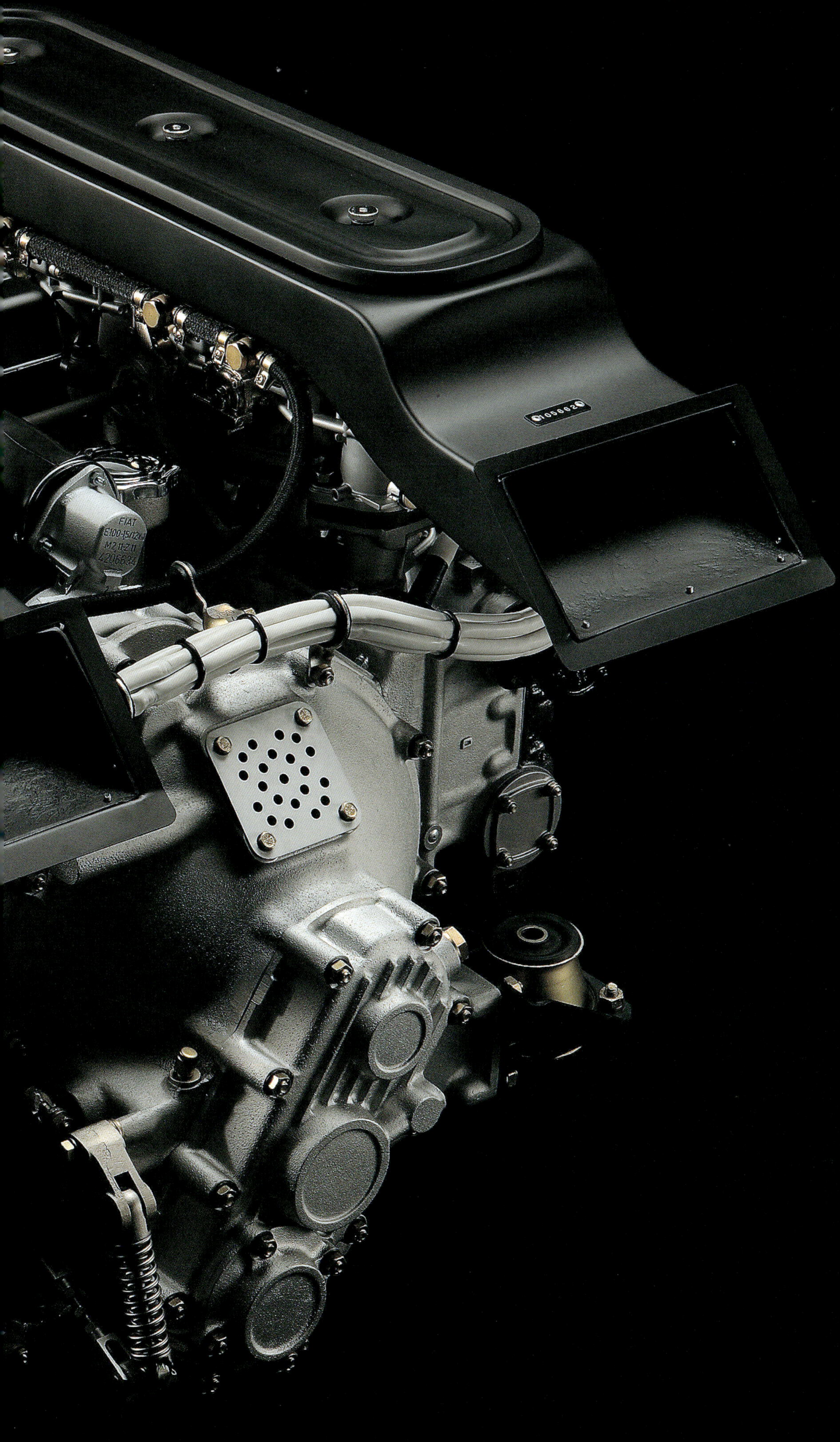
FIAT

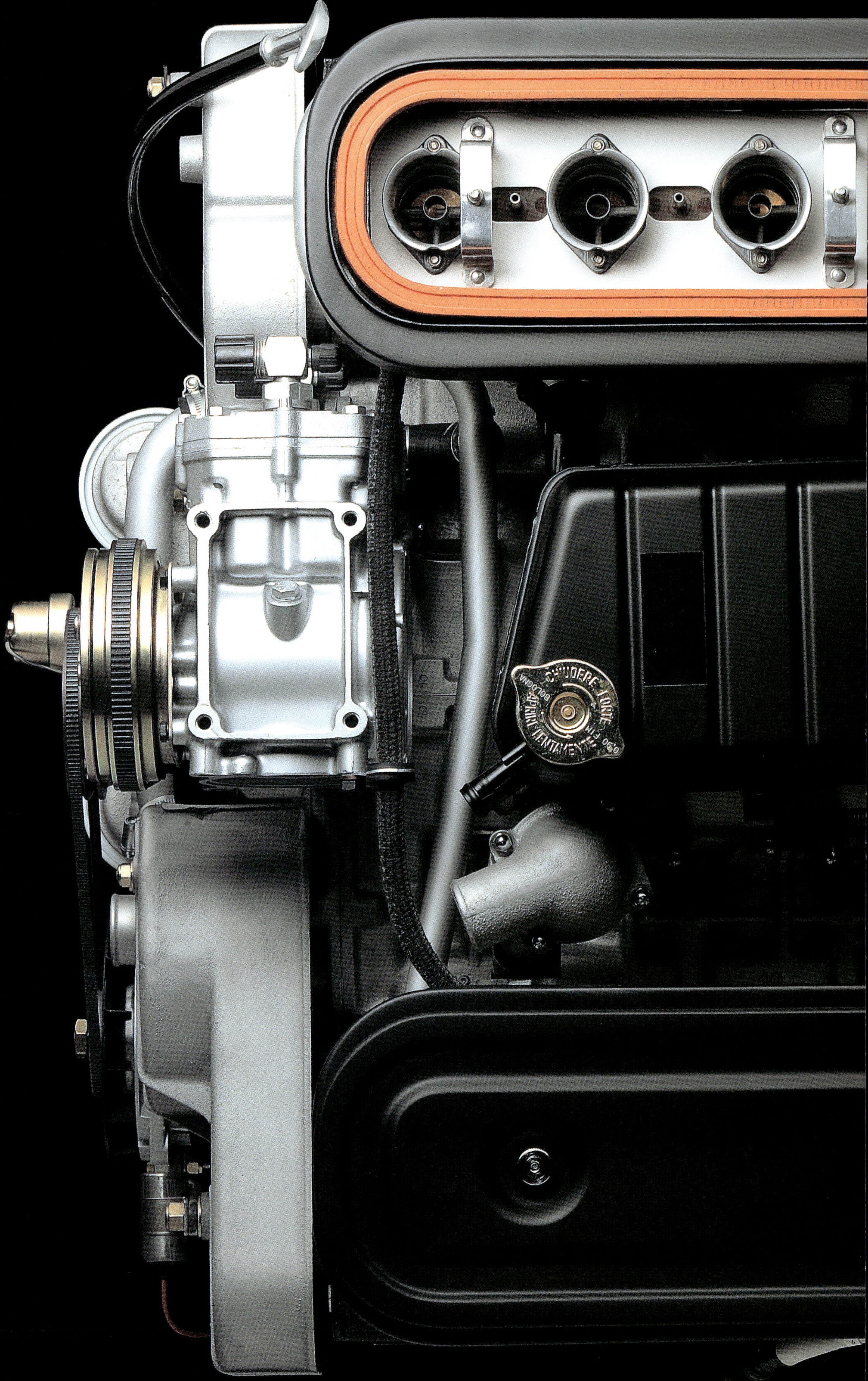

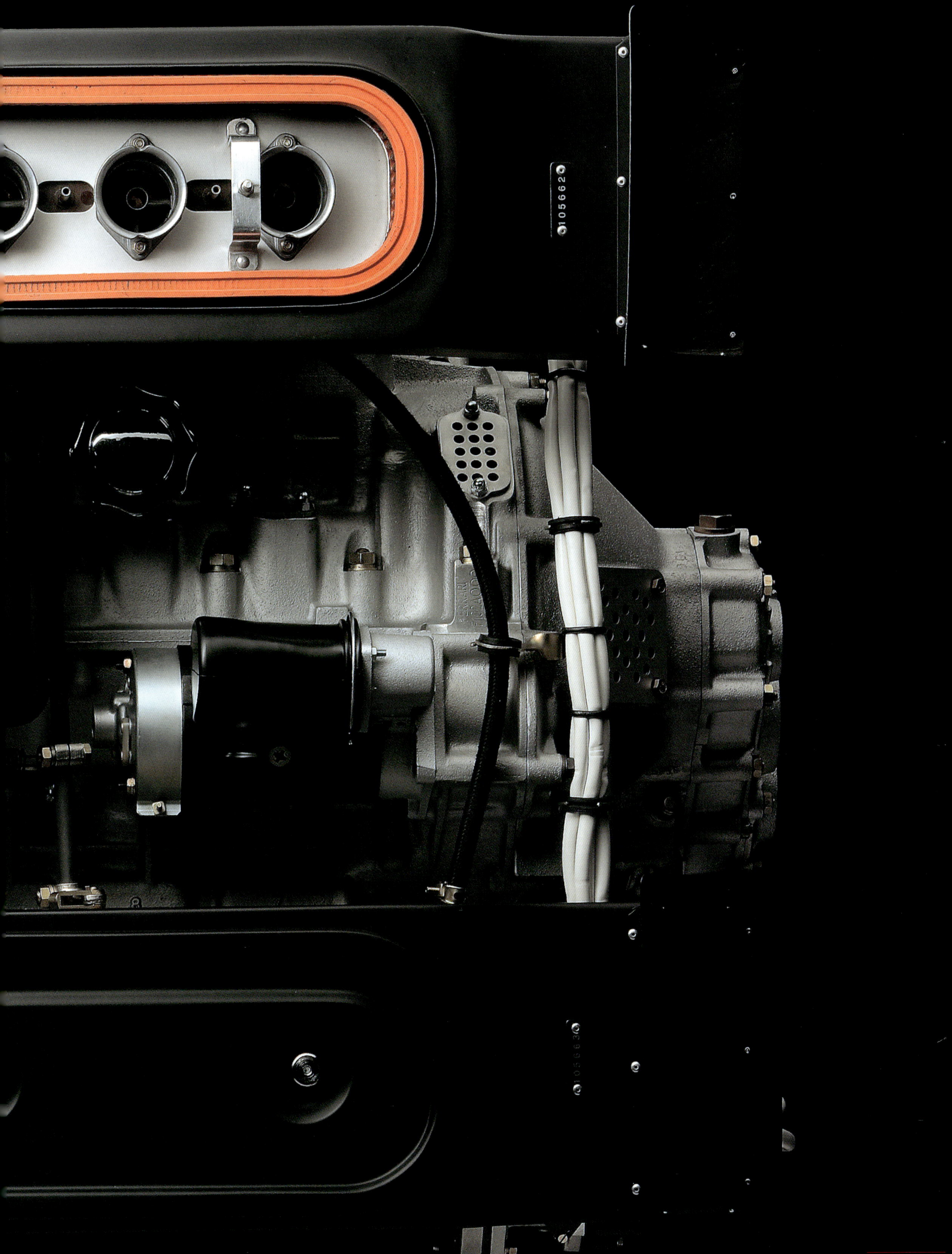
105662
105663

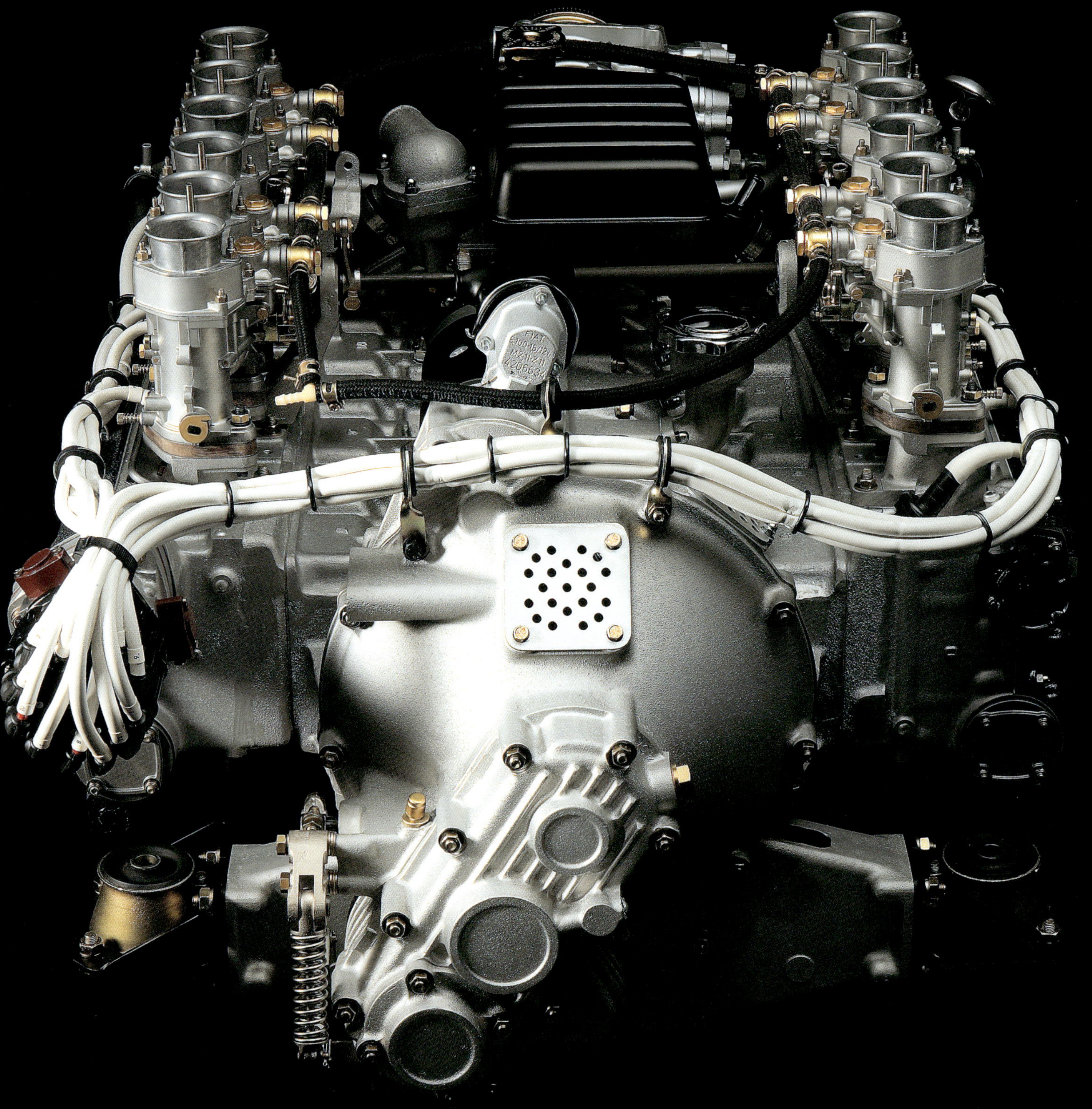

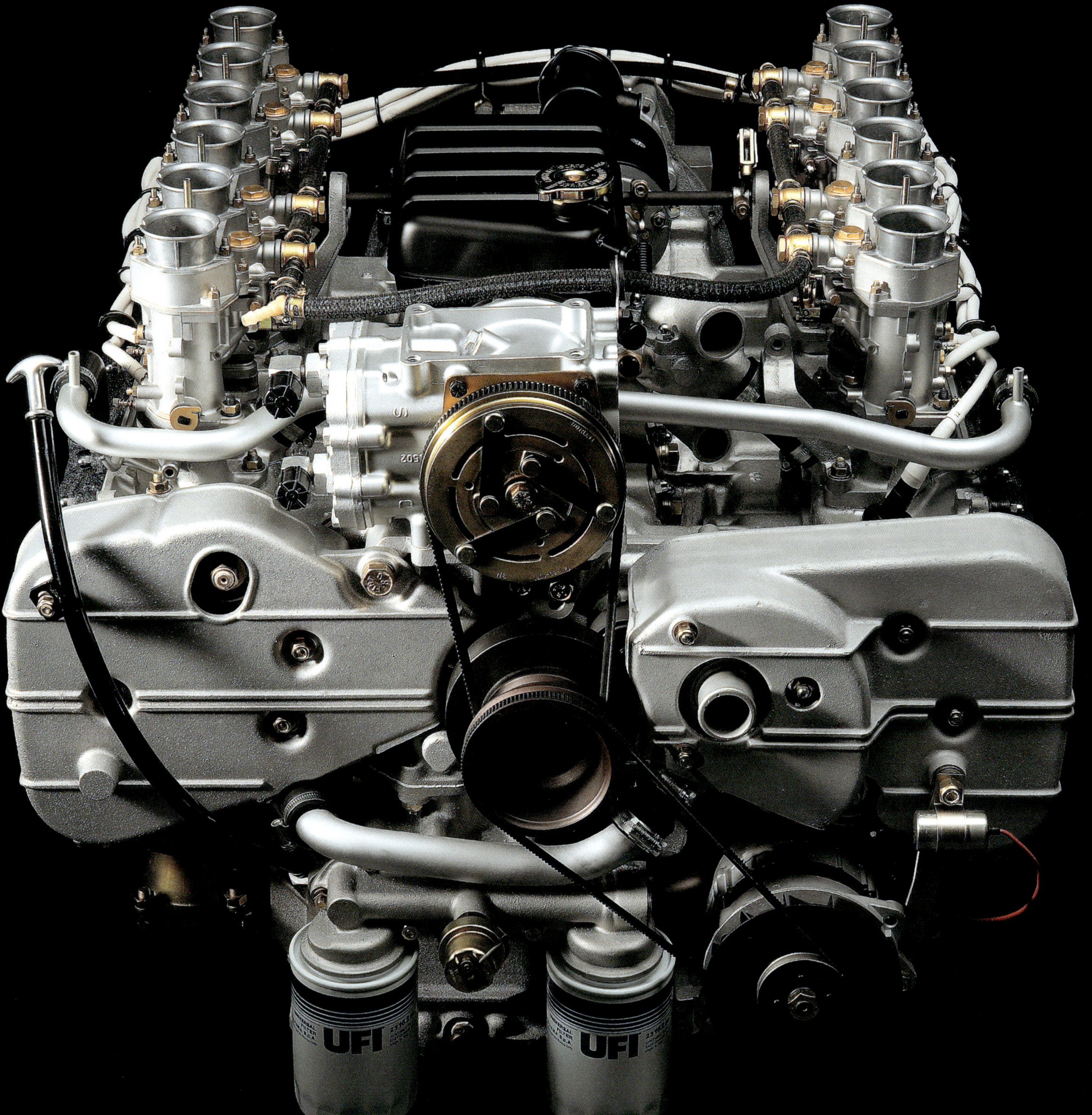
UFI
UFI

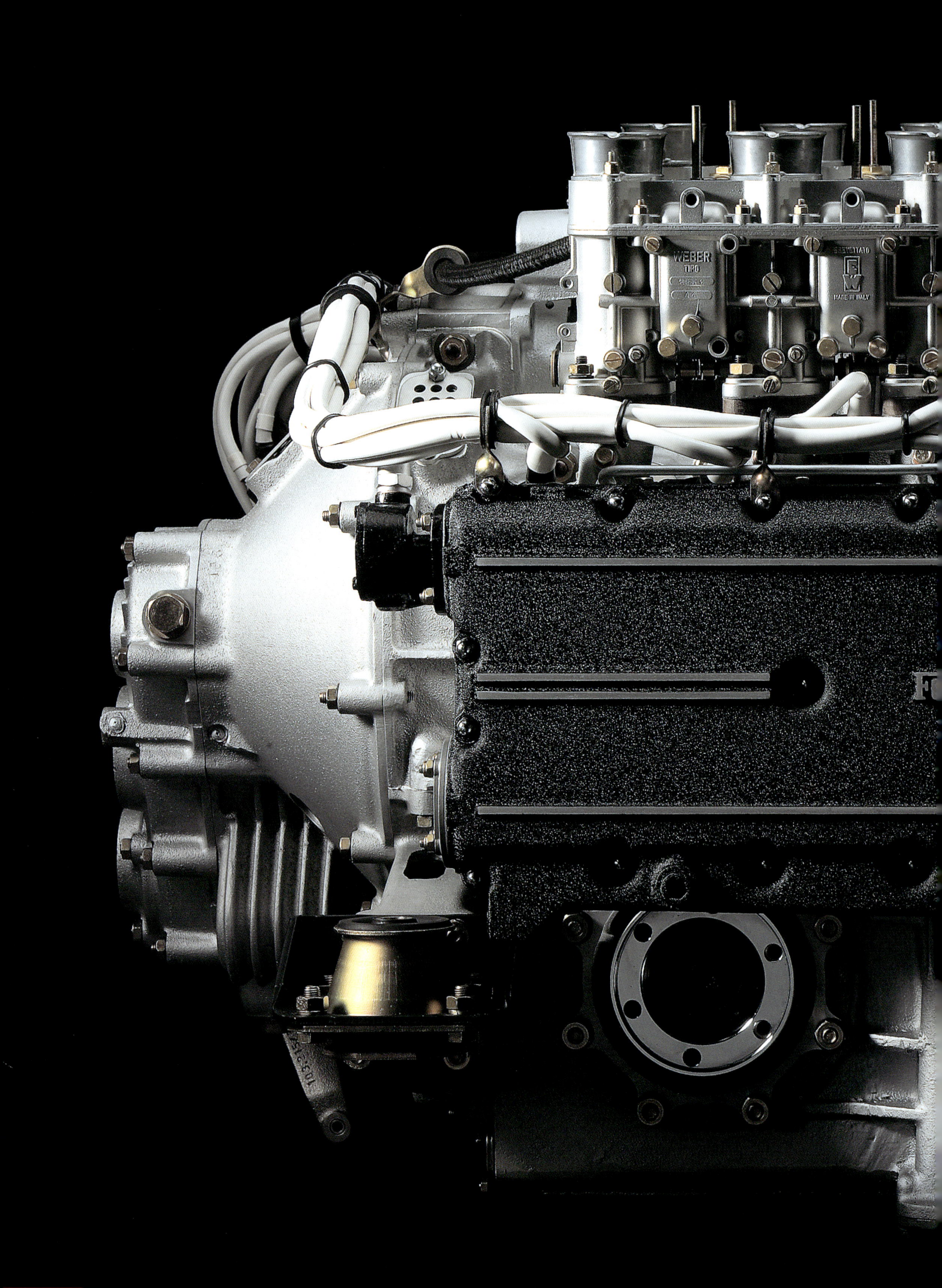
WEBER
TIPO

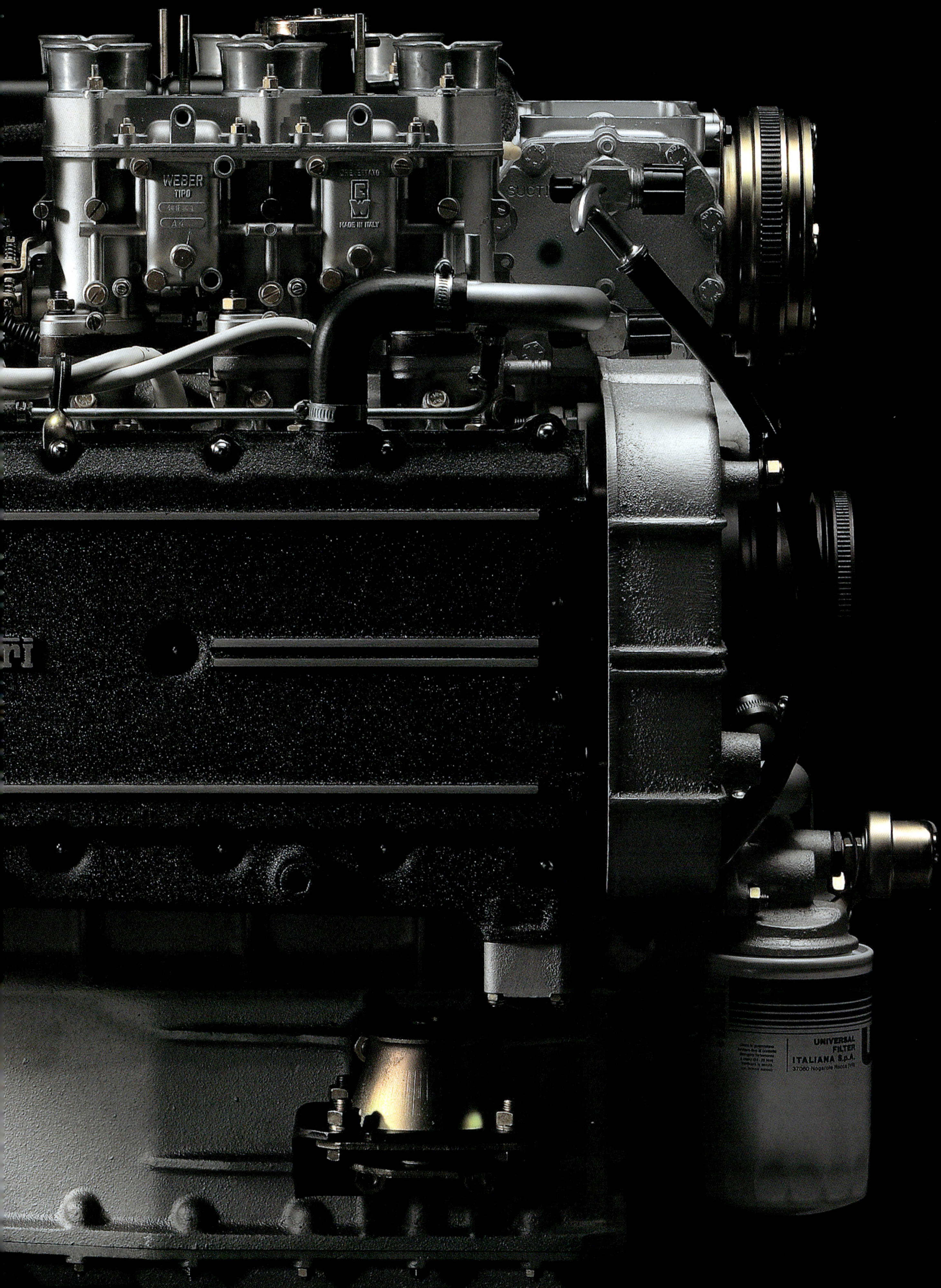
WEBER
TIPO
MADE IN ITALY
UNIVERSAL FILTER
ITALIANA S.p.A.

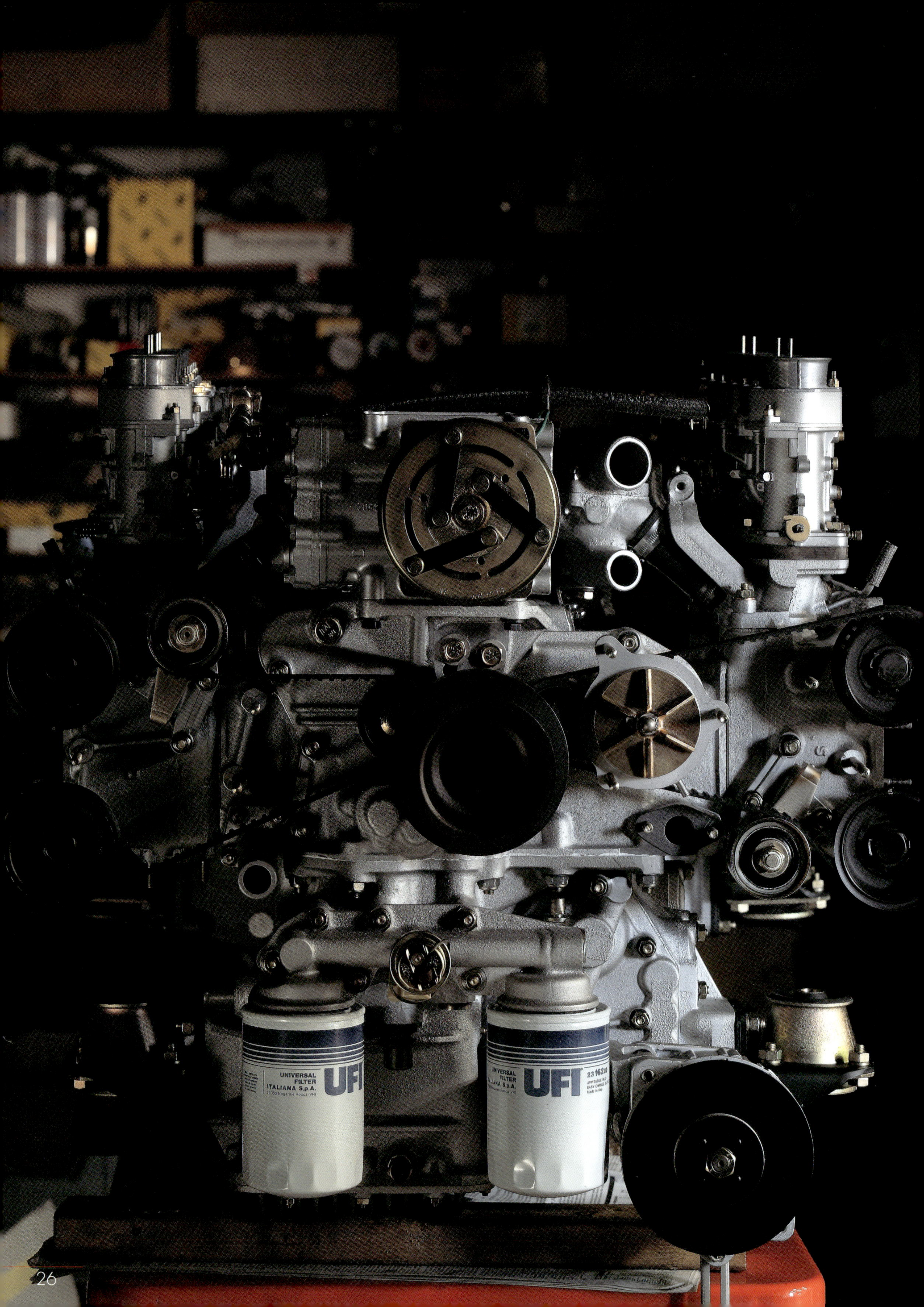
UNIVERSAL FILTER ITALIANA S.p.A.
UFI
UFI

27

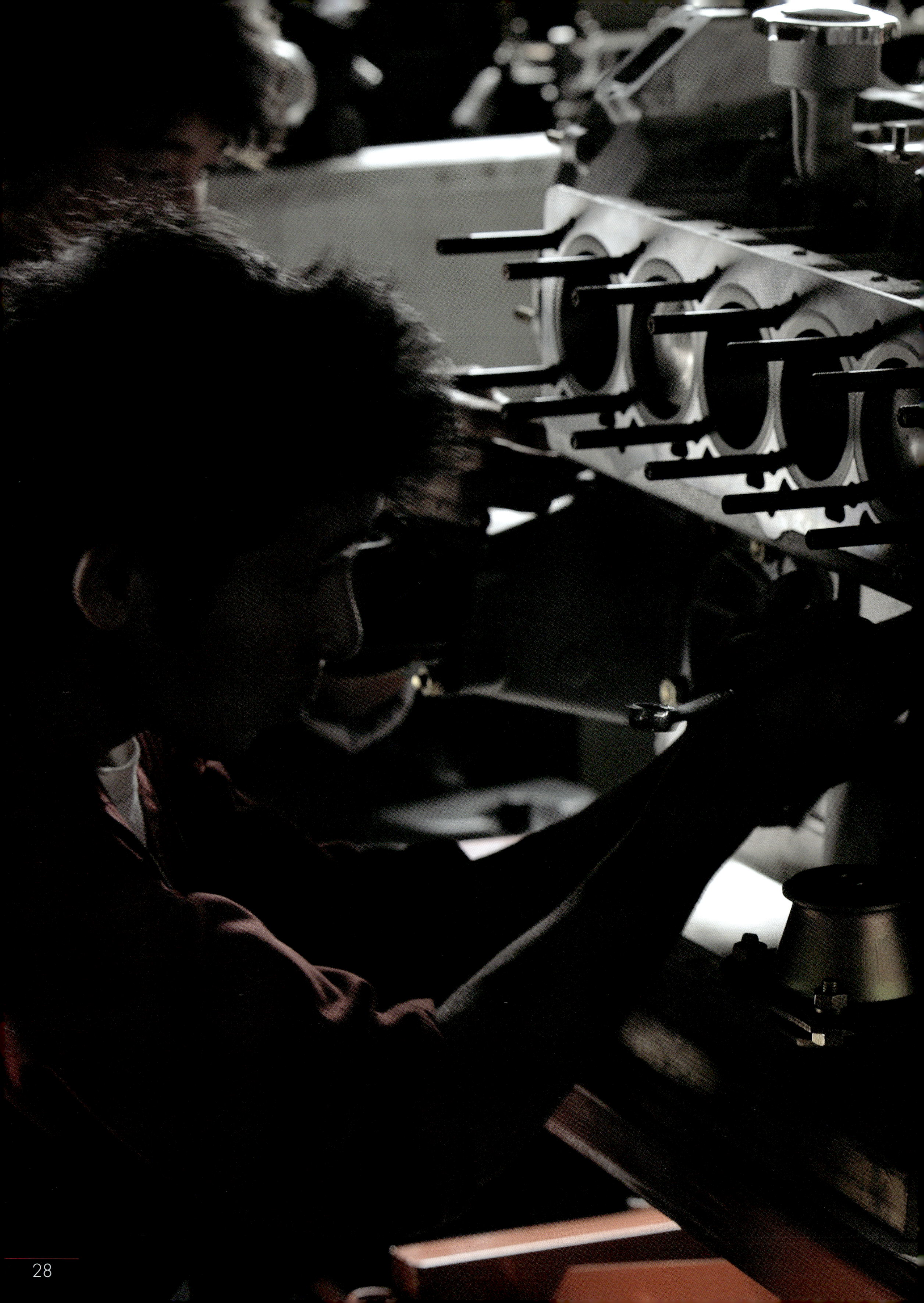

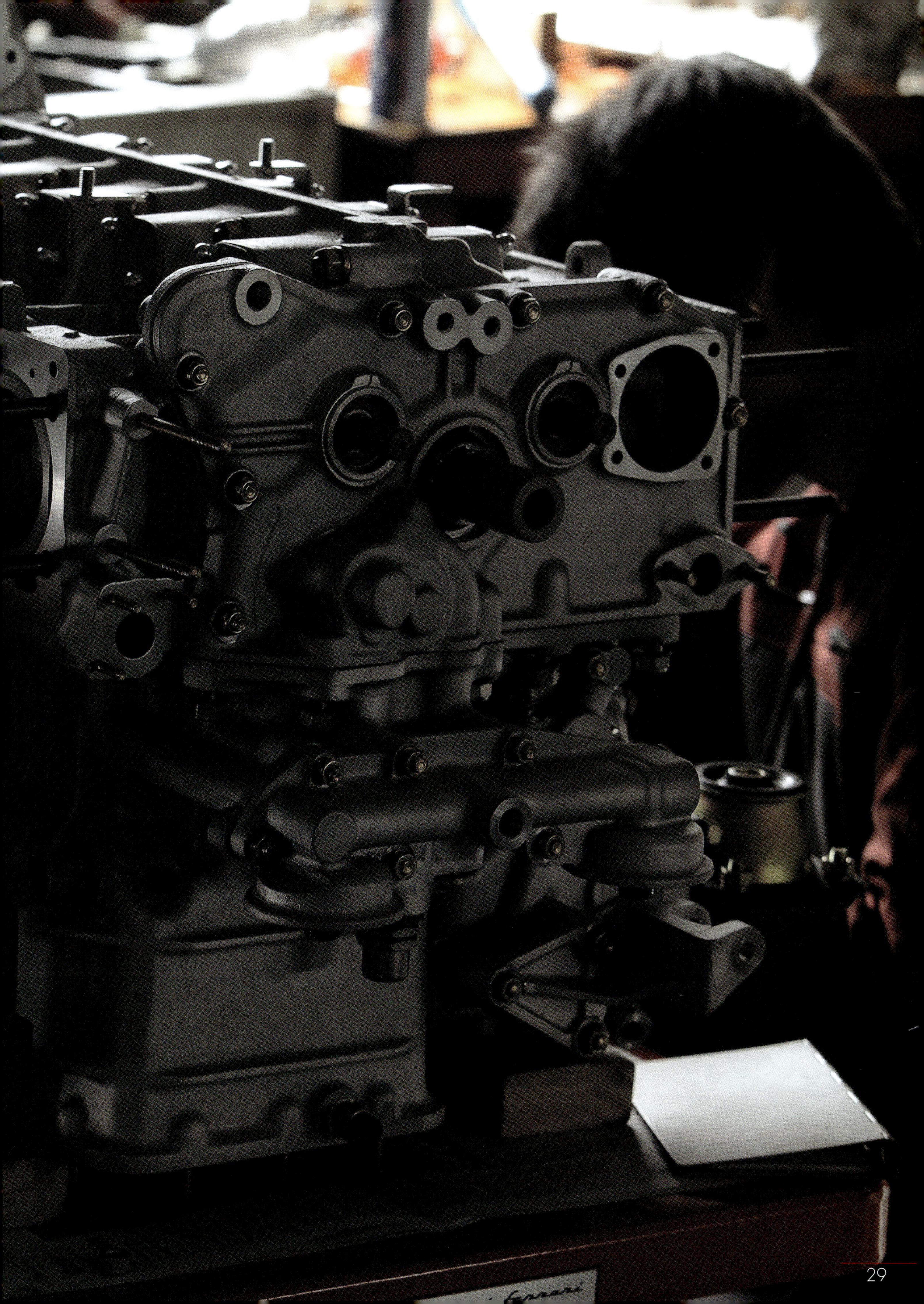

30

31

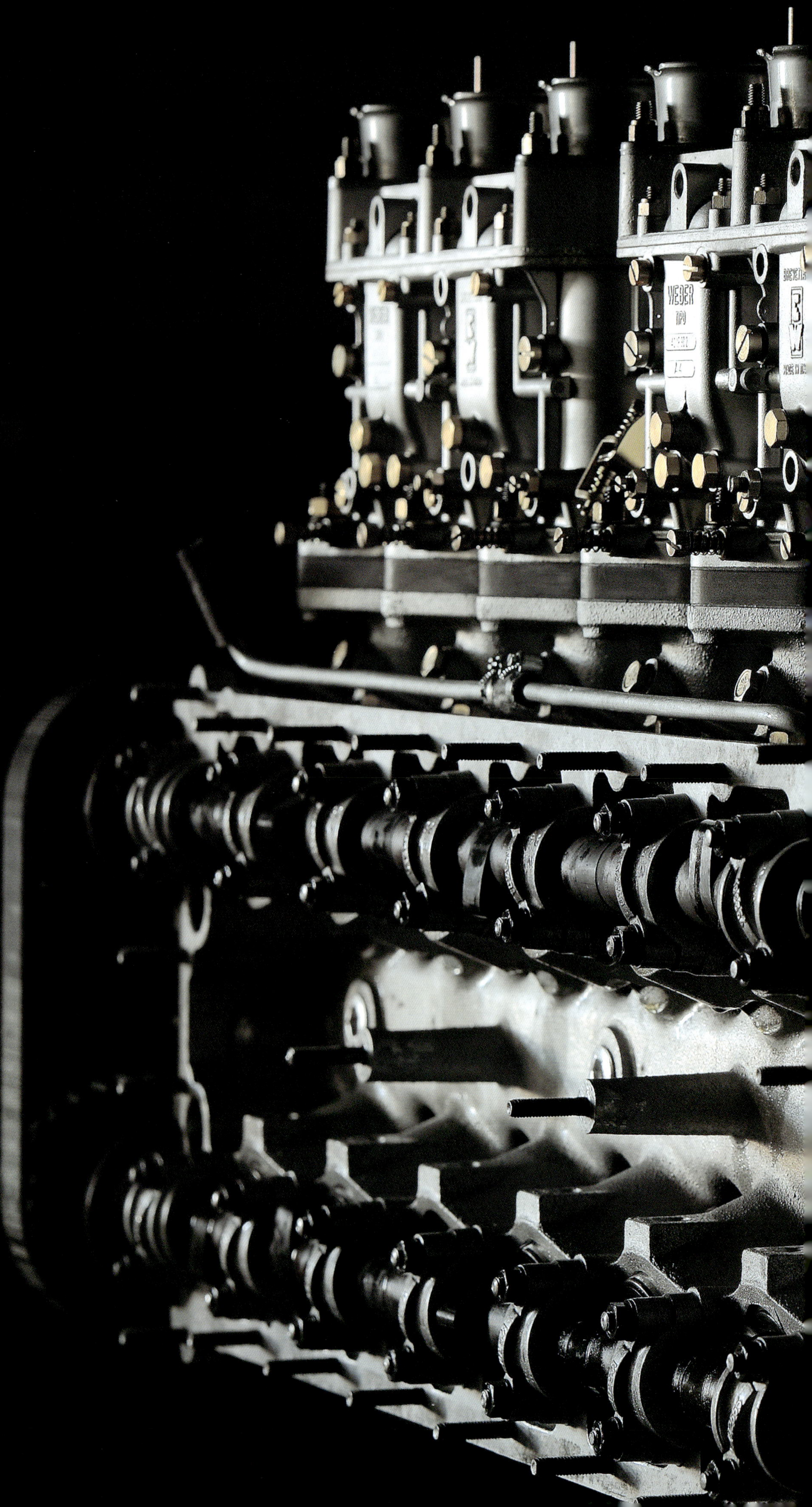
WEBER

33

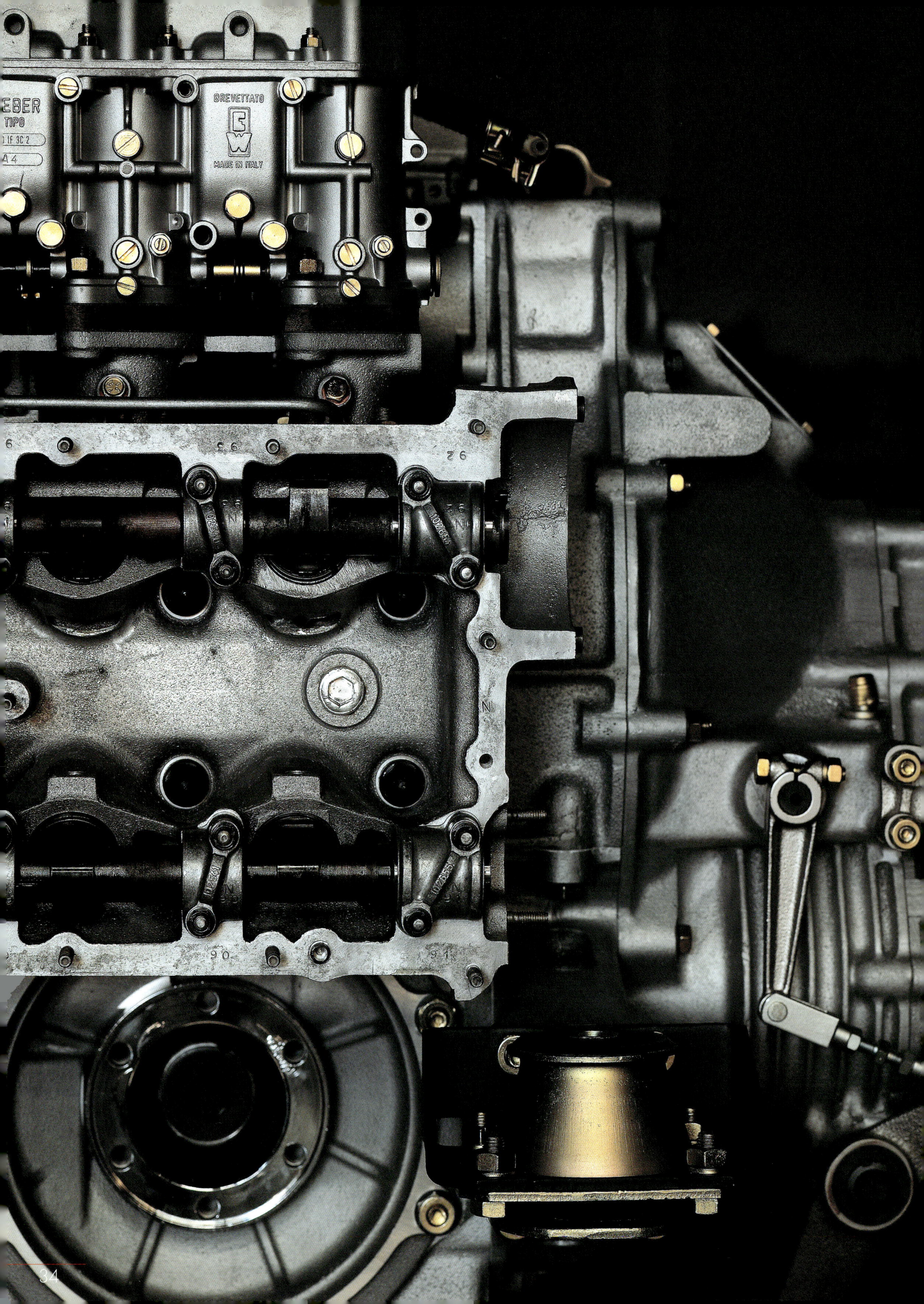
EBER
TIPO
BREVETTATO
MADE IN ITALY

35

36

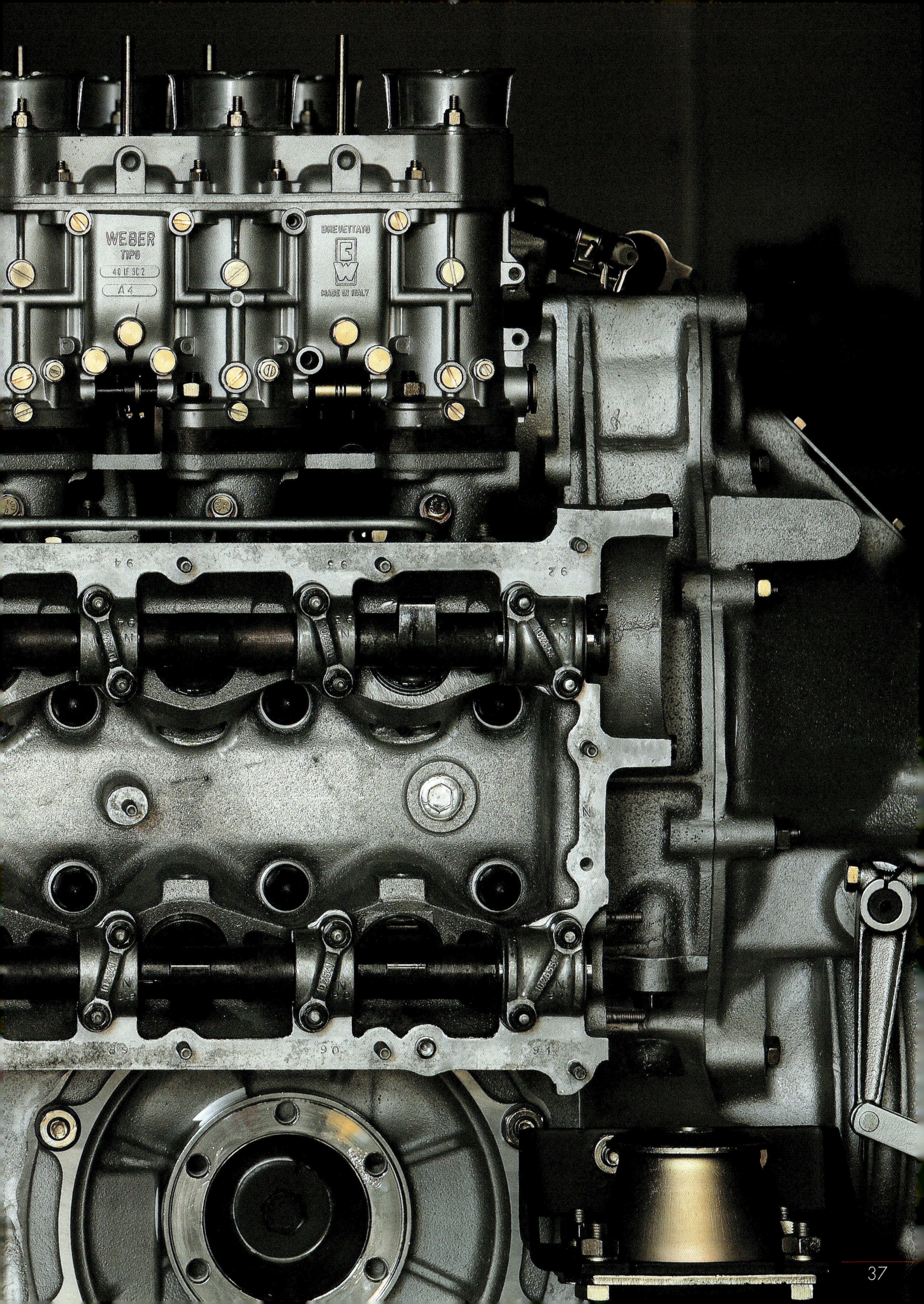
WEBER
TIPO
BREVETTATO
MADE IN ITALY

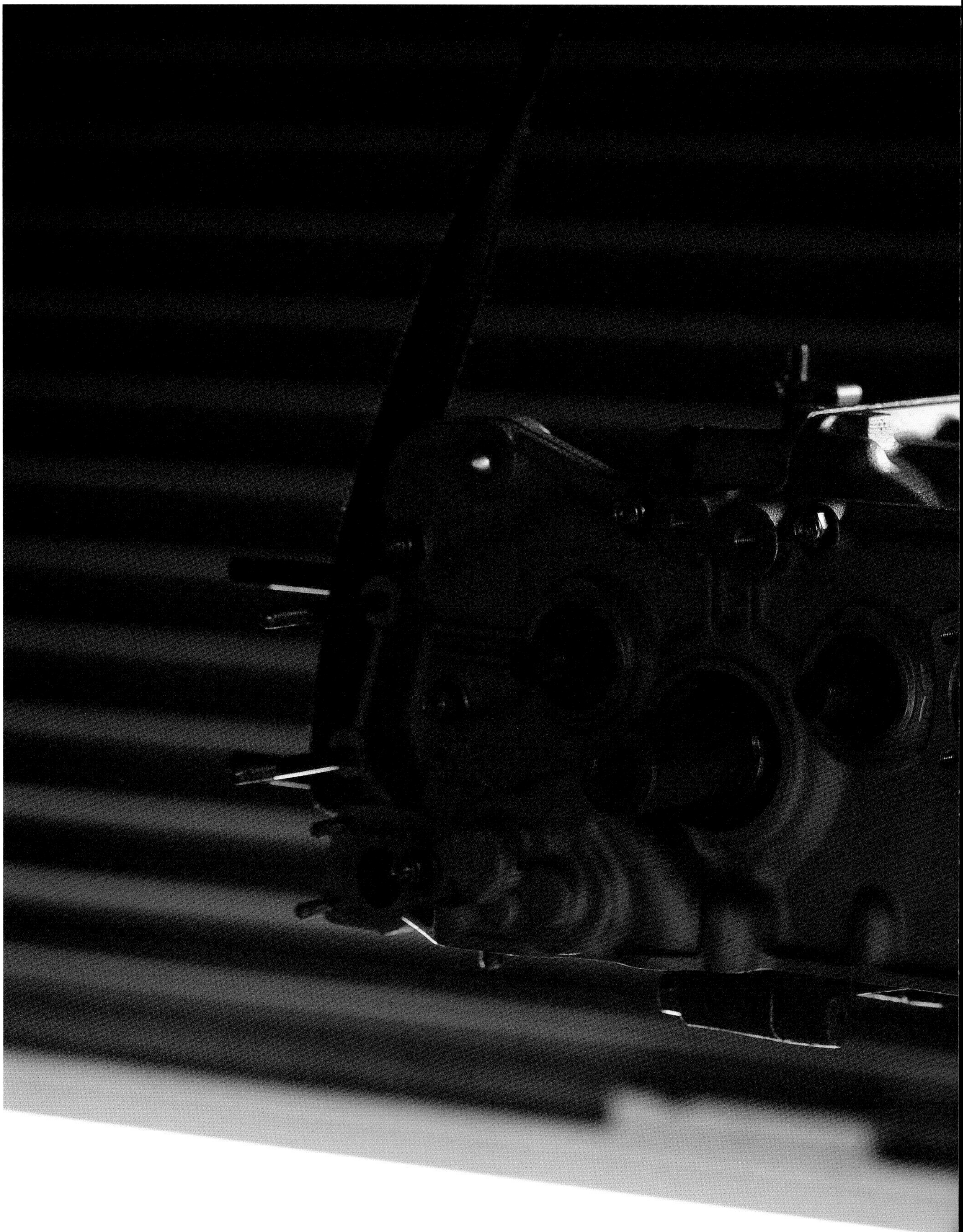

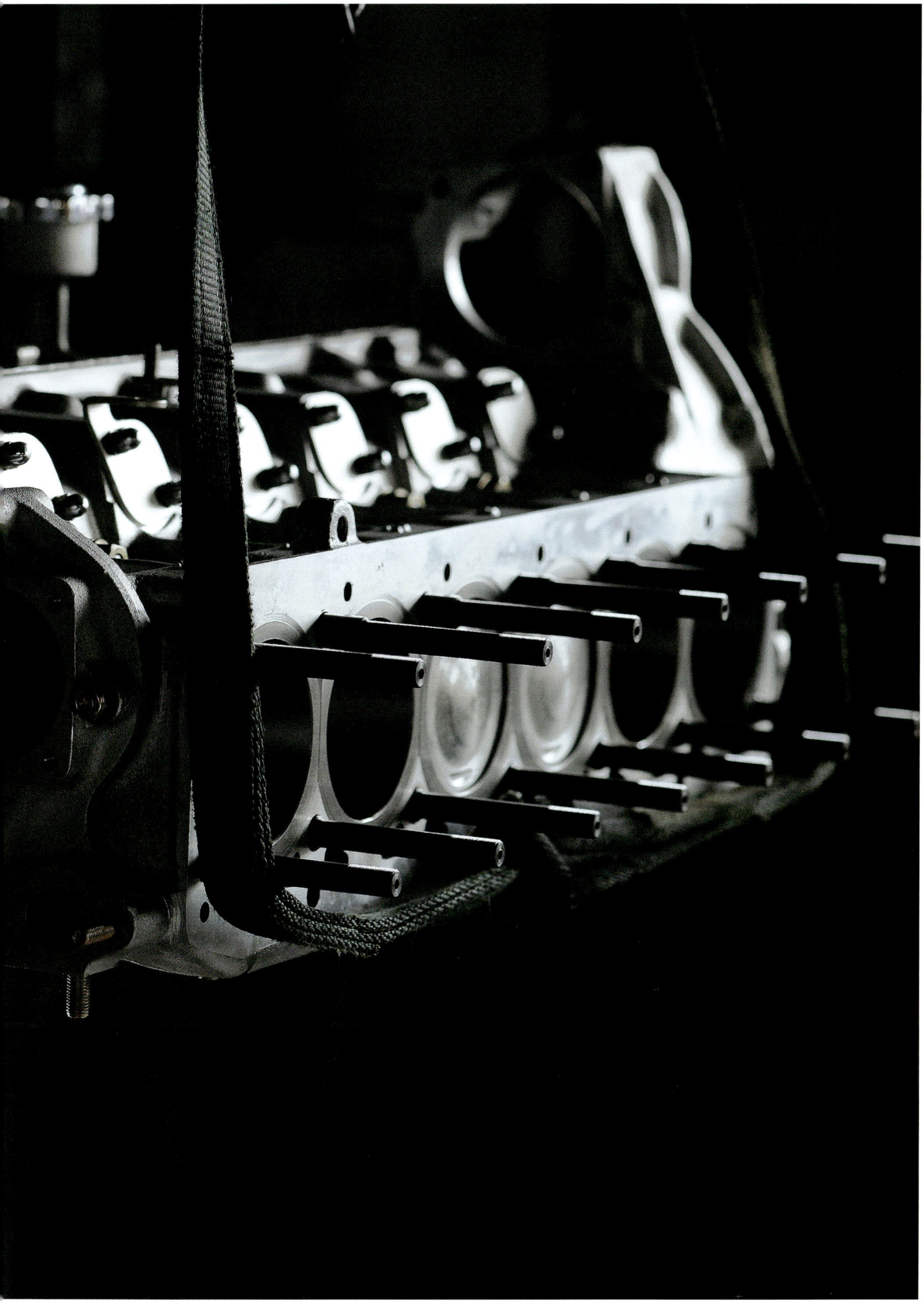

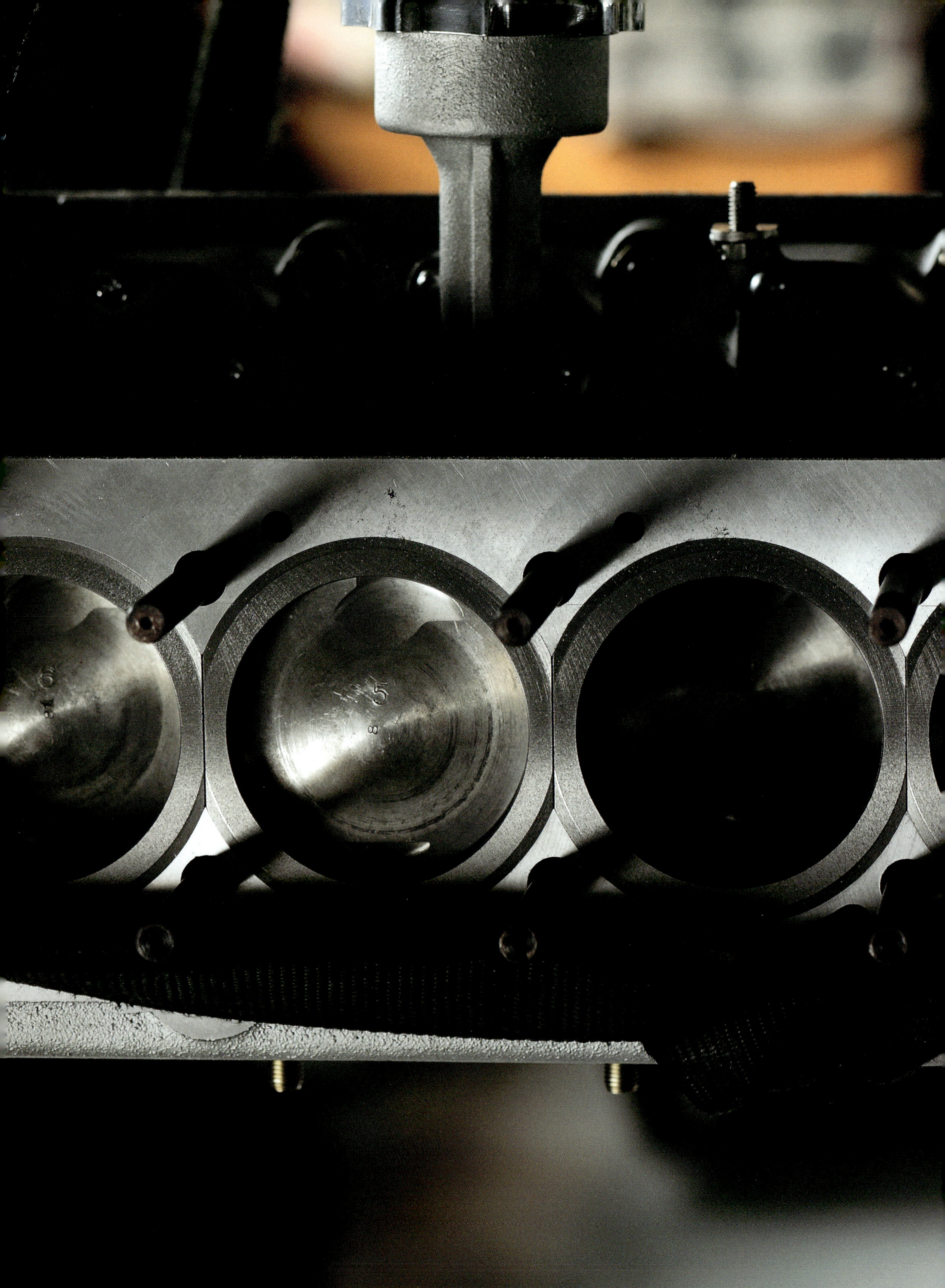

41

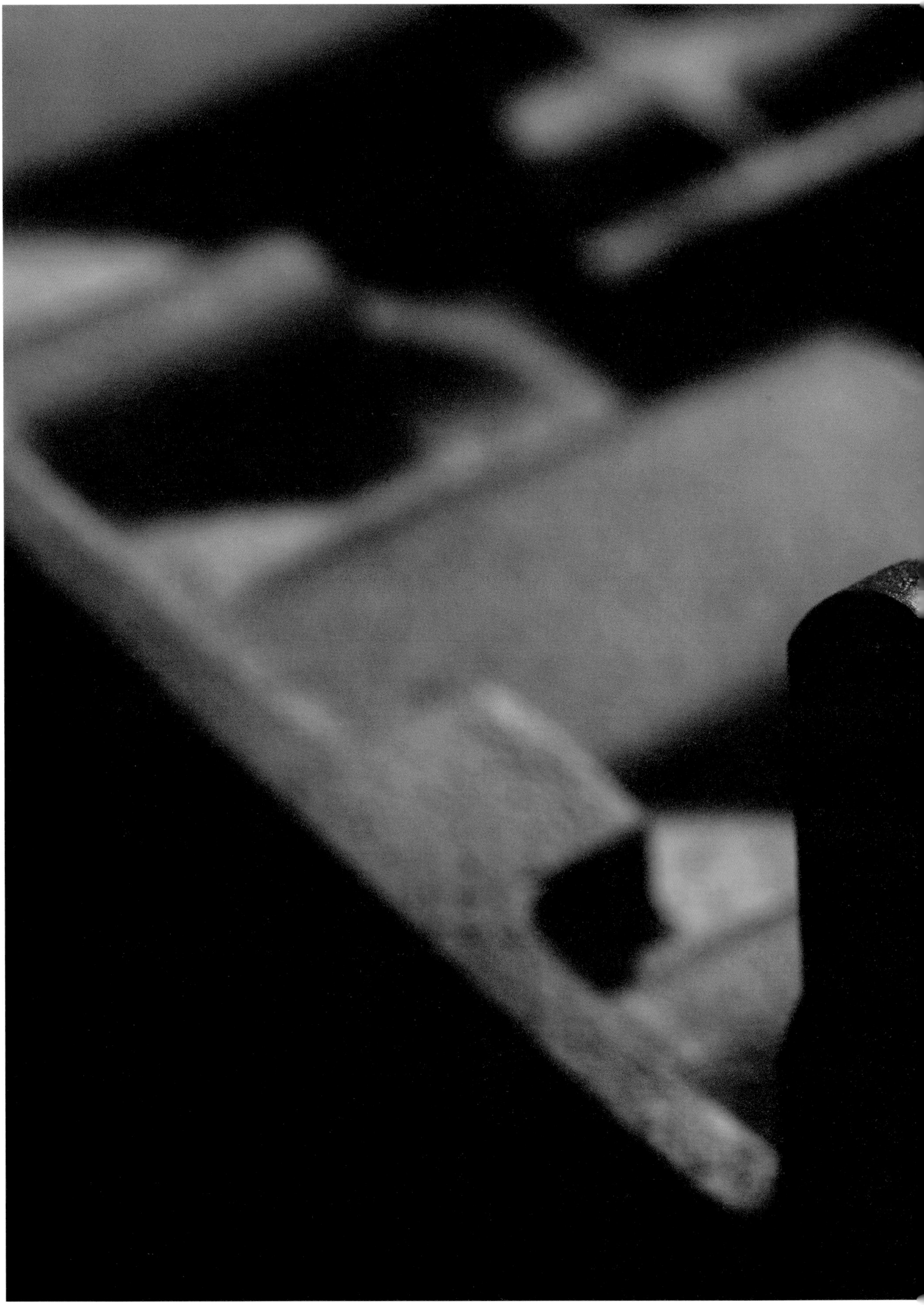

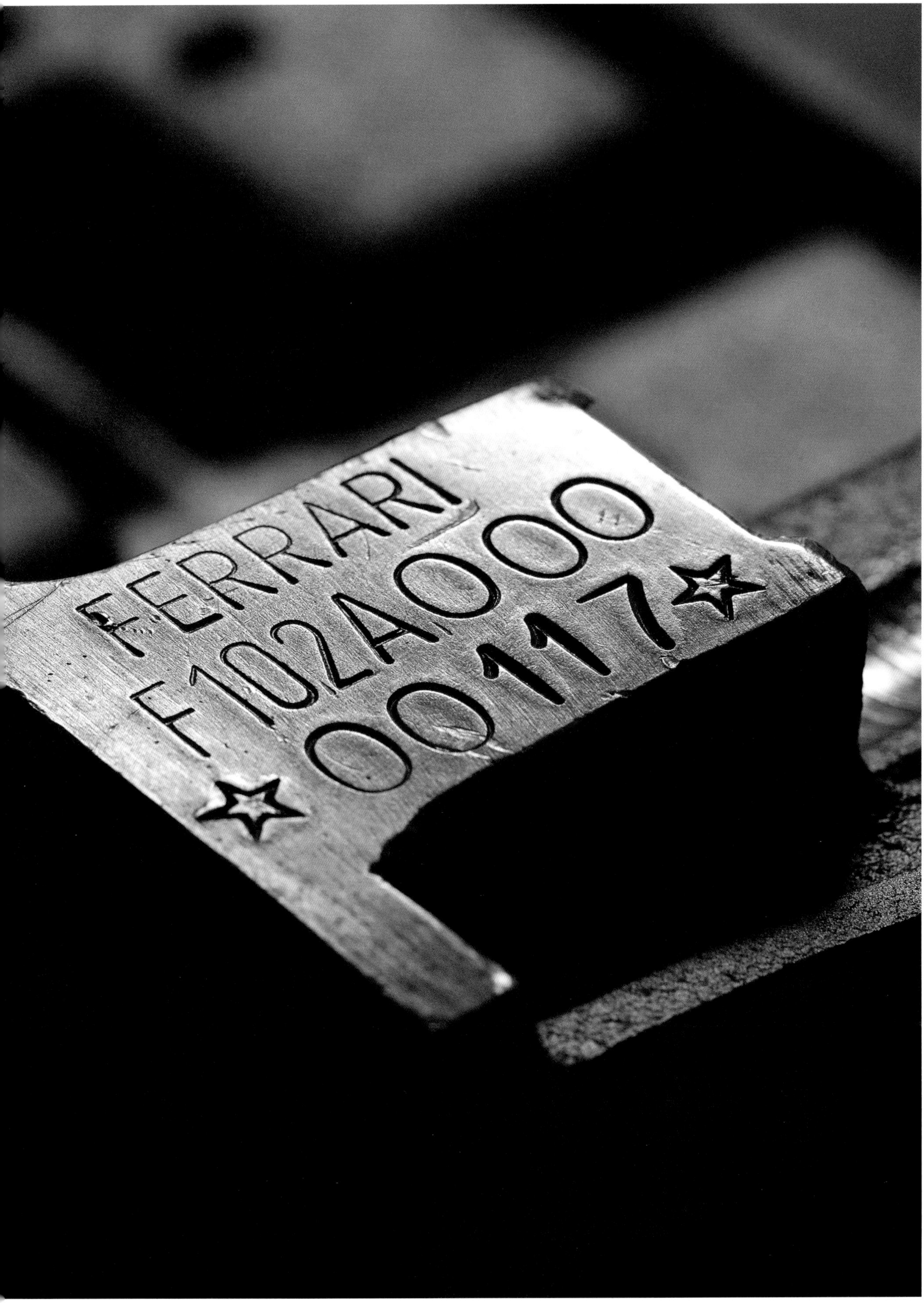
FERRARI
F102A000
00117

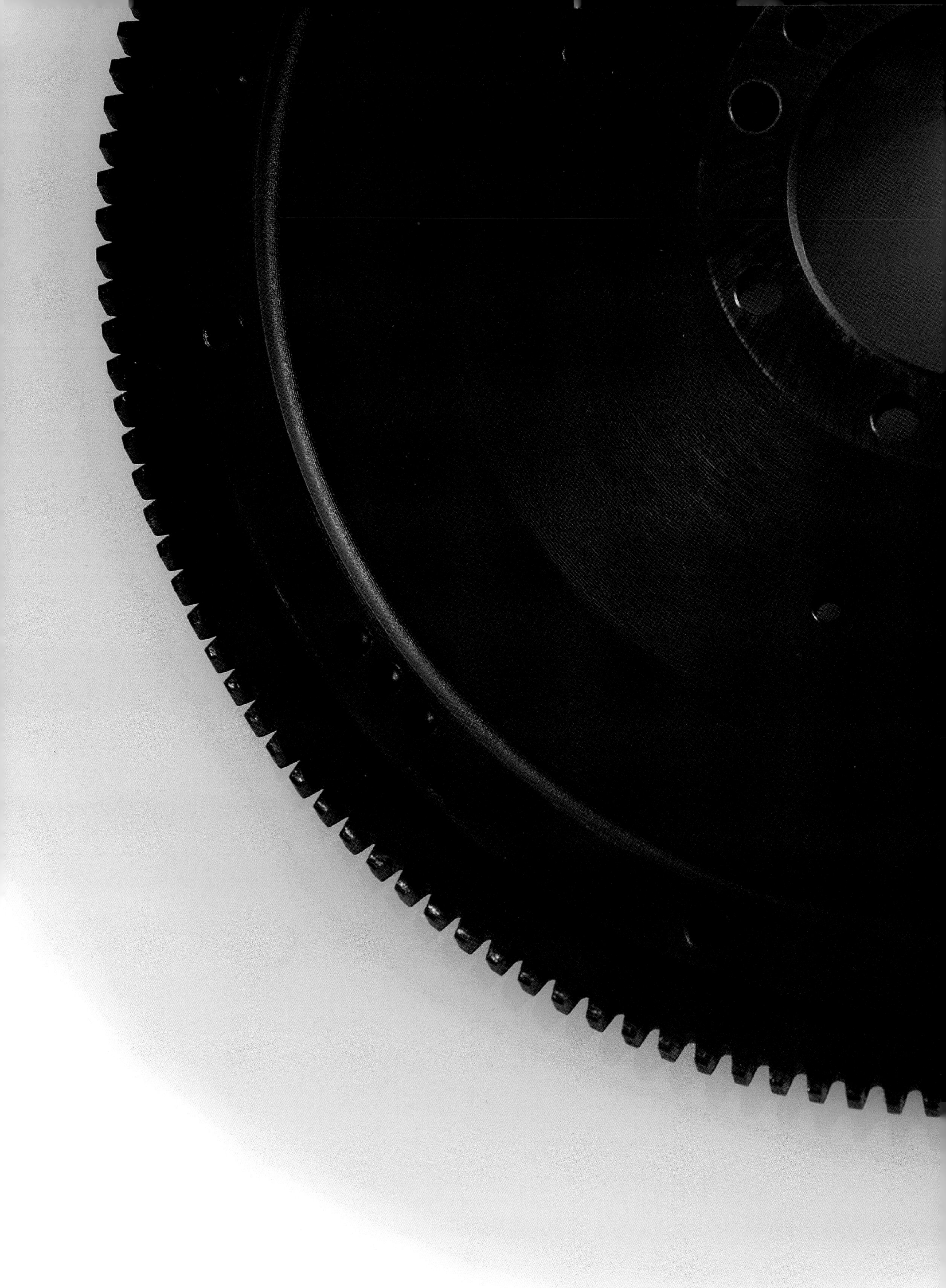

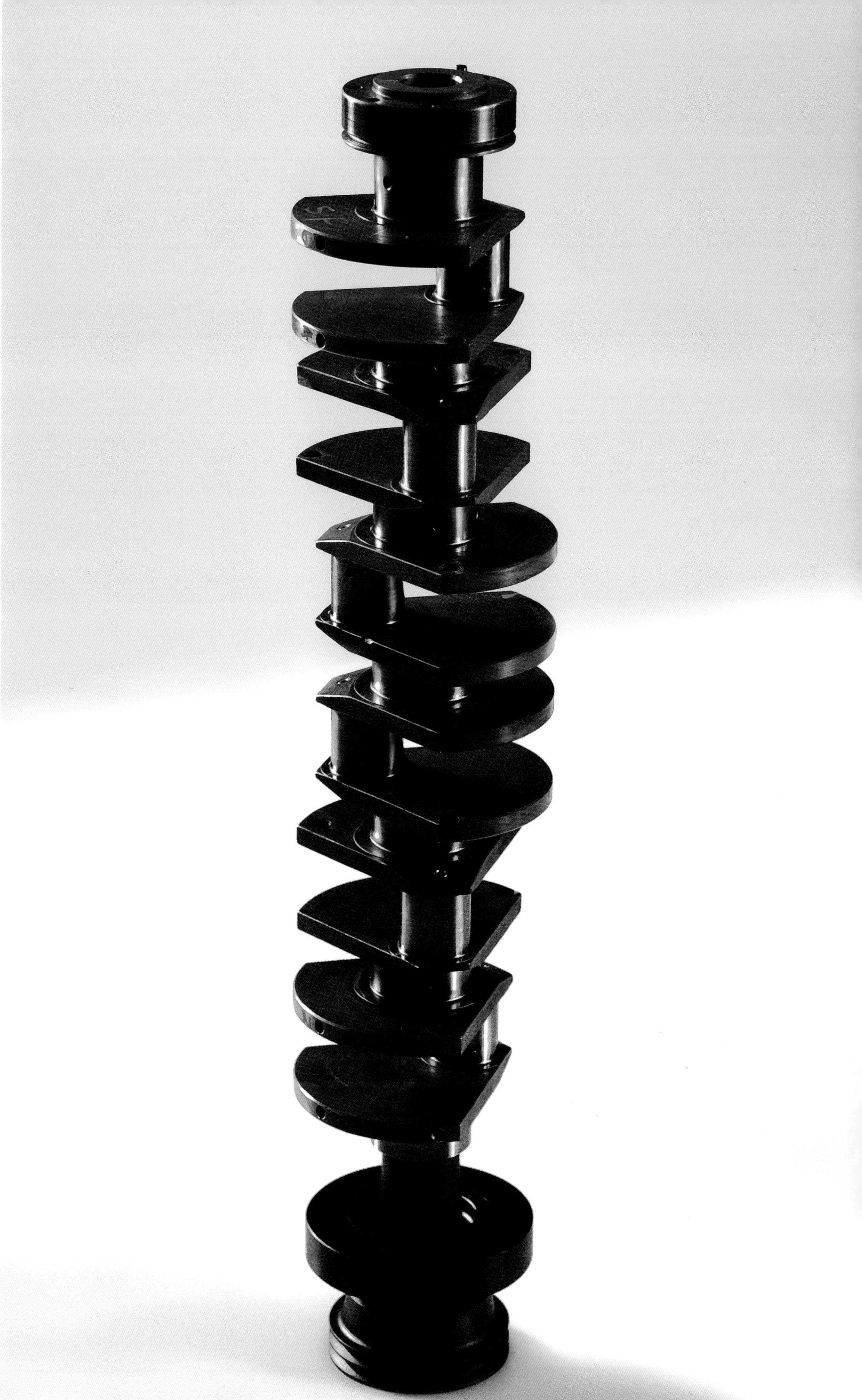

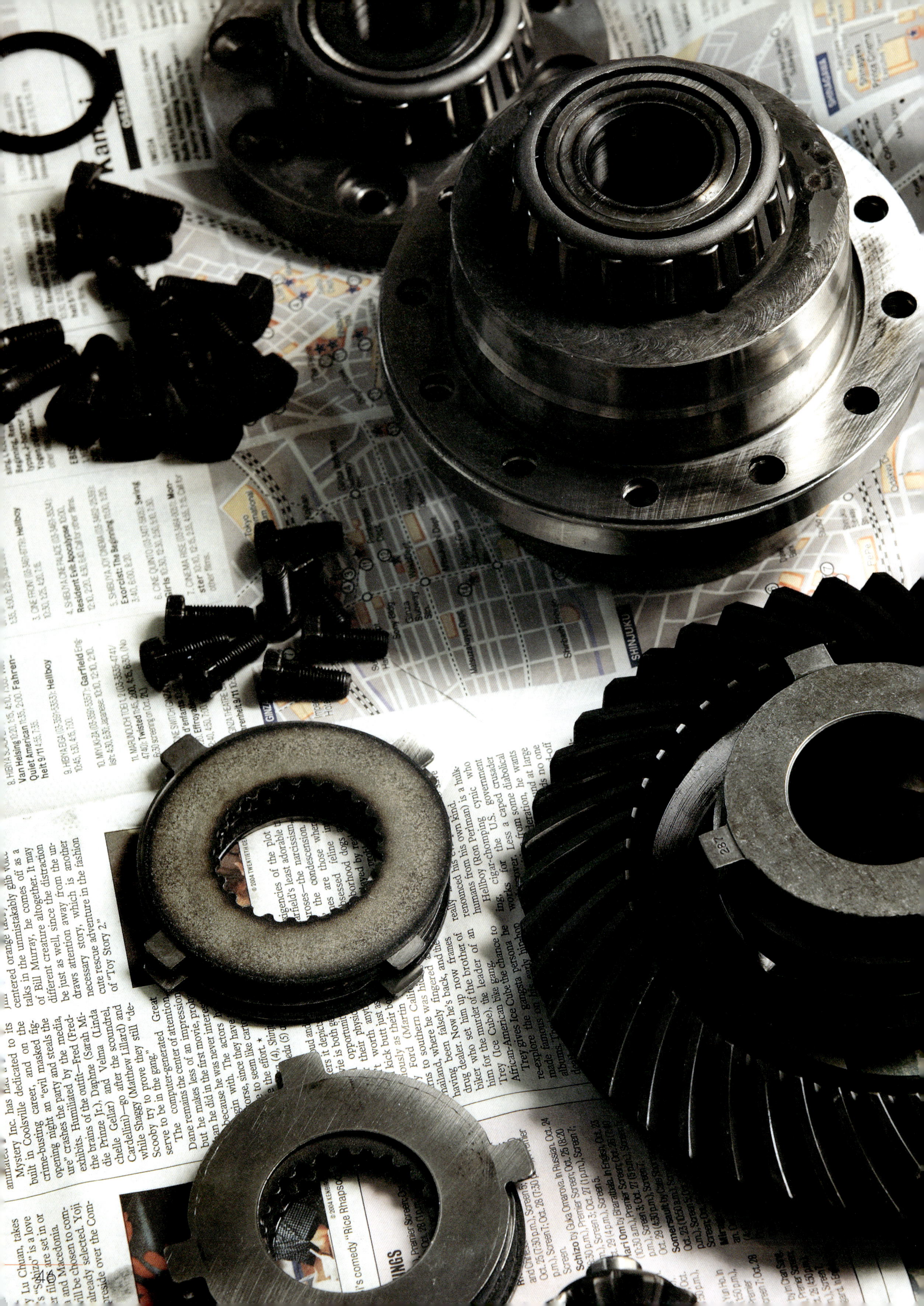
SHINJUKU

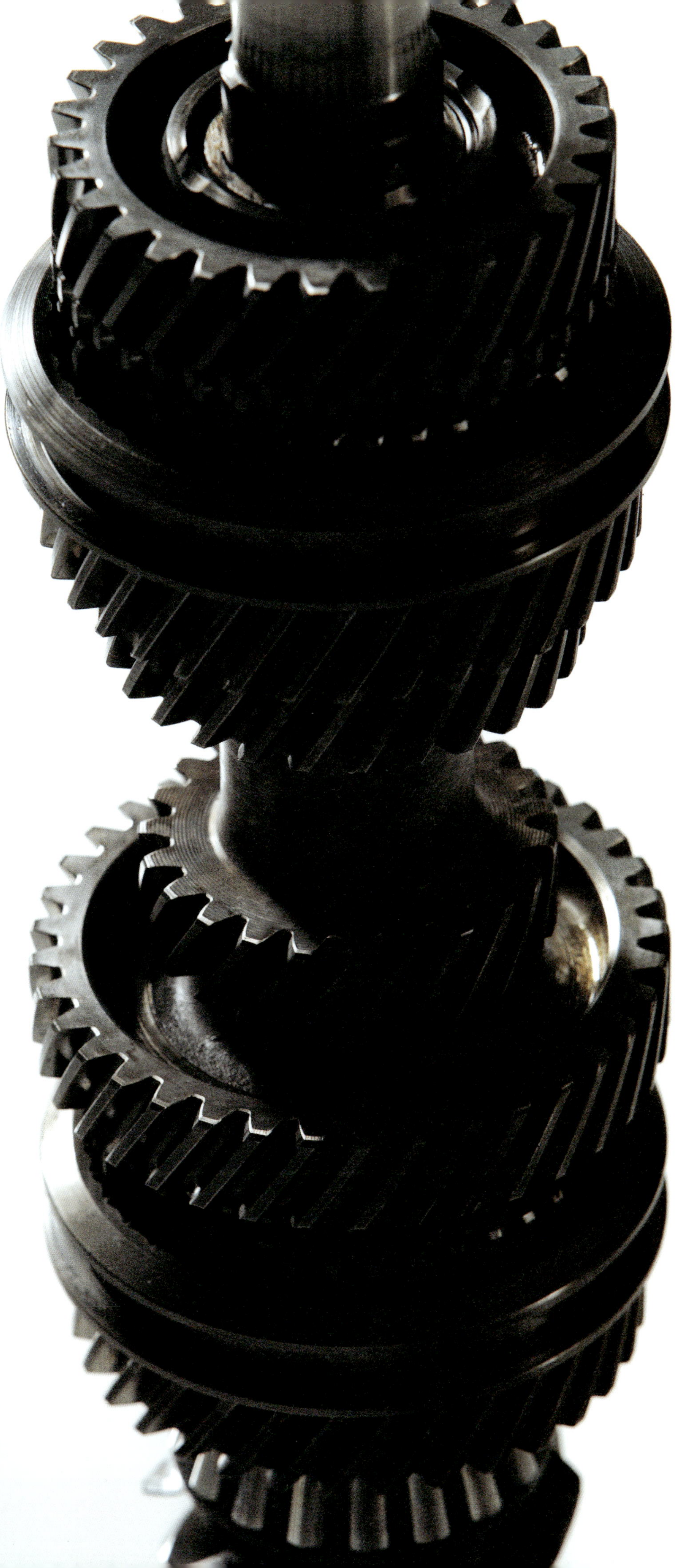

OLIO CAMBIO PONTE

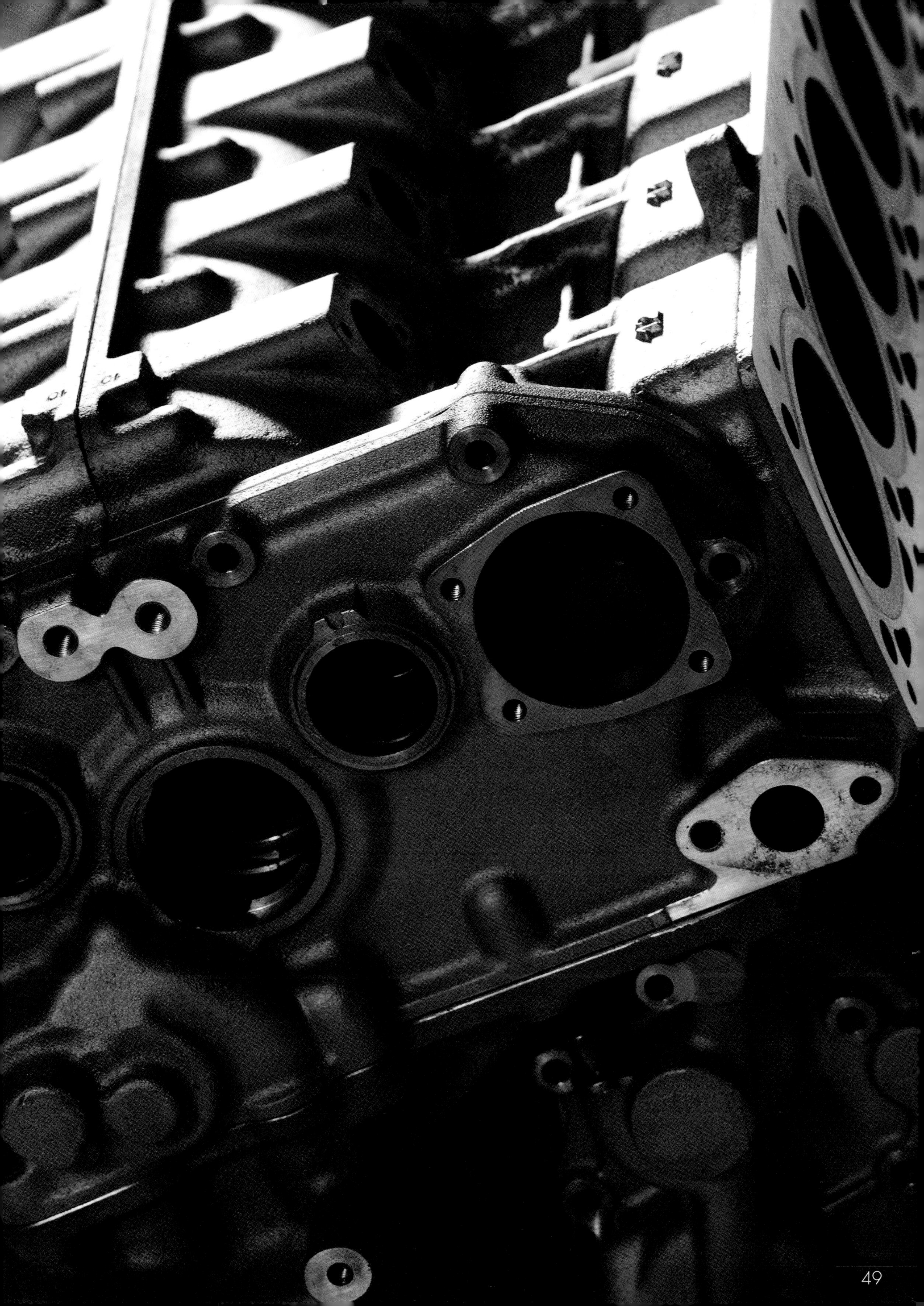

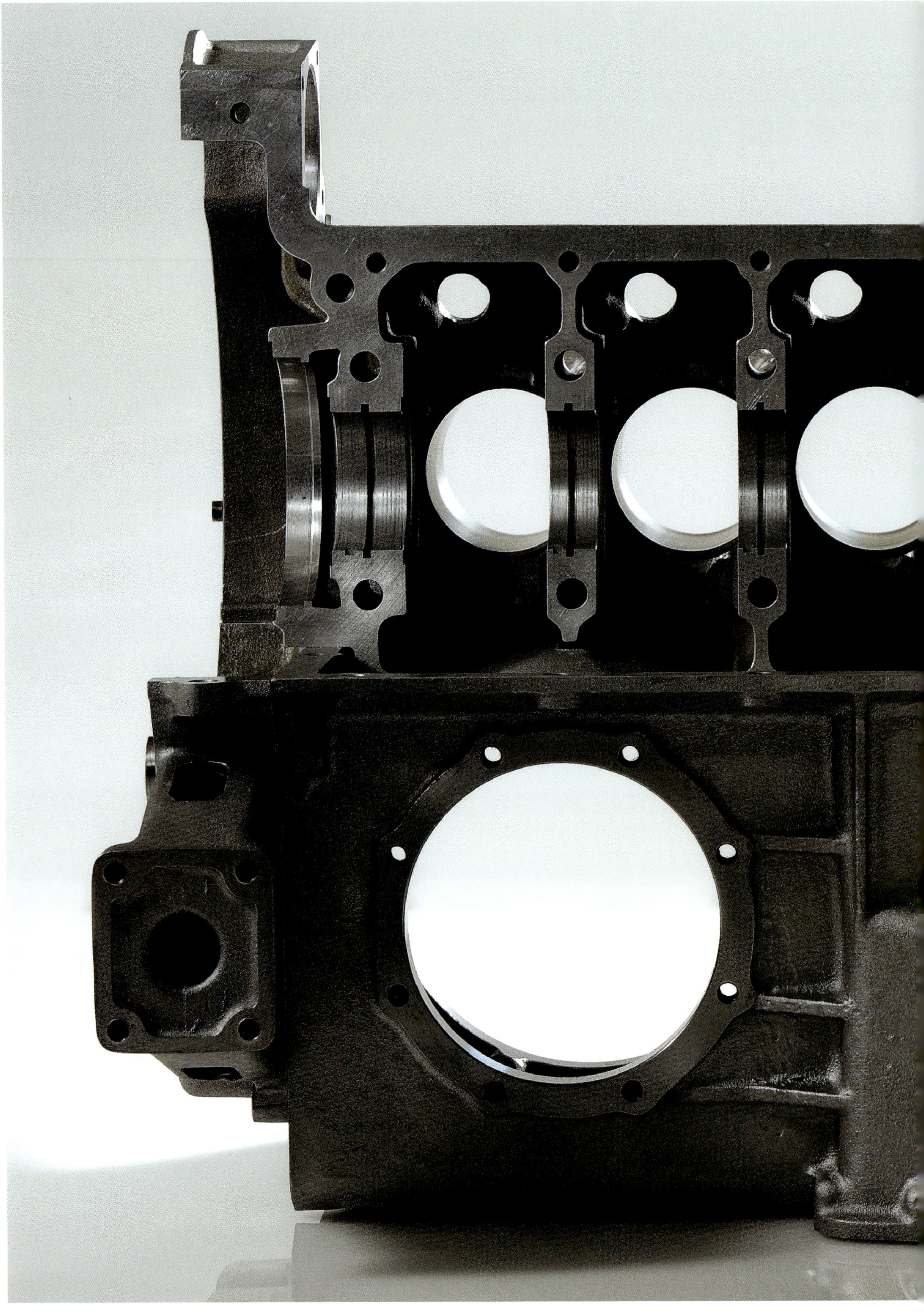

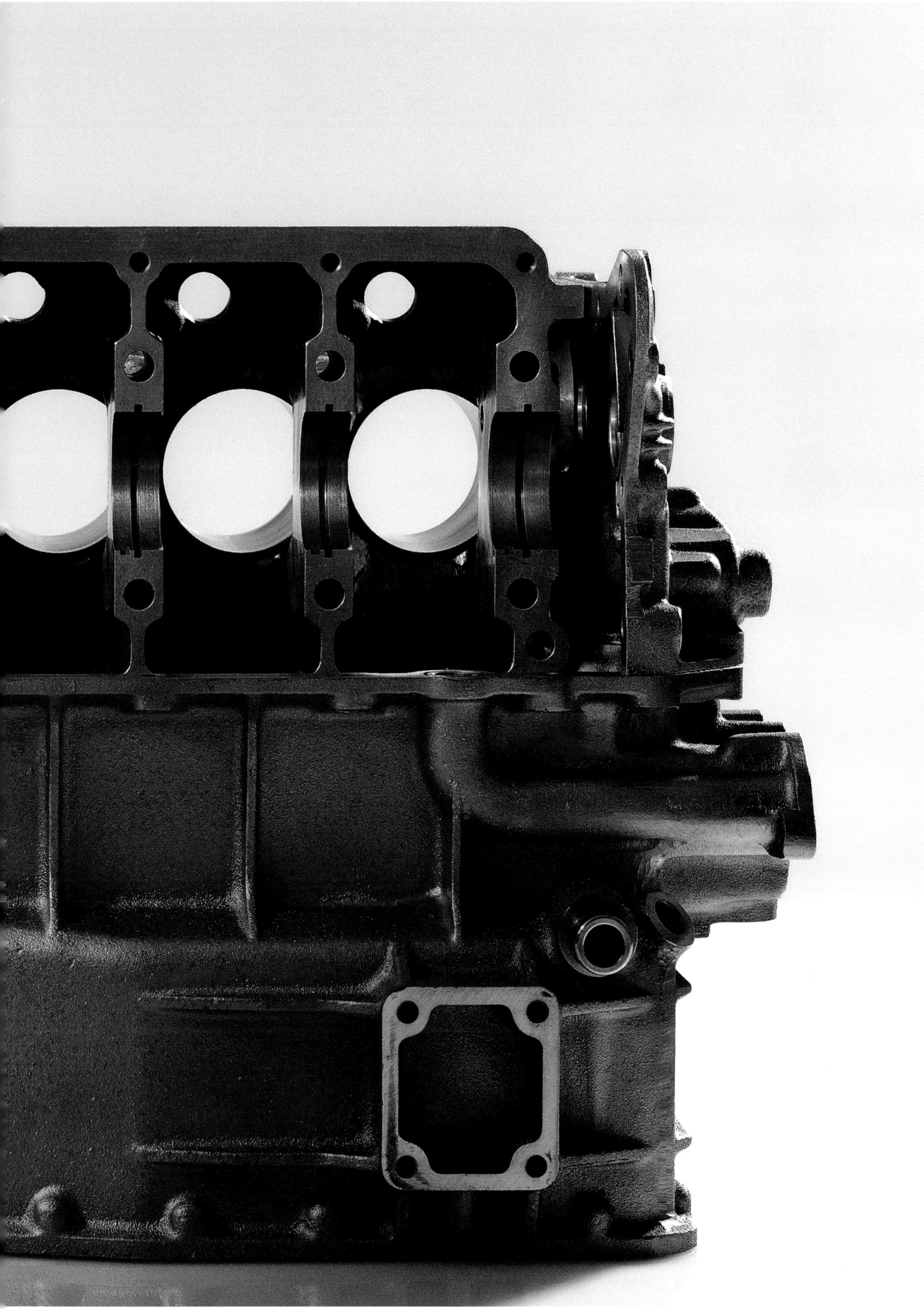

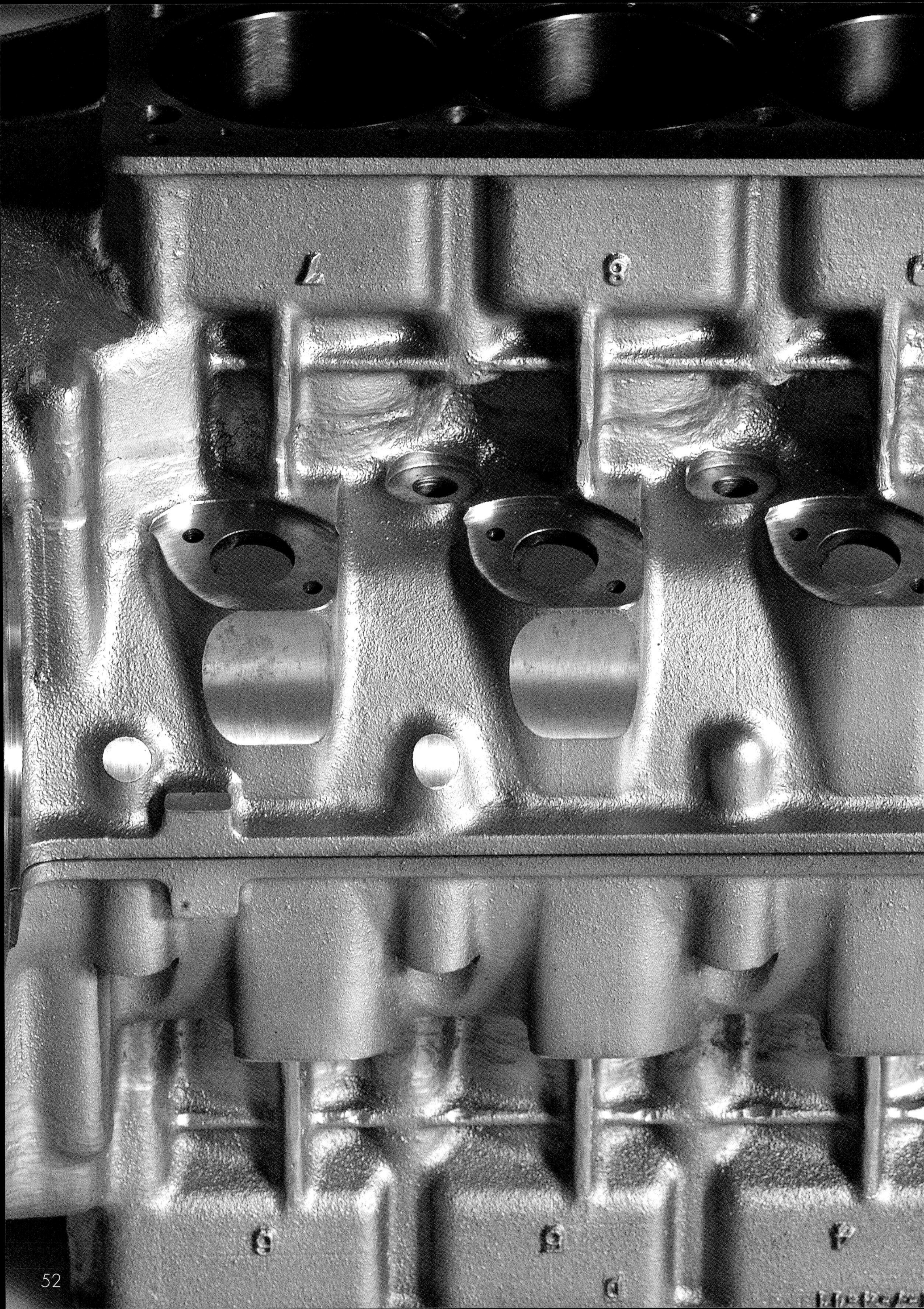

53

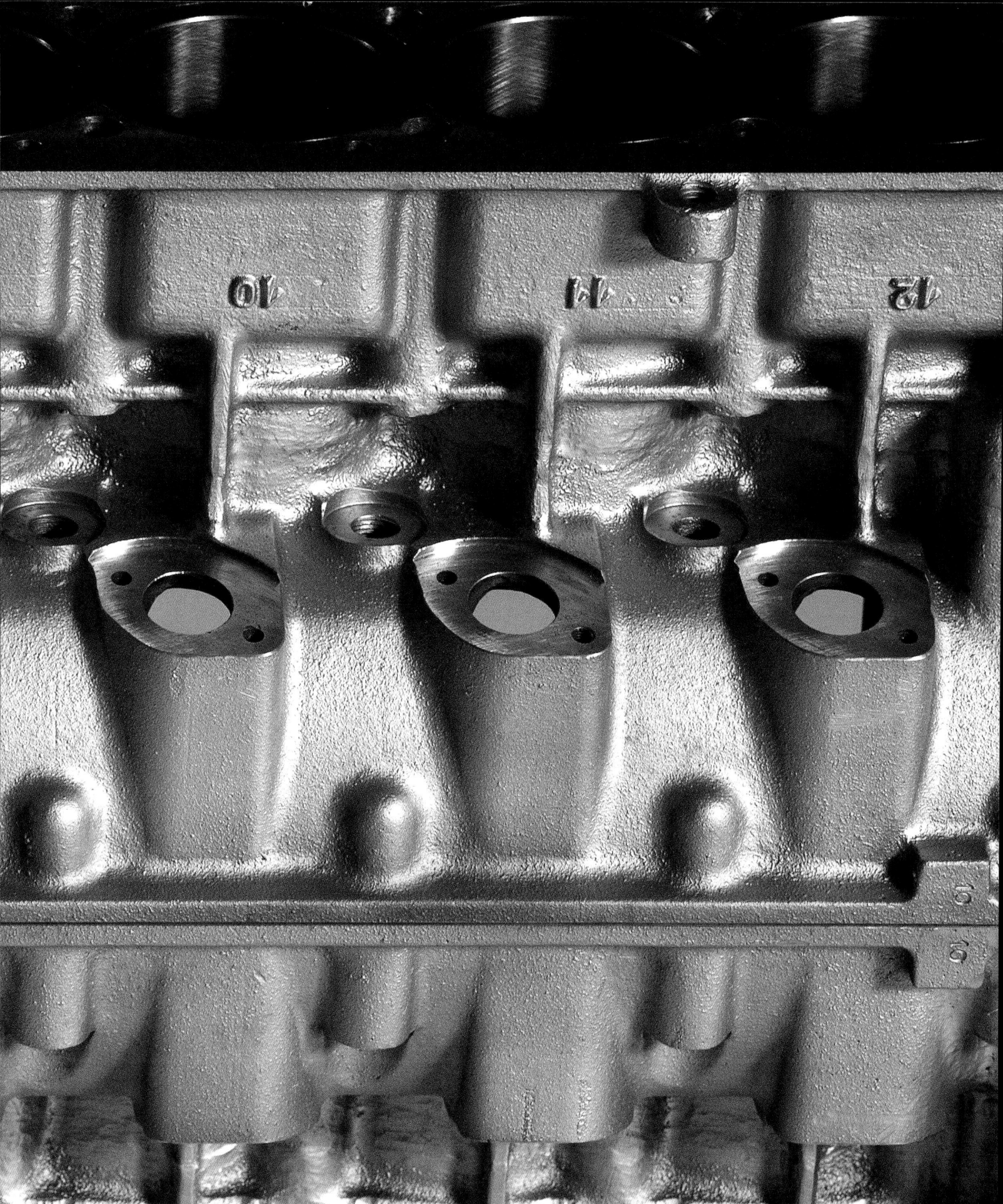

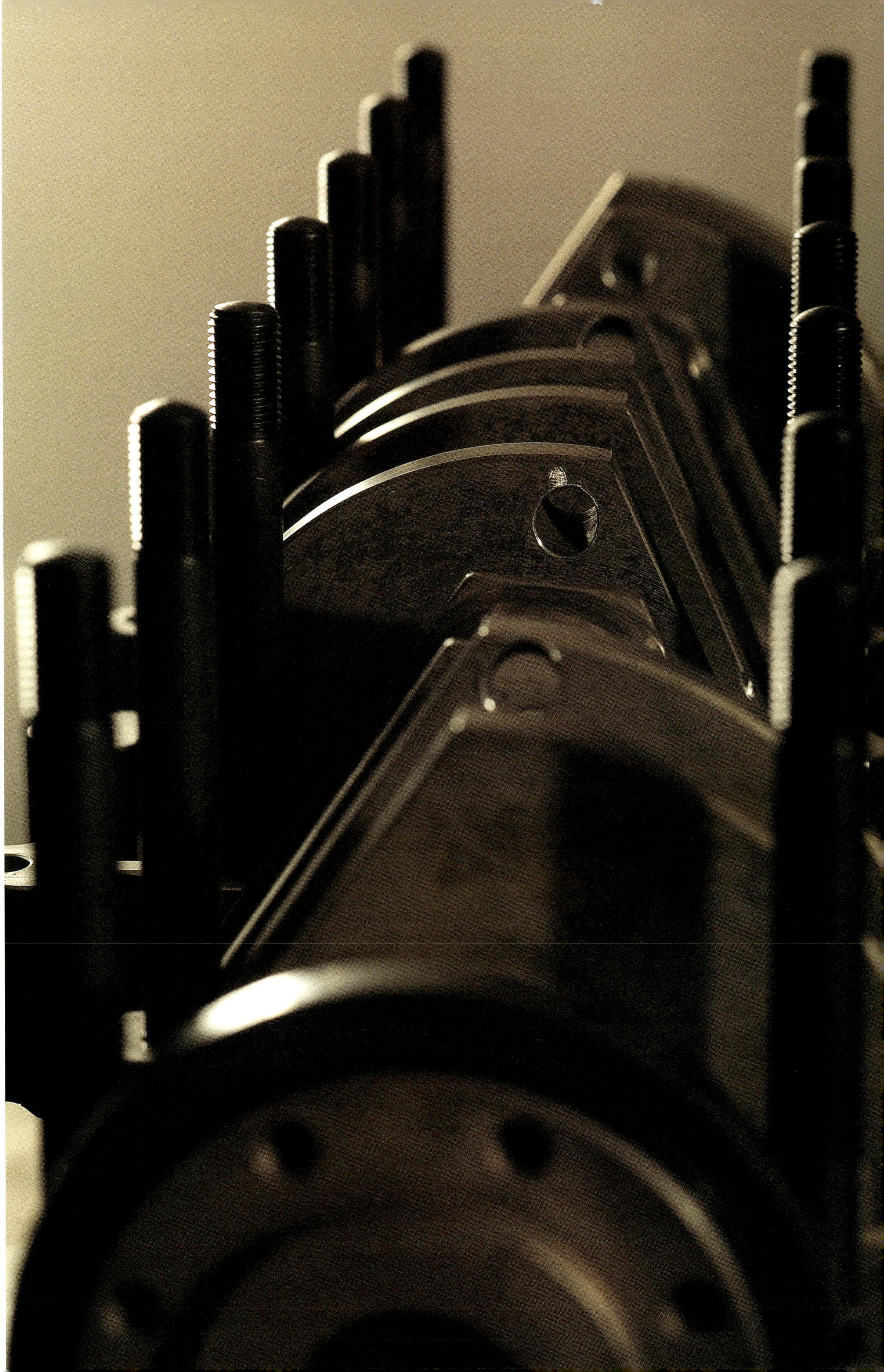

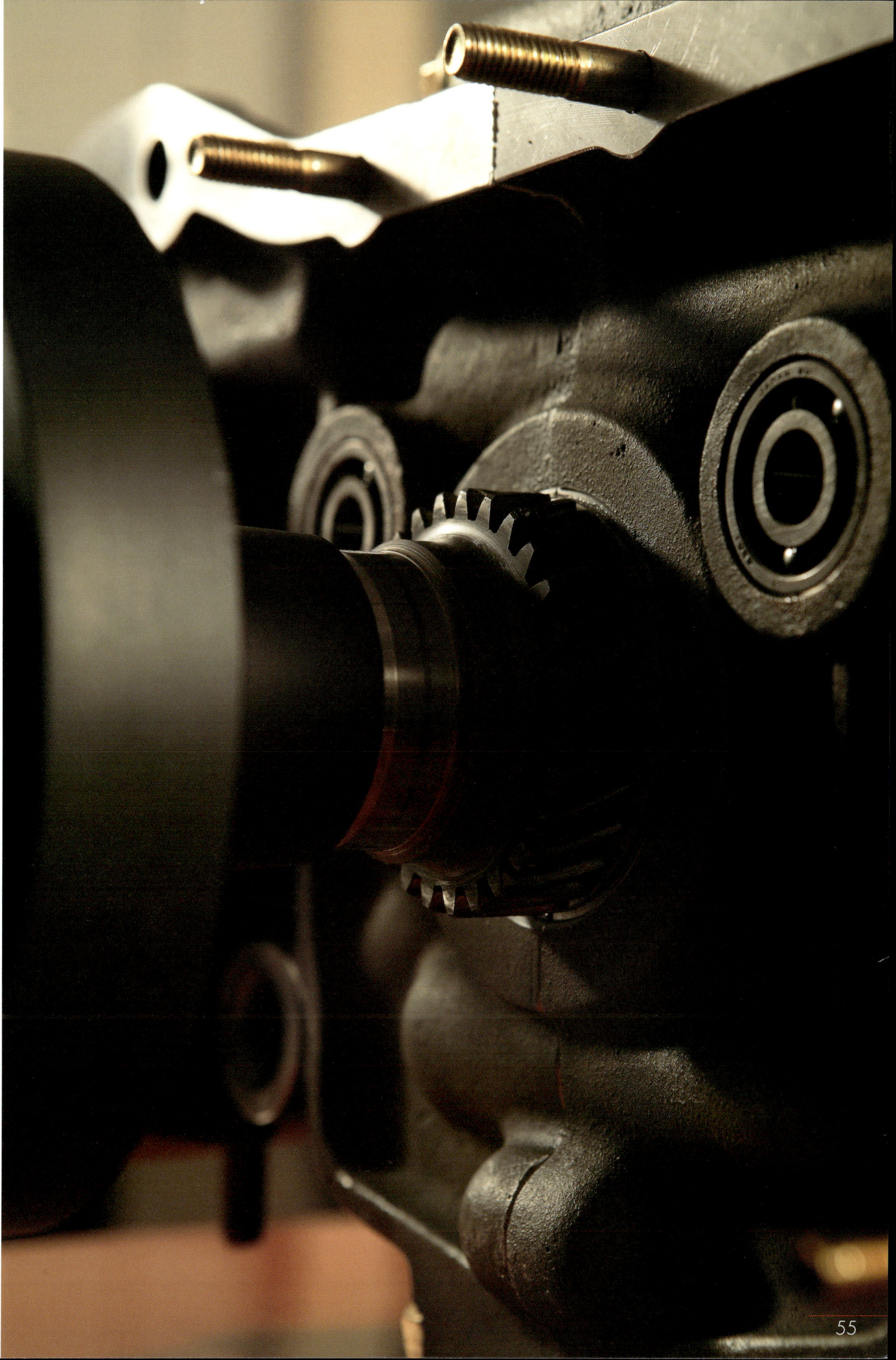

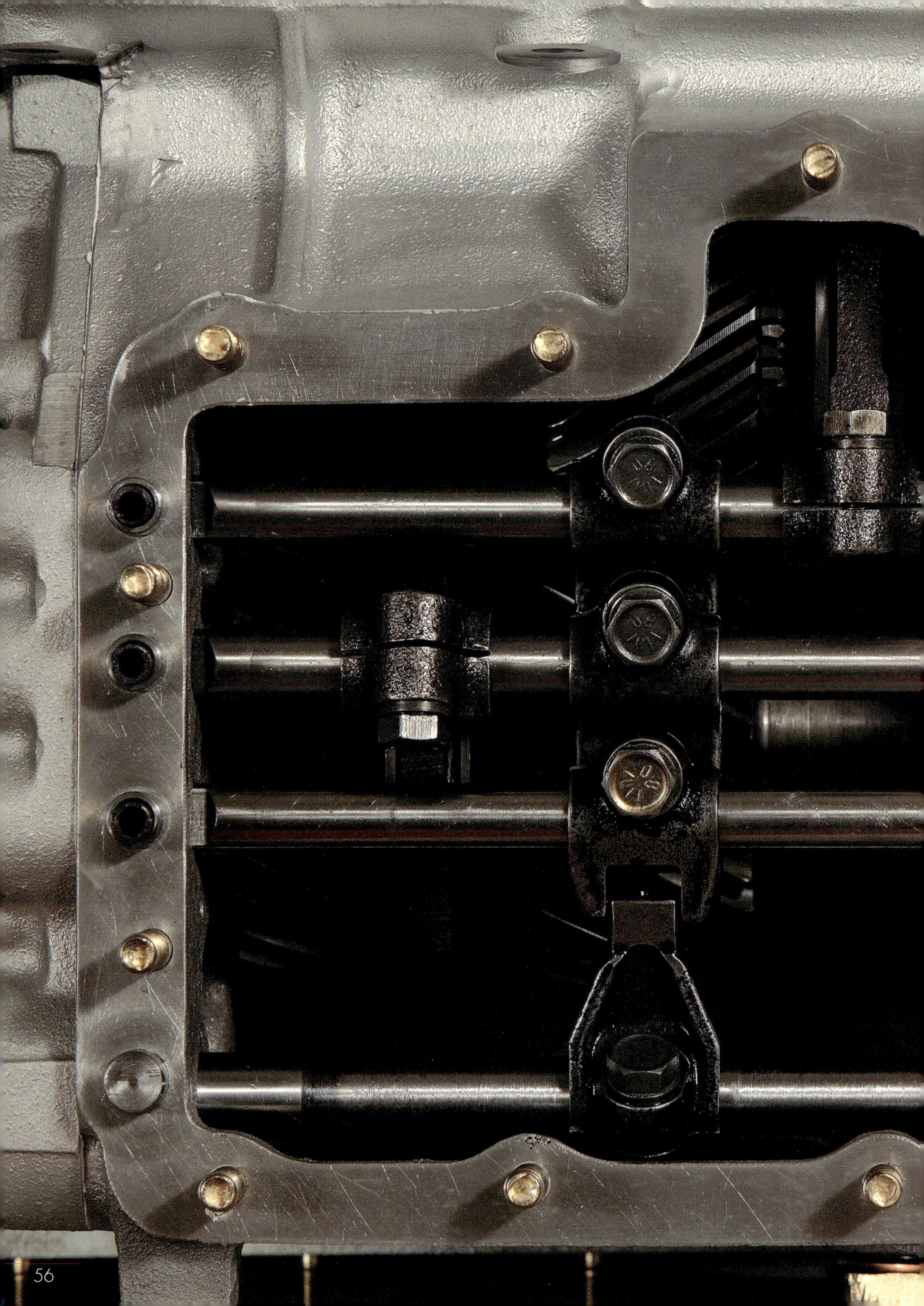

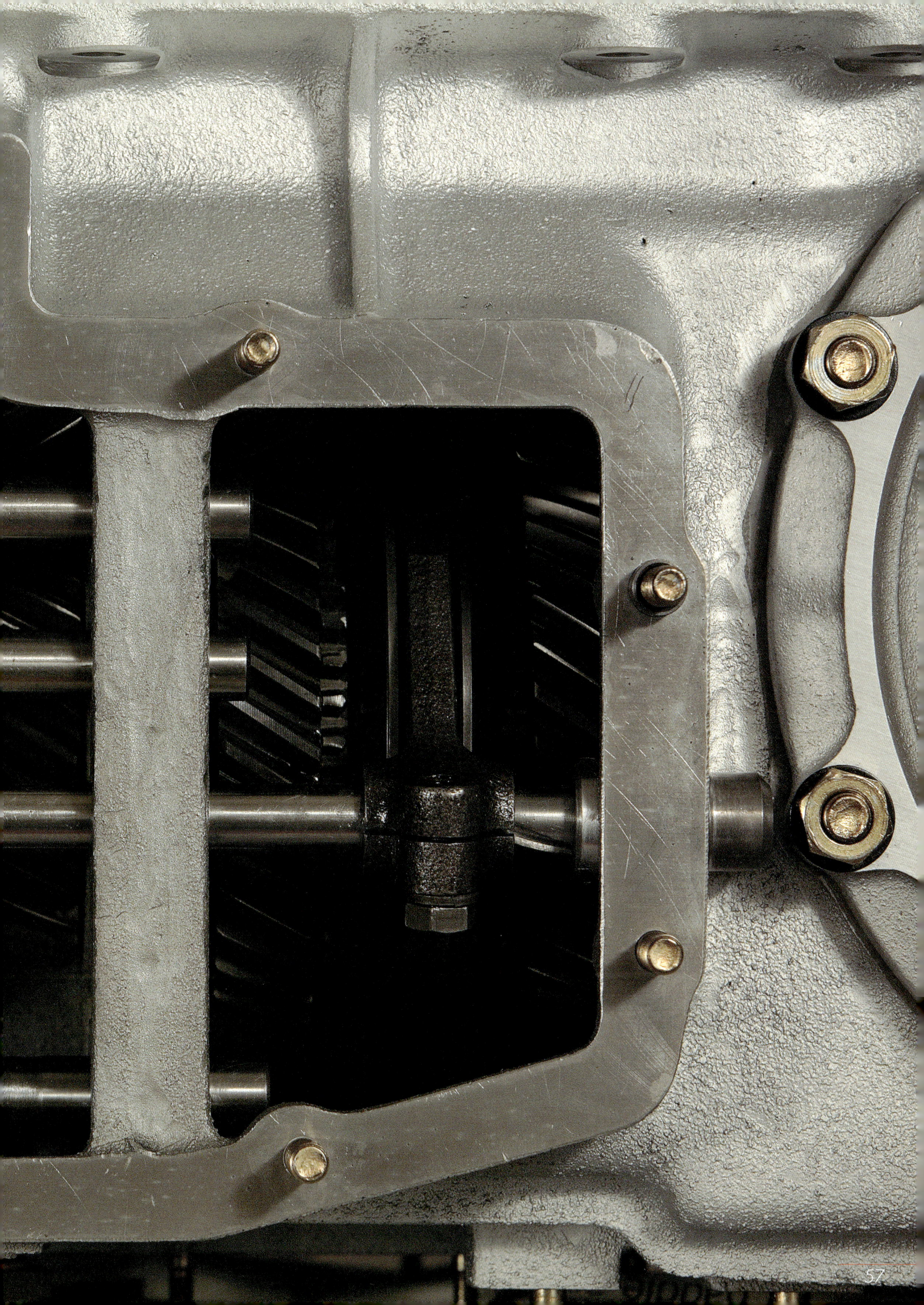

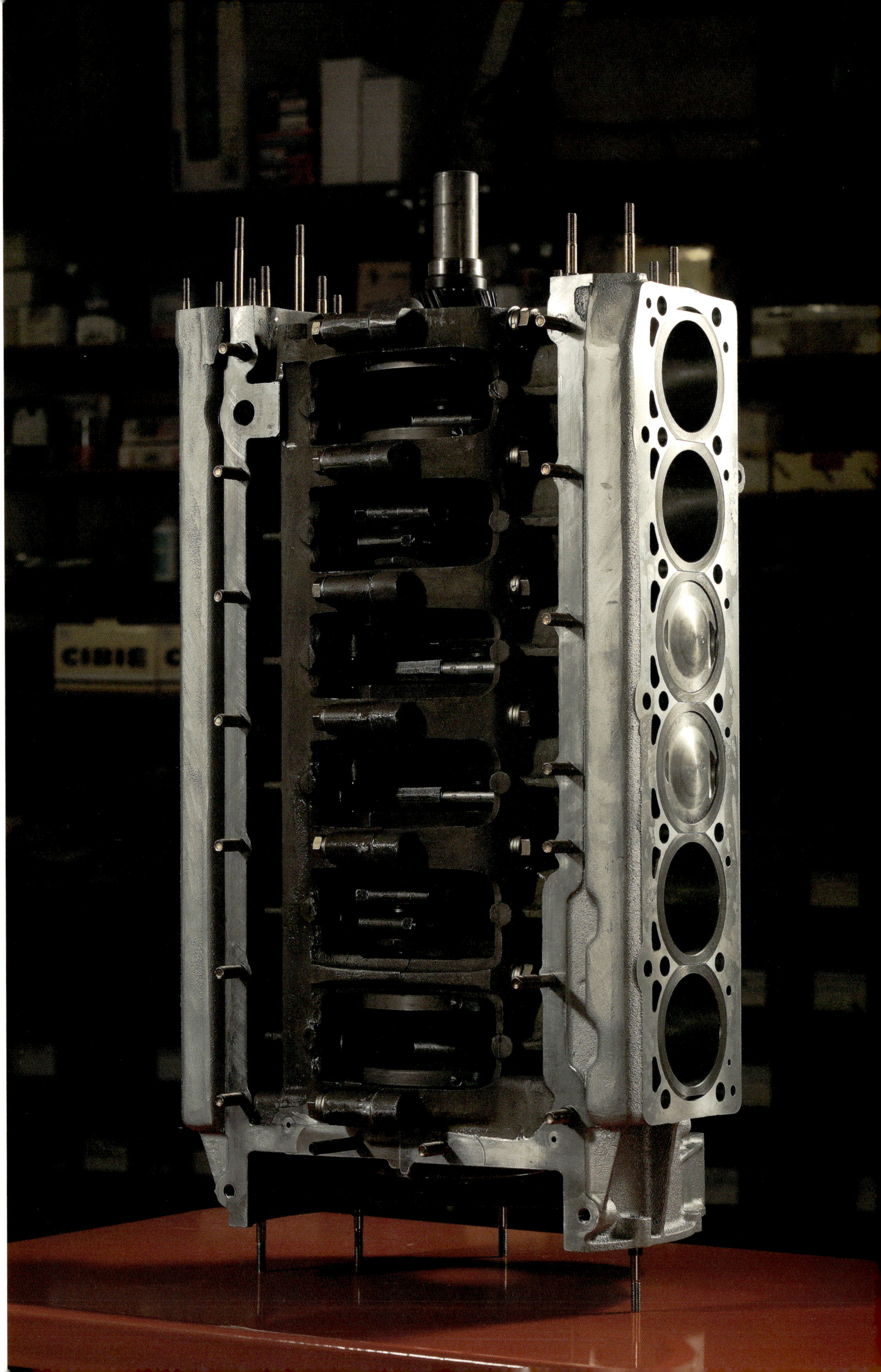
CIBIE

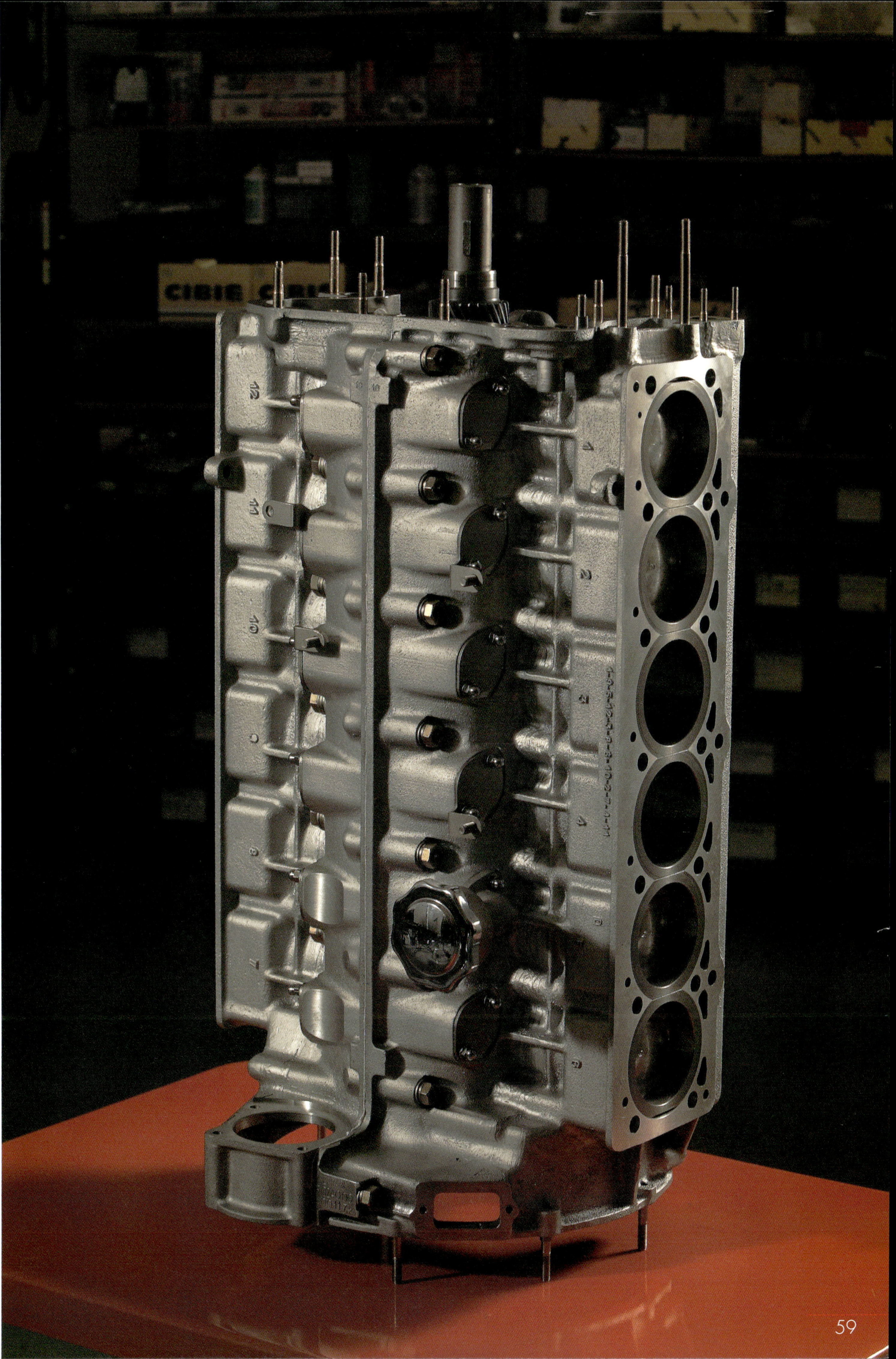
CIBIE

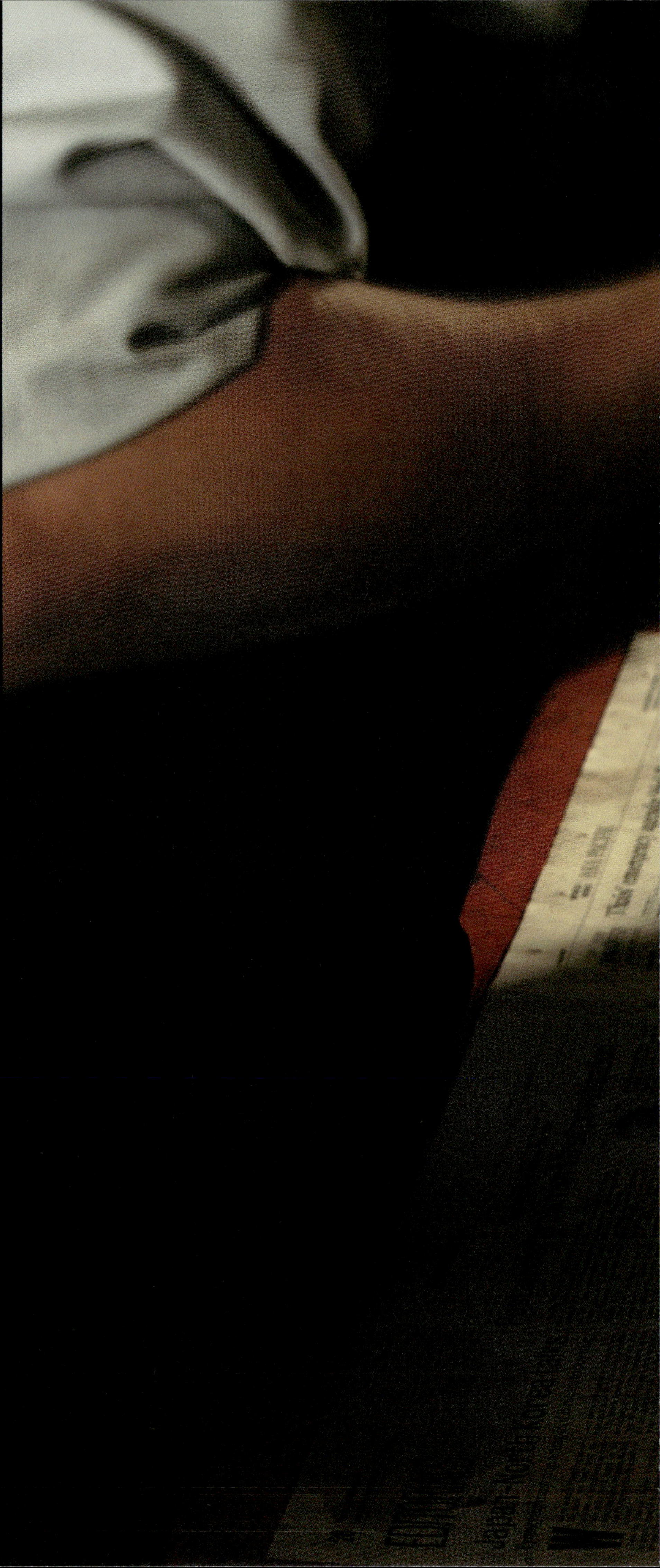

67

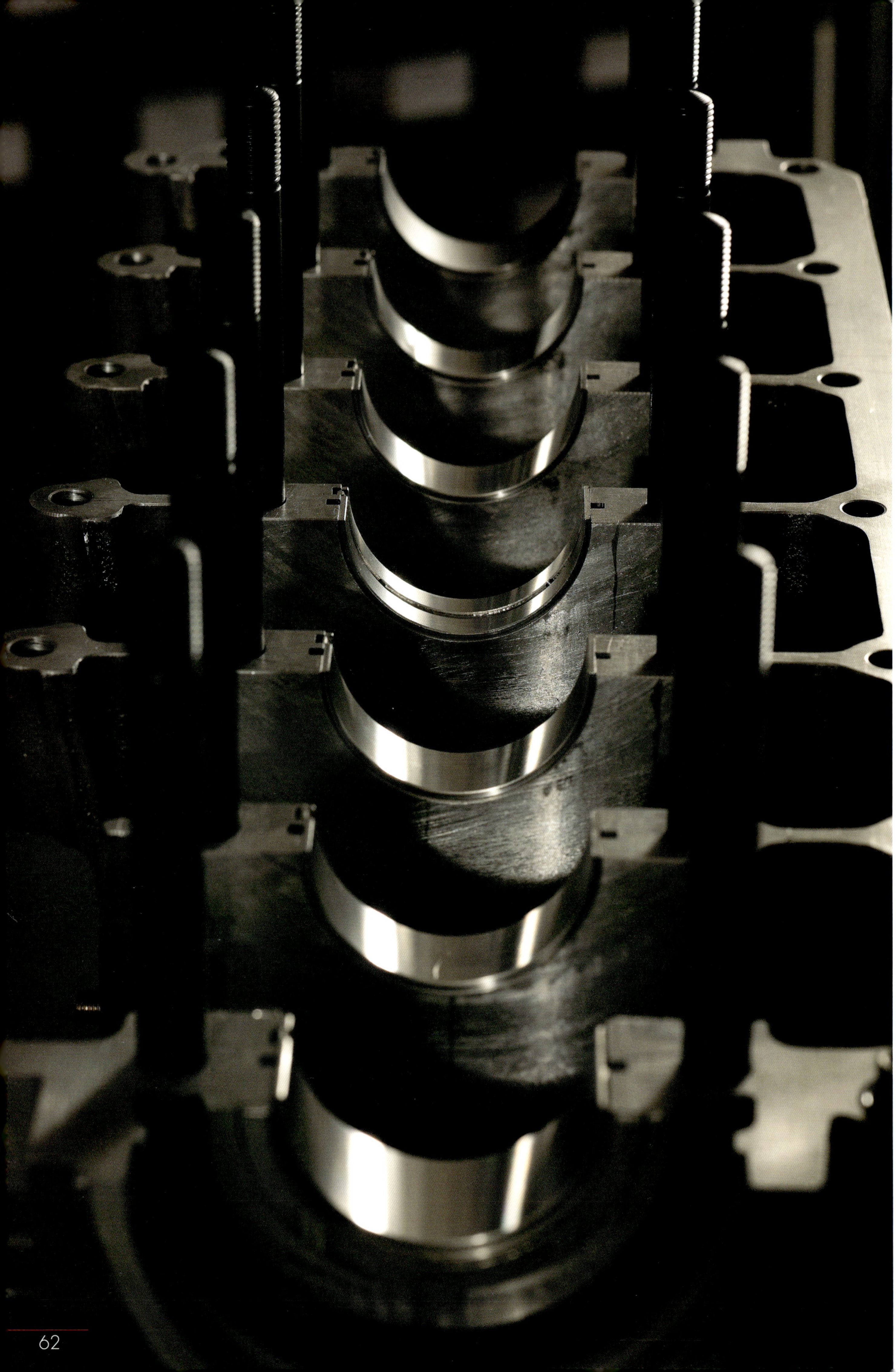

63

Opinion
EDITORIALS
INTERVIEW/
Postal reform plan isn't true privatization
VOX POPULI, VOX DEI
Artist rewriting baseball history with his bat

ASIA/PACIFIC
Thais' emergency agenda: bird flu
EBEL
For 2nd day, rebels shut much of Nepal
Japan is said to delay North Korea food aid
MaxMara

OLIO CAMBIO PONTE

67

解説：個体Ｆ102Ａ00000117エンジン および同Ｆ102AB/ZF/N.85トランスアクスル

Comments: The Engine #F102A00000117 and The Transaxle #F102AB/ZF/N.85

福野礼一郎
Ray Ichiro Fukuno

訳＝佐分利一
Translation=Hajime Saburi

エンジン＃F102A00000117搭載車
フェラーリ365GT/4 BB＃17903（個体）について

本車は2004年4月22日にイギリス・サフォーク州Felixtoweのコンテナヤード（CY）でＦＣＬ貨物として20フィートコンテナに収納されたのち、MAERSK SEA-LAND社の6600TEU型コンテナ船ARTHUR MAERSKに積載され、2004年5月26日に横浜埠頭公社南本牧MC－2号埠頭に到着した。同埠頭内コンテナフレートステーション（ＣＦＳ）にて開梱後6月4日に横浜税関にて通関、改善作業の後7月13日に横浜陸運事務所にて予備検査を取得し、同日千葉県浦安市にある整備工場ソニーズフェラーリに搬入してレストア作業に着手した。上陸後レストア開始までの走行距離は改善作業のための回送の20マイル（32km）のみである。

本書で紹介したエンジン＃F102A00000117およびトランスアクスル＃F102AB／ZF／N.85（以下「本機」）はフェラーリ365GT/4 BB＃F102AB＃17903（以下「本車」）に新車製造時から搭載されているものである。

本車はフェラーリ社が365GT/4 BBの生産および販売を開始してからおよそ7ヵ月後の1974年5月にマラネロで製造された。365GT/4 BBのボディ／シャシとしては109台目（スカリエッティ製造番号＃109）、マラネロにおける組み立て順では通算103台目に相当する（アセンブル番号＃103）。付け加えるなら本車は通算20台目に組み立てられたイギリス仕様右ハンドル車である。当時の生産管理では右ハンドル車はロット生産されており、本車製造時にもアセンブル番号＃98から＃111に至る14台の右ハンドル仕様365GT/4 BBが連続して組み立てられた。ただし各車に与えられたVINは必ずしも組み立て順の通りにはなっていない。当時のVINは同時に製造されていた365GT2+2と混流した連続番号（ただし奇数のみ）で、1975年9月以降はこれに308GTBも加えた3車混流の連続（奇数）番号になった。

Hilary A. Raab, Jr. の著書 "Ferrari Serial Numbers Part1" に掲載されている注釈によれば、同時期に作られた車両は365GT/4 BBの "2nd. Design" に相当するという。同書では＃17185〜＃17535の25台を "1st. Design"、＃17543〜＃18213の215台を "2nd. Design"、＃18217以降＃19445までの残りの147台を "3rd. Design" として分類している。その根拠については明確にされていないが、少なくとも最初の25台を "1st. Design" とした理由は、全387台の生産車のうちその25台だけがサーボタイプの同期機構（「ポルシェ・シンクロ」）を備えたトランスミッションを装備していたからだと思われる。これらの初期型トランスアクスル（F102A型）はギヤトレーンの構造・構成だけでなく、トランスアクスルケース自体の形状／仕様も大きく異なっていた。本機トランスアクスルケースには "F102AB／ZF／N.85" の打刻があるが、これは「キー・タイプの同期機構（「ワーナー・シンクロ」）を備えたZF製トランスミッションを装備する改良仕様F102AB型の85台目」の意である。サーボシンクロタイプの初期型25台を含めれば通算110台目のアクスルケースということになり、117番目のエンジン、109番目のボディ／シャシ、103番目のアセンブル順という一連の製造番号とつじつまが合う。

本車はMARANERRO CONCESSIONARES Ltd. を通じてイギリスに輸出され、1974年6月24日にチェシャー州のIan Anthony Ltd.から同州在住のオーナーへ納車された。以後の30年間をイングランドにあって4人のオーナーの下で過ごした。二番目のオーナーは15年2ヵ月におよぶ保有期間中にざっと2000マイルしか走行しなかった。また四代目オーナーは9年2ヵ月の間にわずか800マイルしか走行しなかった。新車からの積算走行距離はおよそ8000マイル余に過ぎない。だがその事実が数々の証拠によって疑問の余地なく立証されているとしても、30年間ほとんど放置されていたも同然の車両を日本に持ってきてそのまま使用に給することは到底できないため、車検取得後ただちにパワートレーンを完全に分解し、各部を点検するとともに入念なオーバーホールと総括的なコスメティックレストレーションを実施した。前者はプロの手に委ね、その合間に後者を車両の所有者である著者が自分で行なうという段取りである。

パワートレーンのレストレーションに要した手間はスリーブなどの製作を含めたオーバーホール作業に約230時間、主にDIYで行なったコスメティックレストア作業がおよそ350時間であった。

一方車両本体の状態は非常に良いのだが、それでもペイントと内装はどうしてもやり直さざるを得ず、足周りのレストアも含めればボディ／シャシに対してもおそらく今後1500時間以上の作業を必要とすると思われる。しかしそれは現時点で進行中の話であり、本書内容とはまた別のテーマである。

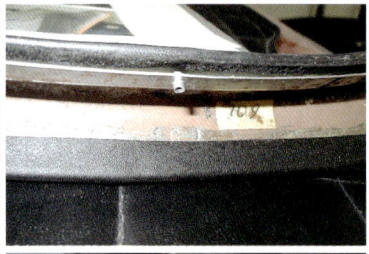

当時のフェラーリのVINはシャシ、ステアリングコラム、シャシプレートの3ヵ所に打刻されているが、ボディ／シャシ各部を分解していて発見するのは、むしろ至る所に落書きのように描かれているスカリエッティ製造番号（本車の場合＃109）である。それらはシャシの鋼材の各部、あらゆる内装材の裏側、天井の内張りの下に隠されたルーフパネル端部のレインフォースメント、そしてボンネットの裏の遮熱材を剥がしたその下（!）などに白いチョークや打刻によってこれでもかとばかりにマーキングされている。チョークによるマーキングはもちろん水で洗うだけで容易に落ちてしまうため、これらの存在はボディやそのパーツがまったく未レストア未交換の状態に保たれてきたという何よりの証明である。

About the Ferrari 365GT/4 BB #17903 with engine #F102A00000117

The engine #F102A00000117 as well as the transaxle #F102AB/ZF/N.85 (hereinafter referred to as "the unit") described in this book were mounted on Ferrari 365GT/4 BB #F102AB17903 (hereinafter referred to as "the vehicle" or "#17903") from the time of its production.

The vehicle was produced in May 1974 at Maranerro, approximately seven months after Ferrari commenced production and sale of the 365GT/4 BB. It was the 109th (Carrozzeria Scaglietti Production Number #109) body/chassis of the 365GT/4 BB, and the cumulative 103rd according to production records at Maranerro (Assembly Number #103). To be more specific, this vehicle was the 20th British version with right-hand drive. In production management of those days, the right-hand drive vehicles were produced in lots. When the vehicle was produced, 14 units of 365GT/4 BB, assembly numbers #98 through #111, were produced at the same time. However, the VIN (Vehicle Identification Number) given to each vehicle is not necessarily in order of assembly. The reason for this is that the VIN then were affixed in continuous odd numbers together with the 365GT2+2 which was produced at the same time. After September 1975, when the 308GTB was added, the numbers became continuous odd numbers for the above three car lines.

According to the book "Ferrari Serial Numbers Part 1" written by Hilary A. Raab, Jr., vehicles manufactured during that period correspond to the "2nd Design" of the 365GT/4 BB. In this book, 25 units from #17185 through #17535 are called as "1st Design", while 215 units from #17543-#18213 are categorized as "2nd Design" and the remaining 147 vehicles from #18217 till #19445 are referred to as "3rd Design." Although the reason for this categorization is unclear, it is assumed, as far as the first 25 units are concerned, that they were called "1st Design" because out of the entire production of 387 units, only those 25 cars were equipped with transmissions having servo-type synchronization mechanism ("Porsche synchro"). Those early versions differed considerably not only in structure and construction, but in terms of shape and specifications of the transaxle case itself. On this unit's transaxle case, there is a stamping "F102AB/ZF/N.85", which may indicate that this transaxle is the 85th axle-case built for transmission with a key-type synchronization mechanism ("Warner Synchro"). Should this be the case, the axle-case from the initial 25 units fitted with servo-synchro type would be the 110th unit. This is fully coherent with the series of production numbers such as the 117th engine, 109th body/chassis and the assembly order of 103.

This vehicle was exported to England through Maranerro Concessionares Ltd., and was delivered by Ian Anthony Ltd., of Cheshire on June 24, 1974 to the first owner living in the area. For the next 30 years, the vehicle stayed in England going through four owners. The second owner drove only approximately 2,000 miles in the fifteen years and two months he had the vehicle, and the fourth owner registered a mere 800 miles during nine years and two months' ownership. The cumulative odometer reading from initial production is only slightly more than 8,000 miles. In spite of the fact that these facts are proven beyond any doubt from various evidences, I was not at all inclined to drive the vehicle "as is", knowing that it was virtually left unattended for nearly 30 years. Therefore, immediately after obtaining the "Shaken" (Japanese roadworthiness registration) I decided to take the entire power-train apart in order to check the various components and carry out a complete overhaul as well as comprehensive cosmetic restoration. The former was entrusted to the hands of professionals, while the latter was to be carried out by this author who is the owner of the vehicle. The time required for restoration of the power-train was approximately 230 hours for the overhauling job including production of sleeves, etc., and another approximately 350 hours for the cosmetic restoration which was mostly a "DIY" or Do It Yourself-work. On the other hand, while the overall condition of the vehicle itself is extremely good, the paint job and interior had to be redone, and that together with the restoration of the running gear will eventually amount to more than 1,500 hours for body/chassis. That, however, is a matter which is on-going at this time and therefore a totally different theme from the contents of this book.

車載速度計の距離表示はレストア開始の時点で8052マイルを示している。この数値が新車以来30年間の真の走行距離であることを証明しているのは、無数の書類の存在に加えてすべての機械構造的要素が示している客観的な状況である。シリンダ内壁は100分の1～2ミリしか摩耗しておらず、5速ギヤのシンクロ機構にはほとんど噛動痕が看取できず、内装を取り去った車内はワイヤハーネスや電気系を含めてまったく新車同様の状態で、驚くべきことにボディ／シャシ各部の塗装の下にもごくわずかの錆しか認められなかった。構造上バラでも分解すればその痕跡が残る速度計自体にも、手を触れたと思しき形跡は一切認められなかった。

前オーナーより譲り受けたドキュメント類。革製のオリジナルドキュメントケース、オーナーズマニュアル84／73、パーツリスト89／73、輸入元(MARANERRO CONCESSIONARES Ltd.)発行の記録簿、新車保証書(以上新車時付属品)およびカタログ83／73など。いずれも痛みはほとんど見られず新品同様の状態だった。この他13年分のMOTテスト証明書原本、過去における重整備時の作業明細、過去の中古車販売時に発行された真正証明書、そして古びた31本の8トラックカセットテープまで含まれていた。

Historical Facts of #17903

Date	Mileage	Evidence
24 June, 1974		Registration warranty & motor vehicle inspection certificate. Dealer: Ian Anthony Ltd.
10 November, 1974	627mile	350/500mile inspection record
30 April, 1975	1682mile	900/1250mile inspection record
8 December, 1976	3900mile	Sold as used car: Ian Anthony Ltd.
8 May, 1981	5353mile	MOT certificate
29 June, 1984	5457mile	MOT certificate
23 March, 1990	5643mile	MOT certificate
8 April, 1992	5929mile	Vehicle maintenance record
23 June, 1992	5948mile	MOT certificate
30 April, 1993	6338mile	Vehicle maintenance record
5 May, 1993	6347mile	MOT certificate
13 May, 1994	6705mile	Vehicle maintenance record
5 July, 1994	6854mile	Trade-in document: William Loughran Ltd.
27 July, 1994	7089mile	MOT certificate
15 September, 1994	7221mile	Sold as used car: William Loughran Ltd.
28 July, 1995	7342mile	MOT certificate
8 October, 1996	7502mile	MOT certificate
2 October, 1997	7812mile	MOT certificate
31 July, 1998	7955mile	MOT certificate
9 October, 1999	7972mile	MOT certificate
5 September, 2000	7981mile	MOT certificate
27 November, 2003	8001mile	Odometer reading, photo from Duncan Hamilton & Co.
26 April, 2004	8011mile	Vehicle maintenance record & MOT certificate at the time of change of ownership.

*MOT is a mandatory annual test of safety and roadworthiness aspects of vehicles over a certain age in the UK.

エンジンの分解
Disassembly of the Engine

73

アルミ砂型鋳物部品の生産技術的考察

よく知られているように70年代末に至るまでフェラーリのエンジンの主構造部分は焼結粘土製の中子を併用したアルミ砂型鋳物によって作られていた。フェラーリが自社内にアルミ砂型鋳物工場を設置し原形木型から鋳造／加工までを一貫して行なうようになったのは1954年のことで、これによって独自の材料レシピによる品質／生産性の向上や設計変更に対する柔軟な対応などが可能となり、レーシングマシン作りにおいてはとりわけ強みとなった。

もちろん1990年代以前には部品の正確な三次元的形状を決定する設計手法は事実上存在しなかった。設計者が行なうのは一般的に言えば断面形状および主要寸法と加工公差の決定、おおまかな外観の指定だけであり、実際の部品の細部形状は生産技術に委ねられることがほとんどだった。砂型鋳造の場合で言うなら部品の外観細部の形状を決定していたのは砂型をひとつひとつ作る際の原型雄型となる木型を作る木型職人だった。

365GT/4 BB用パワーユニットの木型を製作するに際してフェラーリの職人が念頭に置いていたのは、出来うる限り部品を肉薄に作ることだったと思われる。この結果エンジンの各部品の外観は、内部のメカニズムの正確な反映といってもよい様な独特の機能美を呈するに至った。このような複雑な形状を木材料で作るためには多大の労力と熱意、製作技術を要することは想像に難くないが、各部に配した細かいリブや凝ったR面形状など、時には楽しんで作っているとしか思えないような繊細な造形がそこここに散見されて、まったく見る者を飽きさせない。

多くの専門書はフェラーリのエンジンの鋳物素材として「シルミン」という名を掲げている。シルミンはシリコンを10%程度含有した鋳造用アルミ合金の代表的な素材の一般名称であり、もちろんフェラーリだけの特殊なものではない。Alは凝固の際の収縮が大きく溶解時にガス吸収してピンホールを作りやすいので、鋳造用材料の場合合金元素の添加量を増やし、融点を下げ、強度的に若干妥協してでも鋳造性を重視したレシピを作るのが通常である。Siの添加もそのためだが、Siを入れると結晶が粗大になって機械的性質が低下するため、少量のNaを加えて結晶の微細化を図ることが多い。この合金を通常シルミンと呼んでいるが、さらに少量のMgやCuを添加して耐力、高温強さ、疲労強さ、切削性を改善したものもある。前者をガンマシルミン、後者を含銅シルミンなどと呼称する。フェラーリ独自の材料レシピが例え存在するにせよ、いずれにしろ1%以下の金属元素の添加を云々する内容のはずであり素材の根本的な特殊性を意味するものではない。今回のコスメティックレストア作業においてはすべてのアルミ砂型鋳物部品の表面をガラスビーズでショットブラストし、ガスケット面等の切削加工部をペーパー研磨／再切削加工したが、表面硬度が純アルミと変わらないくらい柔らかく（HV60～70程度と類推）比較的ねばりが少なくて研磨・切削の切れ味がよく、酸／アルカリ等で容易に黒く変色することから、主要部品の材質はAl-Si-Cu系（含銅シルミン系）ではないかと推察する。

この時代から生き残ってきた古いフェラーリ車のエンジン外装部は銀色の塗料で塗装してあることが多く、そのためもあって「新車時から塗装仕上げだった」とする認識もあるようだが、少なくとも70年代当時著者が新車で見たフェラーリに塗装仕上げを施したエンジンは一基もなかった。アルミは表面の酸化が早くしかも不均等に進行するため塗料の密着性に劣り、専用の下地処理を必要とする（陽極電解処理やジンククロメート塗装などのアルミ用特殊下地塗装等）ため、自動車部品の場合塗装仕上げはほとんど行なわれていない。

フェラーリでは当時アルミ砂型鋳物パーツの表面に製造工程でサンドブラストを施していた。写真にそれを示す一例を掲げる。各部を観察すれば、バリ取りやヤスリがけ等の手作業の後、切削加工ラインにおける機械加工の前にブラストが行なわれていたことは明白である。鋳造時の砂落としと均質な外観のために鋳造した品物をブラスト加工するのは珍しいことではない。したがって当時の工場における生産工程は①鋳造②手作業によるバリ取りとパーティングライン処理③サンドブラストによる砂落としと手加工部の外観処理④内面部塗装（新品時ダークライムグリーンのツヤ消し）⑤機械加工⑥手加工による機械加工エッジ部C面取り、という手順であったと推察できる。エンジンのアルミ部品すべてについて精査したがいずれも同じ工程を示唆していた。

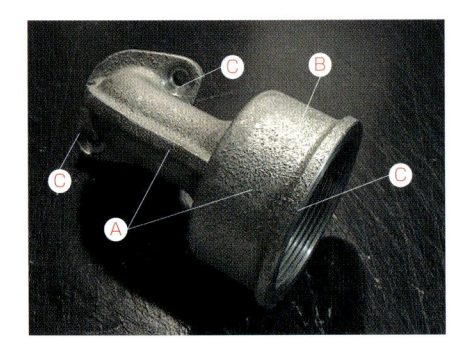

アルミ部品の製造工程が伺われる一例。A部には手加工によるヤスリがけが施してあるが、キズミで観察するとサンドブラストはその作業を終えた後に行なわれていることが分かる。B部にはたまたまブラストが上手にかかっていないためアルミ鋳物独特の非常に光沢のある鋳造時の鋳肌がそのまま残っている。C部は機械加工がブラストの後に行われていたこと、ブラストが後年のレストア作業によるものではないことの二点を示している。

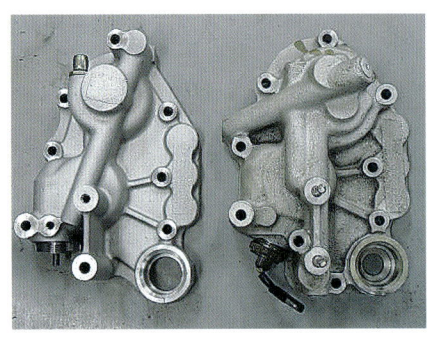

木型職人が見せる類いまれな造形力。トランスアクスルケース前面につくトランスミッションシャフトのエンドカバー部である。左がレストアを終えた本機のもの、右は512BBi（F110A型）用。形状は内部メカニズムの正確な反映で、例えば右端のひょうたんの用な奇妙な形状は三本の変速用フォークシャフトの末端部である（その下の開口部がシフトリンケージ出口）。

Study on Production Technology for Aluminum Components made by Sand Castings

It is widely known that until the end of the seventies, the major components of the Ferrari engines were produced by aluminum sand castings using sintered clay core. In 1954, Ferrari started continuous casting/processing using wooden patterns at its own aluminum sand casting facility. This enabled improved quality and productivity through use of original material recipe as well as coping flexibly to design modifications, which obviously was of special advantage in producing racing machines.

Of course, in the days prior to 1990's, there virtually was no design methodology to decide precise three dimensional shapes of components. Generally speaking, a car designer's responsibilities were limited to deciding major specifications, tolerance allowances and general exterior design. Therefore, in most instances, fixing the detailed shape of components was entrusted to production engineers. For example, regarding sand castings, the decisive factors in fixing the outer details of parts were the wooden pattern which was the original male die. These were made by gifted wood pattern craftsmen. The Ferrari craftsmen in making the wooden patterns for power units of the 365GT/4 BB made them as thin as possible. As a result, the various components of the engine were unique in way of functional beauty and precision of the inner mechanism. It is not hard to imagine the magnitude of effort, passion and manufacturing technique required in fabricating such a complicated form with wooden material and looking at delicate moldings such as minute ribs and elaborate R-surface shapes, etc., one is inclined to believe that the craftsmen enjoyed doing such a delicate work. This is something which has a special appeal to a keen observer.

In most professional literature, "Silumin" is mentioned as the casting material for Ferrari engines. Silumin is a generally accepted name for a representative material for aluminum alloy casting having approximately 10% Silicon content, and of course not particular to Ferrari. As Al (Aluminum) has large contraction during solidification, pinholes are liable to occur from gas absorption during smelting. Therefore, it is customary in case of casting material to increase the amount of alloy element additive in order to lower the melting point and concoct a recipe focusing on casting capabilities even by compromising slightly in strength. Addition of Si (Silicon) is also for the same purpose, but as it will lower the mechanical characteristics from rougher crystallization, a small amount of Na (Sodium) is added to make the crystallization as minute as possible. This alloy is normally called as Silumin, but there are cases where small amounts of Mg (Magnesium) or Cu (Copper) are added to improve durability, strength against high temperature, anti-fatigue properties and cutting characteristics. The former is called "γ-Silumin" while the later is referred to as "Cu-Silumin." Even if Ferrari's peculiar material recipe exists, it will be a matter of discussing addition of alloy elements of below 1%, and not a matter of arguing the fundamental particularity of the material. During the cosmetic restoration jobs carried out at this time, surfaces of all components made by aluminum sand casting were shot-blasted by glass beads, and all parts made by milling such as gasket surfaces, were polished by abrasive paper but the surface hardness was found to be almost as soft as pure aluminum (assumed to be in the range of HV60-70). From this as well as the fact that viscosity was relatively low with favorable polishing/cutting properties and as the color changed to black rather easily by acid or alkali, it is conjectured that the quality of materials for the major components are of Al-Si-Cu (Cu-Silumin) character.

In most instances, the exterior parts of the surviving old Ferrari cars from this era are painted in silver paint, which lead to the assumption that "They were painted from the very beginning." However, at least in the '70s, there was not a single painted engine among all the brand new Ferrari cars inspected by this author. As oxidation occurs fast and unevenly on aluminum surfaces, resulting in poor paint adherence, exclusive substrate treatment (special substrate painting for aluminum such as anode electrolysis treatment or zinc chromate painting) is required. Therefore, paint finish is seldom seen on automotive components.

In Ferrari's production process of those days, surfaces of parts made by aluminum sand casting were sand blasted. Photographs showing this process are shown. By observing the respective components, it is obvious that after the manual jobs such as removal of burrs and filings, and prior to milling on the machining line, blast was applied. It is not unusual to blast-process the cast components to remove sand from casting as well as to achieve a uniform exterior. It is assumed that the production processes at the factory then were; ①casting ②manual work to remove burrs and parting line process ③sand removal by sand blast and exterior treatment of hand-produced parts ④inner surface painting (matt dark lime green on new cars) ⑤machining ⑥manual work to remove blemishes caused by milling process. Detailed investigations of all aluminum components in the engine were suggestive of the same production sequences.

1977年6月にマラネロの生産ライン上で撮影した512BBのパワーユニット。アルミ表面にはもちろん塗装は施されておらず、さりとて砂型鋳造の鋳肌のままでもない。高圧でサンドブラストを施した典型的な表面である。ナット類にはこのころから亜鉛クロメートめっきに変わって上等なニッケルめっきが使われ始めたが、テスタロッサの時代に下ると再びクロメートに逆戻りした。

F102A型およびその改良版F102AB型パワートレーンの設計

　F102A型およびその改良版F102AB型パワートレーンは、1970年代初頭に設計され1990年代中盤のF512M用F113Gユニットに至るまで23年間の長きに渡って作られた一連のミドシップ搭載用フェラーリ12気筒パワーユニットの、その初期のモデルである。設計の基本方針がパワートレーン・パッケージとしての小型・軽量化にあったことは設計概要を鳥瞰するだけでも明らかだが、実設計における小型化（＝軽量化）の手法は一口に言えば「フェラーリ既存メカニズムの踏襲および統合」であったと言える。クランクシャフトからの出力をクラッチを介したのちベルハウジング外側に置いた3列のギヤで等速ギヤ伝達し、エンジン直下に置いたトランスミッションのインプットシャフトに送るという「2階建て」構造は、1966年に発表されそののち市販に移された206GT用135BS型65度V型6気筒およびその発展型135CS型（246GT用）パワートレーンの設計を踏襲したものである。12気筒化にあたっては重心高を下げるためエンジンに水平対向型レイアウトを採用しており、これがBB（Berlinetta Boxer）という車名の由来であるが、エンジンそのものの基本設計は365GTB／4用（以下俗称名「デイトナ」）251型60度V型12気筒の流用である。ボア・ストローク比、ボアピッチ寸法、シリンダスリーブ設計仕様、クランクシャフト・ジャーナル径／長、コンロッド小端部・大端部径とセンターディスタンス、バルブ挟角、バルブトレーン構造などの基本設計はもとより、各主要部品製造時の寸法およびその公差までデイトナ用251型のものをそっくり使っている。メカニズムの実際としてもこのエンジンはデイトナ用60°V12の180°レイアウト版に他ならず、よく言われているような同時期のフェラーリの水平対向型4ベアリング式レーシングエンジンとの血縁関係は設計的に見ると一切存在しない。もちろん左右分割方式のクランクケースなどのエンジン主構造は母体となったV型エンジンとは根本的に大きく異なっているわけで、基本設計データや部品そのものを流用するというその開発手法に設計的誤算が生じ易いことは想像に難くない。

　前記の通りトランスアクスルは206／246GT用（および後の308／328系用）同様エンジン直下に置かれているが、パワートレーンを縦置き搭載とした関係上、デファレンシャル中心軸はトランスミッションの入／出力軸と並行にではなく、ハイポイドギヤを介してケース後端部にこの場合直角に配置されている。この設計はむしろ275GTB／4で採用されデイトナに引き継がれたFRレイアウト用のトランスアクスルケースに酷似しており、シフトフォークおよびそのシャフトの配列・機構、点検パネルのレイアウトなどにも多くの共通点が見られる。おそらく初期の25台に搭載されたサーボ式同期機構付きトランスミッションの主要パーツは、デイトナ用トランスアクスルのものを一部流用していたと思われる。デファレンシャルユニット自体もデイトナ用とほぼ同構造だが、直上にエンジンを据える都合上リングギヤ・ピッチ円径を小型化せざるを得ず、歯車設計上の許容応力設定がデイトナのものに比べ大幅に低下している。このような妥協にもかかわらずエンジンとの構造的干渉は回避できず、エンジン側も構造的に譲歩したことが伺われる。

　F102A型およびF102AB型パワートレーンは、長大なデイトナ用の60°V12エンジン、クラッチ、ドライブシャフトおよびトランスアクスル機構のすべてをV12エンジン単体一基分ほどのスペースに収めようとした大胆かつ冒険的な構想のパワーユニットである。しかしながら本書で指摘するように機関設計の根幹に関わる多くの問題をかかえており、設計的配慮および開発が不足していたことは明らかである。1973年9月発行のカタログ83/73はエンジンの最高出力として380bhp/7700rpmという値を標榜していたが、ほぼ同時期に印刷され車両1台につき1冊ずつ搭載されていたオーナーズマニュアル84/73には、344bhp/7200rpmという遥かに低い数値が記載されていた。補器類の選定やプーリ比などの設定も含めたその設計仕様を詳しく検討すれば、いずれにせよF102AおよびAB型パワートレーンの設計が7000rpmを常用するような超高性能エンジンを意図したものではなかったことが分かる。例外はかぶり易いコールドタイプの点火プラグと超高性能車並みに濃い空燃比の設定だが、これこそが365GT/4 BBをとりわけ気難しく扱い難いクルマにしていた理由であることを想起するなら、人々が長い間抱いてきたイメージとは裏腹なその本質が垣間見えてくるだろう。すなわちこれは「実用性を身につけたレーシングエンジン」ではなく、他のほとんどのフェラーリ・ロードカーのものがそうであったように「レーシングカー的な演出を施した乗用車エンジン」に他ならないのである。

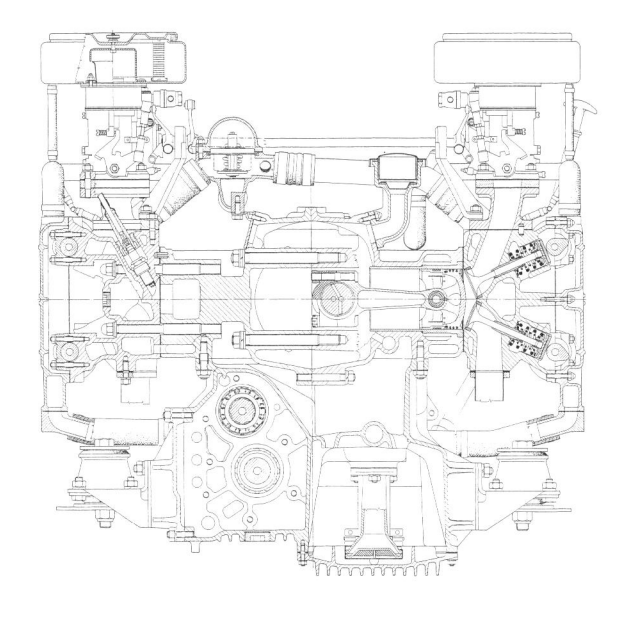

180度V型エンジン直下にトランスミッションを置いた二階建て構造を示す。図は一番シリンダ付近の断面で、トランスミッション部と隣り合うエンジンオイルタンクとの位置関係が分かる。デファレンシャル部の横断面については別項参照。この図ではエンジン直下に随分スペース的な余裕があるように見えるが、デファレンシャル収納部では寸法的にぎりぎりで、両者干渉している。ケース各部は砂型鋳造の限界といえるまで肉薄である。
〈Istruzioni per le Riparazioni（以下「サービスマニュアル」）No.95990807より転載〉

Design of Type F102AB Power-Train

The engine type F102A and transaxle F102AB (hereinafter referred to as "Type F102AB power-train"), designed in early 1970's was the very first model of the series of Ferrari's 12 cylinder power unit to be mounted on mid-ship cars, and had a long lifespan of 23 years until the mid 1990's when the F113G power unit for Ferrari F512M appeared. From a glance at its design outline, it is clear that the basic design policy was to make the power-train package as small and light as possible, and the actual design method to attain this aim was, in a nutshell, "Follow the steps of and integrate the existing Ferrari mechanism." The so-called "Two storied" construction in which the output from the crankshaft is fed via clutch by constant velocity gear transmission to a set of 3 gears at the outer side of bell-housing from where the power is delivered to the input shaft of the transmission located right beneath the engine, was actually inherited from the power-trains of the 65° V-6 engine type 135BS for the 206GT which was announced in 1966 and sold subsequently as well as its derivative type 135CS power-train for 246GT. In making the 12 cylinder engine, a horizontally-opposed layout was adopted to lower the height of center of gravity, and that was the origin of the car's name BB (Berlinetta Boxer). But the basic design of the engine itself was taken from the type 251 60° V-12 engine for the 365GTB/4 (hereinafter referred to by its nickname "Daytona"). Not to speak of basic designs such as bore/stroke ratio, bore pitch dimension, design specifications of cylinder sleeve, diameter and length of crankshaft journal, diameters of small and large end bores of connecting rod, center distance, valve angle and construction of valve train, the production dimensions and tolerances of major components were identical to those of Daytona's type 251. From the mechanism, too, this engine is merely a 180° version of the 60° V-12 for Daytona. Contrary to some theories, there is no blood relation whatsoever with Ferrari's horizontally-opposed racing engine with 4 bearings of the same period as far as design aspects are concerned. Of course, the main structure of the engine such as the crankcase which is divided in left and right parts are fundamentally different from the V-type engine from which it stemmed, and it is not hard to presume that the development method of inheriting basic design data and components themselves will cause miscalculations in design.

As enumerated earlier, the transaxle is located right under the engine as in the 206/246GT series (and later in the 308/328 series), but due to the vertical mounting of the power-train, the center shaft of the differential is not parallel with input/output shafts of transmission but is located in right angle at rear end of casing via a hypoid gear. In fact, this design has a strong resemblance with the transaxle case for front-engine/rear-drive layout which was adopted for 275GTB/4 and subsequently carried over to Daytona, and there are many commonalities such as shift fork and layout/function of its shaft, layout of inspection panel, etc. I assume that the main parts of the transmission with servo-synchro mechanism which were installed in the first 25 units were actually derived from Daytona's transaxle. The differential unit itself is of almost same construction as Daytona, but as it was necessary to make the ring gear pitch diameter smaller in order to mount the engine directly above, the designed specification of the gear was drastically lower than those of the Daytona. In spite of such compromises, it was not possible to evade constructional interference with the engine, and it could be observed that certain structural concessions, were made to the engine.

The F120A and the F102AB is a power unit with a daring and adventurous concept in which the long and big 60° V-12 engine, clutch, driveshaft as well as the transaxle mechanism for the Daytona are all contained in a space as small as size of one V-12 engine. However, as pointed out in this book, there were numerous problems which influenced the fundamentals of engine performance. It is self-evident that there were decisive lack of considerations and development at the time of initial designing. In the catalogue 83/73 issued in September 1973, the maximum output of the engine is given as 380bhp/7700rpm, but in the owners' manual 84/73 delivered with each vehicle and printed at almost the same time, the maximum output is given as 344bhp/7200rpm. However, from detailed evaluation of the design specifications such as selection of accessories and the pulley ratio, it could be perceived in any case that the power trains of the Type F102A and AB were not intended for super-high performance engines which will be operated regularly at 7000rpm. The only exceptions are the cold type spark plugs which are liable to get wet and the rich air/fuel ratio resembling a super-high performance vehicle. But if we recall that these were the reasons for making the 365GT/4 BB so delicate and difficult to tame, the real essence of the car contradicts with the image nurtured by the general public for a long time. In other words, this is not "a racing engine with inherent practicality," but nothing but "a passenger car engine produced with a racing car-like personality," as in the case of almost all Ferrari road cars.

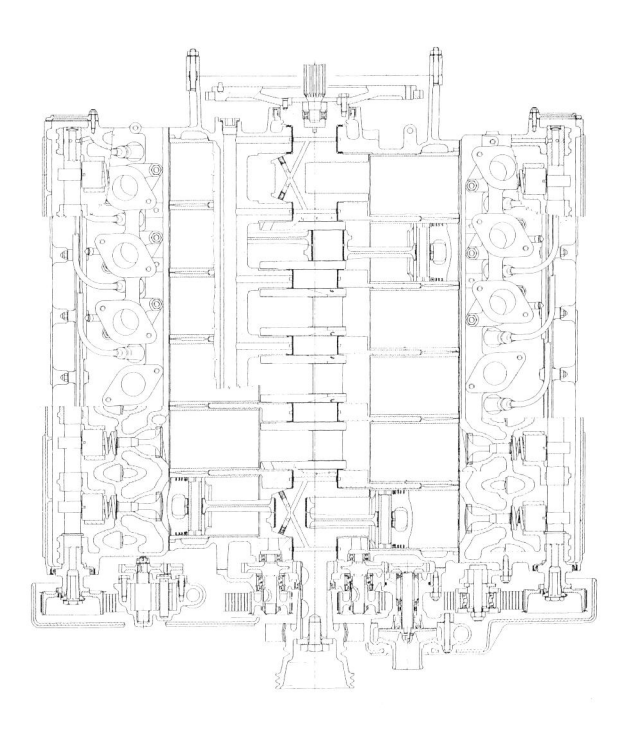

往復運動部の設計はデイトナ用251型エンジンと共用しており、バンク角を180度にした以外基本的に同一のパーツを使用していると考えてよい。カムシャフト駆動機構はチェーンからベルト式に変わったが、それ以外の部分のヘッド周りの基本設計もほとんど251型を踏襲したものである。詳細後述。〈サービスマニュアルNo.95990807より転載〉

クランクケースの設計仕様

レーシングエンジンの世界では水平対向レイアウトの経験をすでに積んでいたフェラーリだが、デイトナ用251型60°V12を180°レイアウト化するに際してそれらの設計がそのまま流用されたわけではない。

水平対向型エンジンはクランクシャフトの保持を左右二分割のケースの結合によって行なっており、直列／V型エンジンのようなメインベアリングキャップを持たない。このためクランクシャフト保持剛性はクランクケースの構造とその締め付け方法の如何で決定する。また基本構造上、高剛性を確保しようとすると設計が複雑化して製造工数および組み立て／整備工数が増えやすい。

本機F102A型用クランクケースはこうした点に配慮しながら量産車用水平対向型エンジンとしてまったく新たに設計された物である。全体に構造はシンプルで生産性が高くかつ軽量で、ウエットライナーの冷却性を各気筒均一化するためにサイドウォータギャラリーを設けたり、ケース上面にコンロッドボルトの締め付け用アクセスホールを開けて組み立て工数の低減を図るなどの工夫も見られる反面、クランクケース剛性およびクランクシャフト保持剛性については高出力・高回転を目指す大排気量エンジンとして十分なものであったとは言い難く、本機固有の問題点の主因もおそらくその点にあると思われる。

Design Specifications of the Crankcase

While Ferrari had ample experience regarding the horizontally-opposed layout in the world of racing engines, such designs were not necessarily adopted in making the Type 251 60° V12 of the Daytona into 180° layout. In case of horizontally-opposed engines, the crankshaft is held by joining the two left/right halves of the casing, without main bearing caps as in the case of in-line/V engines. Therefore, the holding accuracy of the crankshaft depends on the construction of the crankcase and its tightening method. Also, due to its basic construction, the design becomes complicated if high rigidity is to be secured, resulting in increment of production as well as assembly/maintenance processes. Therefore, it could be said that the crankcase of this Type F102A was designed totally anew as a horizontally-opposed engine for a serially produced car by taking such aspects into consideration. Overall, the construction is simple, designed for high productivity and light weight, incorporating such ideas as using side water galleries on wet liner to achieve uniform cooling of each cylinder and lessening the assembly process by making access holes on upper casing to facilitate tightening of connecting-rod bolts. On the other hand, the rigidity of crankcase and supporting rigidity of crankshaft are far from being sufficient for a large displacement engine targeting high revolutions and it is presumed that those are the main reasons for the inherent problems of this unit.

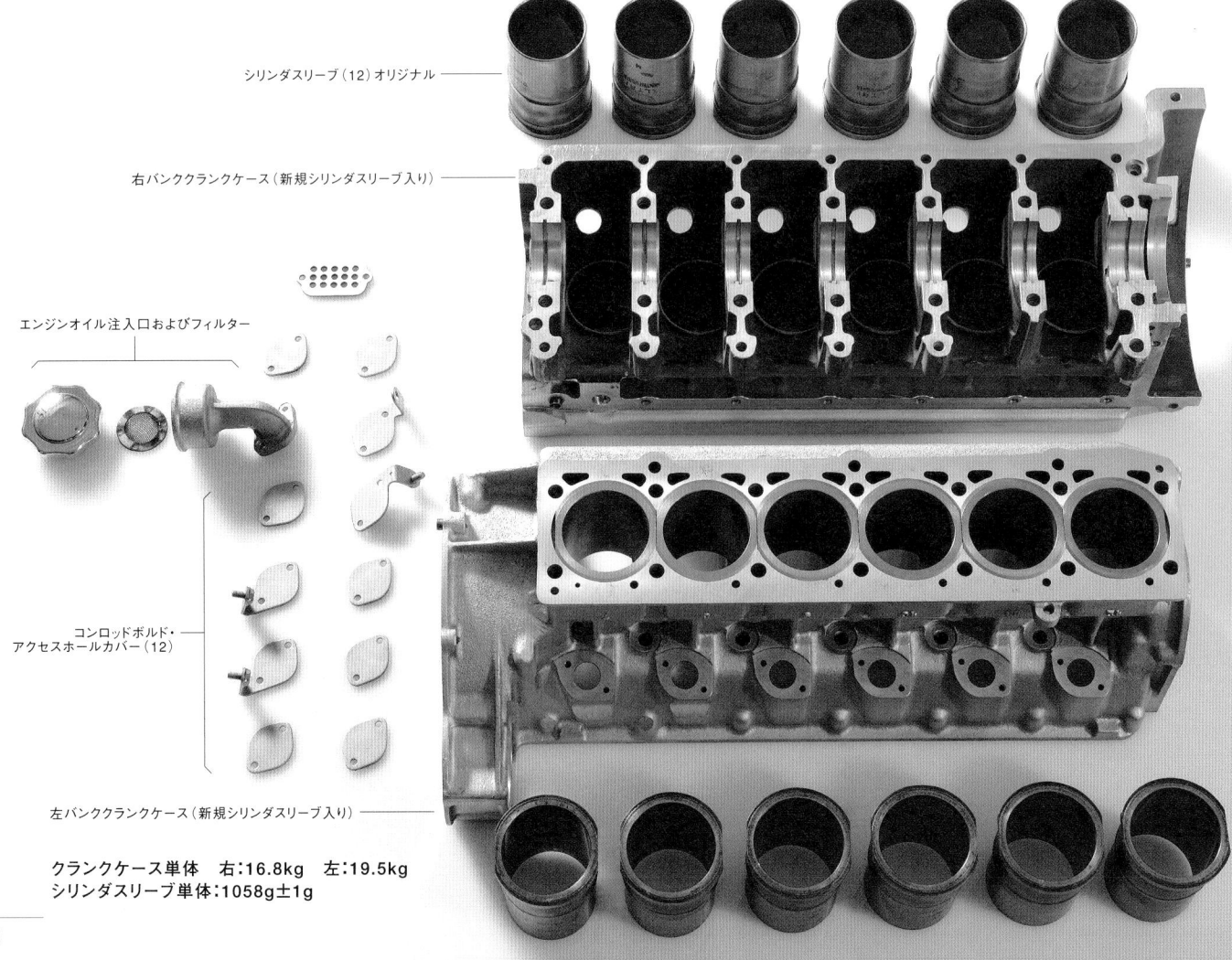

- シリンダスリーブ（12）オリジナル
- 右バンククランクケース（新規シリンダスリーブ入り）
- エンジンオイル注入口およびフィルター
- コンロッドボルド・アクセスホールカバー（12）
- 左バンククランクケース（新規シリンダスリーブ入り）

クランクケース単体　右：16.8kg　左：19.5kg
シリンダスリーブ単体：1058g±1g

クランクケースの製造仕様

Production Specifications of the Crankcase

　クランクケースはアルミ砂型鋳物製左右分割構造で、冷却水路およびオイル通路は中子で抜き、鋳鉄製機械加工のシリンダスリーブ（ライナー）をOリングを介して挿入している。これらの仕様はそれまでの60°V12フェラーリ市販車用エンジンと基を一にしているが、ケースはアルミ砂型鋳造の限界といえるほど薄肉・軽量に作られている。スリーブ／スタッドなしのクランクケース単体重量は右バンク16.8kg、左バンク19.5kg（いずれも実測値）で、4ℓ級V12エンジンとしては異例に小型・軽量であったデイトナ用251型のエンジンブロック本体より20%近く軽い。この時代のフェラーリ・エンジンは市販車用／レーシングカー用の区別を問わず、エンジン内面部に相当する箇所の全域にツヤのないライムグリーンの塗装を施していた。砂落ちの防止とオイル落下性の向上に期待した措置だと思われるが、下地にサンドブラスト以外何らの前処理も施していないため、とりわけヘッド周辺部などは塗膜が剥落しやすく、これがオイルフィルターに詰まるなど逆効果のことの方が多かった。色調から察してクロムを含む塗料だと思われるが、油温をあげたことのあるエンジンでは茶色く酸化変色していることが多く、エンジンの履歴を知るひとつの目安にはなる。

The crankcase is of sand cast aluminum construction divided into left and right sections, with cooling water jacket and oil passage made by a core. Cylinder sleeve (liners) made of cast iron and machining is inserted via an O-ring. While such specifications are identical with the 60° V-12 Ferrari engines used in serial production cars, the case is so thin and light that it could be described as the limit of aluminum sand casting technique. The weight of crankcase itself without sleeves/studs are, in actual measurements, right bank 16.8kg and left bank 19.5kg, or almost 20% lighter than the engine block of Type 251 engine for Daytona, which was exceptionally small and light for a 4-liter class V-12 engine. In both serial production and racing cars, Ferrari engines of those times had matted lime-green colored paint on all inner surfaces presumably to prevent sand dropping from casting mold and improve oil down-flow. However, as there was no pretreatment process other than sand blasting on backing, paint membrane especially around the head area tended to peel off and get stuck in the oil filter, to bring about the opposite effect. Conjecturing from the color tone, the paint must have contained chrome because brownish oxidative discoloring is often noticed in engines operated at high oil temperatures. This is one standard used in determining the engine's history.

　クランクケース下部にオイルパンを配する形式のフェラーリ水平対向型レーシングエンジンと同様ケース下面は開断面構造で、ポルシェのような閉断面ケースに比べると剛性が低くなりやすい基本形態である。本機では右バンク側ケースのベアリングジャーナル部16ヵ所のM14スタッド／ナットおよび外縁部15ヵ所のM10ボルト／ナットで左右ケースを締結しているだけで、結合剛性についてもあまり高い印象は受けない。例えば312B型レーシングユニットは左右ケースにそれぞれスタッドを立てケース相互が締め付け合う設計をしているし、ポルシェ901型は6気筒にもかかわらず閉断面構造の高剛性ケースを35ヵ所で締め付けている。12気筒レーシングエンジンのポルシェ912型では左右締結箇所は50にものぼる。ポルシェのジャーナル部締め付けは伝統的に貫通ボルト式で、本機F102A型のような片持ちスタッドタイプの締結は1.5ℓF1用753型およびその発展型2ℓ771型で試みたのち二度と使っていない。ただし本機ではエンジン下部をトランスアクスルケースと剛結しており、応力をトランスアクスルケースに分担させることで高剛性と軽量性を両立させようとした設計であることが読み取れる（クランクシャフト保持には貢献していない）。〈CATALOGO PARTI DI RICAMBO（以下「パーツカタログ」）No.95990216より転載〉

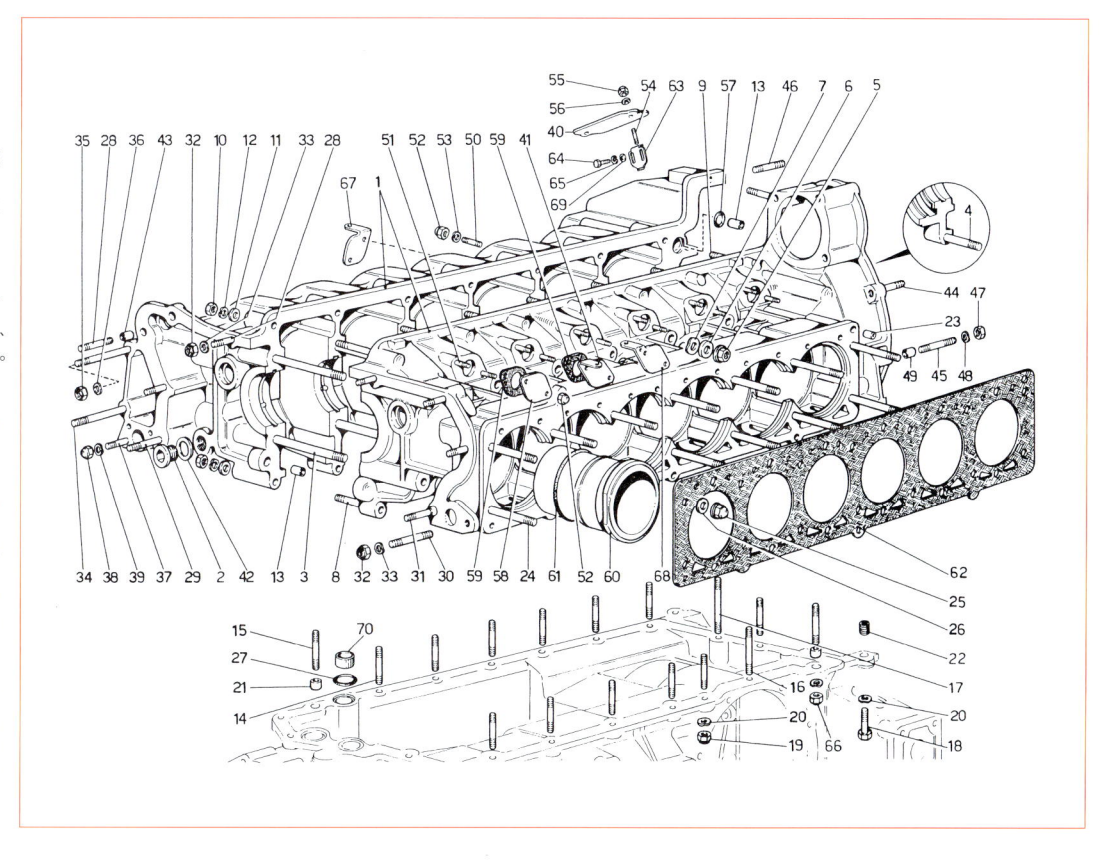

シリンダスリーブのガタつきと
クランクシャフトの湾曲

　本車エンジン#F102A00000117を分解し詳細に点検したところ、全般にその状態は非常に良好で、8000マイルという走行記録を完全に裏付けるものであった。したがって以下の各点は異常で特異な状況と考えられる。①クランクシャフトに中心線上約0.1mmもの湾曲が見られた。また6番/7番メタル（クラッチ側端のふたつ）表面に金属接触痕が見られた。②シリンダスリーブとクランクケースとの間に平均0.06mm、最大0.08mmもの異常なガタつきがあった。③シリンダー慴動面圧縮リング上死点付近に最大深さ0.04mmの異常な摩耗が生じていた。

　うち③は主に本機固有の圧縮リング形式に一因があると見られるため後述する。

　②に関してフェラーリのエンジン重整備に長い経験を持つ古谷康一郎氏（ソニーズフェラーリ）は「ごく近年のものを除きどの時代のフェラーリにも必ず見られる状況であり、特に12気筒ユニットではクランクシャフトが湾曲していない個体の方が珍しい」とする。クランクシャフトが湾曲する一因は連続過負荷あるいは過回転だが、その場合他にも何らかの痕跡が残ることが多く、本車の状況は該当し難い。6番/7番メタルに傷があり、湾曲はその周辺で発生したと考えるのが妥当であること、本機はトランスアクスルのデフギヤ収納部と6番ジャーナル外側部が構造的に干渉するため締結をオミットしており、応力の集中点が6番ジャーナル付近に存在すること、512BB用F102B型以降は右写真に示すように2番ジャーナル外側部締結もオミットしており、おそらく応力を分散させるための何らかの応急的対策であると考えられること、さらにテスタロッサ用F113A型では締結部の設計を改めて全周結合としたことなどから、この現象は当初設計の不備に起因するものではないかと推察する。

　③について設計仕様ではスリーブ挿入部のケース内径寸法最大87.035mm最小86.980mmに対し、スリーブ外径寸法最大86.980mm最小86.960mmと規定し、最大0.075mm最小0.02mmのクリアランスを設けている。常温手作業で挿入できる程度のクリアランスである。この設計公差数値はデイトナ用251型と完全に同一だが、古谷氏によれば251型ではスリーブのガタつきはほとんど発生しないという。ケース剛性が低くその締結剛性も低いクランクケースに対し251型と同じゆるいスリーブクリアランスを適用した結果、使用するうちにスリーブが揺動し過度のガタつきに至るのではないかというのが本書の推察である。

　ちなみにテスタロッサ用F113A型のサービスマニュアルは、冷却したスリーブを常温のクランクケースに圧入するよう特に指定しており、フェラーリがクリアランス設定に関する考え方をのちに根本的に改めたことを伺わせる。

【付記：現在とりわけレーシングエンジンの世界では液体窒素で冷却したスリーブを加熱したケースに圧入するのが常道である。このときのクリアランス設定はゼロ-ゼロもしくはマイナスである】

Clattering of Cylinder Sleeve and Curved Crankshaft

After the engine #F102A00000117 of the vehicle was taken apart to pieces, minute inspection was carried out, and the overall condition was found to be exceptionally good, fully supporting the announced driven distance of 8000 miles. Therefore, I gather the following points to be abnormal and peculiar phenomena; ①along the center line of the crankshaft, there was a curve of as much as 0.1mm and metallic contact scars were found on surfaces of the sixth and seventh metals (the two metals at the end of clutch side); ②there was an abnormal cluttering of average 0.06mm, maximum 0.08mm between cylinder sleeve and crankcase and ③on the compression ring surface near the Top Dead Center, there was an abnormal defacement with maximum depth of 0.04mm. Out of these points, ③will be enumerated later as the cause of the defacement is presumed to be the form of the compression ring which is characteristic of this engine. Regarding②, Mr. Kouichiro Furuya of Sonny's Ferrari, who has long experience in heavy duty overhauling of Ferrari engines, commented "This is seen in Ferraris of all ages except for very recent years, and in V-12 units, it is extremely rare to find a crankshaft which is not curved." One reason for a curved crankshaft is continuous over-loading or excessive revolution, but in such cases there most probably will be other traces, and judging from the condition of this vehicle, it is not applicable in this case. Judging from the fact that there are scars on sixth and seventh metals, the curve obviously developed in that vicinity. On this unit, due to constructional interference between the differential gear housing of transaxle and the outer side of the sixth journal, the joint is omitted, resulting in tension concentration in the area around the sixth journal. As shown in the photograph on the right, after the Type F102B for 512BB, the joint at outer side of the second journal is also omitted, presumably as a sort of emergency measure to disperse tension. Furthermore, because in Type F113A for Testarossa, the design of the jointing area was changed to fully circumferential joining, it is conjectured that the phenomena was the result of error in the initial design. As for ③, the design specifications stipulate the inner diameter of the case where the sleeve is inserted to be maximum 87.035mm and minimum 86.980mm, while the outer diameter of the sleeve is prescribed as maximum 86.980mm, minimum 86.960mm, setting the clearance at maximum 0.075mm, minimum 0.02mm. This clearance is in the range which enables insertion by hand work under normal temperatures. This designed tolerance value is fully identical to that of Type 251 for Daytona, but according to Mr. Furuya, there is almost no clattering of the sleeve in Type 251. In this book, we submit that the excessive clattering came from shaking motion of the sleeve caused by adopting Type 251's loose sleeve clearance values on the case having low rigidity and crankcase with equally low joining stiffness. Incidentally, the service manual of Testarossa's Type F113A specifically stipulates that cooled sleeve should be pushed into the crankcase at normal temperatures. This indicates Ferrari subsequently made fundamental change in design policy regarding clearance settings. [The author's remarks: Nowadays, especially in the world of racing engines, it is normal to insert sleeves chilled by liquid nitrogen into heated crankcase. The clearance setting in this case is zero-zero or minus.]

メカニカルレストア　　　Mechanical Restoration

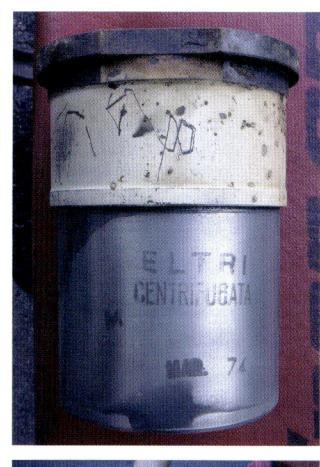

クランクシャフトの湾曲は修正した（後述）。問題はクランクケースとの間にガタつきが生じ、慴動面上死点付近が異常摩耗していたシリンダスリーブである。新品部品は現在メーカーからは供給されていないが、世界中探せばNOS（New Original Stock＝いわゆる純正デッドストック部品）は見つかるはずだ。しかし当時の設計の部品では幾ばくも走らぬうちに再びガタつきが生じることは明らかであると思われるし、ピストンとの寸法関係も非摺動面（上死点より上部／下死点より下部）で測定すると新造時からかなりばらついていたことが分かったため、素材からスリーブを製作するのが最も得策と判断した。すなわち製作に際して使用する位置（シリンダ番号）をあらかじめ決めておき、スリーブ外径は使用部位のクランクケース側挿入部の内径に、またスリーブ内径はそこに入るピストン（元々番号がふられ位置が決まっている）の外径に合わせてそれぞれ切削寸法を決定すれば、全シリンダにおいてクランクケース－スリーブ間およびスリーブ－ピストン間のクリアランスを均一にすることができるからである。安全性に鑑み、各クリアランスは設計上の最小許容値（製造公差によって生じるクリアランスのバラつきの下限値）とした。すなわち前者が0.015±0.005mm、後者が0.025±0.005mmである。エンジンオーバーホールの常識としてヘッドボルトはすべて新製しヘッド取り付け面は切削加工した。それ以外のスタッド、ボルト、ナット、ワッシャは著者の希望によってレストアしたオリジナル部品を再使用した。メインベアリングはすべて新品に交換した。

The curved crankshaft was corrected as enumerated later. Now, the problem is the cylinder sleeve which showed excessive wear on the surface near Top Dead Center. Although new parts are no longer supplied by the manufacturer, NOS (New Original Stock, the so-called genuine dead stock parts), probably can be found if a world-wide search is undertaken. However, as it is obvious that parts made according to design specifications of those days would develop clattering before accumulating much mileage, and as it became clear that numerous measurement errors existed at the time of manufacture in relation with the pistons (above Top Dead Center and below Bottom Dead Center), it was decided that it would be best to fabricate the sleeve from appropriate material. By predetermining the position to be used (cylinder number), the outer diameter of the sleeve should be decided based on inner diameter of insertion position on crankcase side, while inner diameter of the sleeve should match the outer diameter of the piston (originally numbered to show the position) to be inserted. By determining the respective cutting dimensions in this way, it was possible to standardize the clearances between crankcase ⇔ sleeve and sleeve ⇔ piston on all cylinders. For safety's sake, respective clearances were set at the minimum permissible value on design basis (lowest value of discrepancies in clearance error caused by production tolerance). In other words, the clearances were 0.015 ±0.005mm for the former and 0.025 ±0.005mm for the latter. In accordance with the common sense of engine overhauling, all head bolts were made anew, and mounting surface of the head was processed by cutting. By the author's wish, restored original parts were reused for other items such as studs, bolts, nuts and washers. All main bearings were replaced with new parts.

オリジナルのシリンダスリーブの状態。上部にカーボンが溜まっていくためクランクケースに挿入されている状態ではしっかり固定されているように見えるのだが、クランクケース／スリーブ両者を洗浄後あらためて挿入してみると、元来かなり大きいクリアランス設定をさらに上回るガタつきが発生していた。スリーブに平均0.06mmものガタがあったのではスリーブ－ピストン間のクリアランスに如何なる注意を払ったとしても徒労である。スリーブには12本ともにMAR.74の刻印（薬剤刻印）があり、新車時挿入のオリジナルであることは間違いない。スリーブの重量は実測単体で1058g（＋1g－0g）である。

スリーブを抜いた状態のクランクケース。左が本機、右は512BBi用F110A型のもの。設計および生産技術的にはほとんど両者同一だが、木型は別のもので砂型分割線の位置も異なる。おそらく生産上の都合（木型の損傷等）による変更だろう。

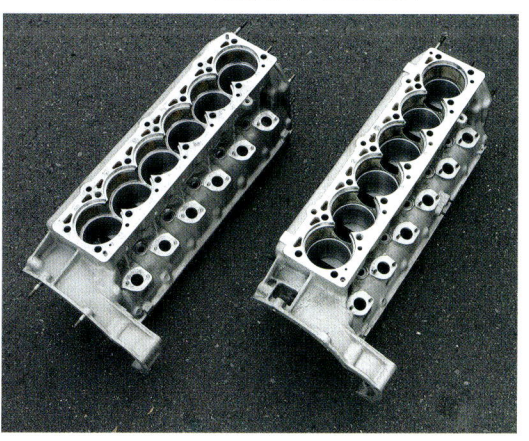

本機（下）ではデファレンシャル部と干渉する6番ジャーナル外側締結部をやむなくオミットしているがF110A（上）では2番ジャーナル部も省略（矢印）。クランクシャフト保持剛性をさらに低下させてでも応力集中を回避しようとした応急措置と推察する。

コスメティックレストア　　　　Cosmetic Restoration

いささか馬鹿げているし、メカニズムにとって少しも有益でないばかりか逆に少々のダメージすら与えかねないことを承知の上でコスメティック面でのレストアを行なった。

すべてのスタッドボルトはいったんケースから抜き、すべてのボルト、ナット、ワッシャと共にブラストと再めっきを行なった（めっきおよびその考証については119ページ参照）。

クランクケース本体は入念に洗浄・脱脂したのち、切削部分をマスキングしてからガラスビーズで全体をブラストした。様々なトライアルの結果、細目の#150ビーズを0.42～0.45kg／m²の高圧で一気に噴射したときに新品時に最も近い艶と肌が得られた（新造時表面はサンドブラスト処理であった－前述）。ガラスビーズが摩耗していたり噴射圧力が低かったりすると、黒ずんだ酸化／腐食皮膜が取れにくく、また表面が白くくもってツヤがなくムラの多いみすぼらしい仕上がりになりやすい。薬品に浸漬する方法もテストしてみたが、表面の酸化／腐食状態に応じて仕上がり具合が異なるためやはりムラになりやすかった。結局新品時に近い表面を得るには新造時と同じ方法（高圧ブラスト）を施行するのが最も有効である。

クランクケースについては内面のグリーン塗装の大半が残っており色・状態ともに良かったため、あえて剥離せず、ブラストがかからないようマスキングを施して現状を維持した。

スタッド脱着は工場に依頼し、めっきは専門業者に委ねたが、それ以外の作業はすべて著者が自分で行なった。

Cosmetic restoration was carried out although I was fully aware that it is somewhat ridiculous and also not beneficial at all for the mechanism, with a possible risk of doing some damage. All stud bolts were pulled out of the case, to be sandblasted and re-plated together with all bolts, nuts and washers. (For plating and its investigation, refer to page 119). As for the crankcase itself, after a careful washing and degreasing, the cut surfaces were masked before the whole unit was sandblasted with glass beads. As the result of various trials, it was found that a quick injection of fine #150 beads at high pressure of 0.42-0.45kg/m² produced gloss and surface closest to original production. (It was mentioned already that the surfaces were treated with sandblast when it was newly built). If the glass beads were worn out or if the injection pressure was too low, it was difficult to remove the blackish traces of oxidation and corroded membrane, causing whitish clouding without luster and blurr, resulting in a shabby finish. Immersion in chemicals was also tested, but the finish tended to be uneven depending on oxidation of the surface and state of corrosion. After all, it was found out that the most effective method to attain the surface closest to initial production was to carry out the same process (High pressure sandblasting) as the time when it was newly produced. As for the crankcase, since most of the green paint on the inner side was intact with good colors and condition, I did not dare to remove the paint and decided to maintain the present condition by masking the surface to protect from sandblasting. Except for removal and assembly of studs which was entrusted to a workshop, and asking the professionals to do the plating job, all other works were done by the author himself. The advantage of DIY(Do-It-Yourself) is that one is able to try out, think through and decide things without hurry until full satisfaction is attained.

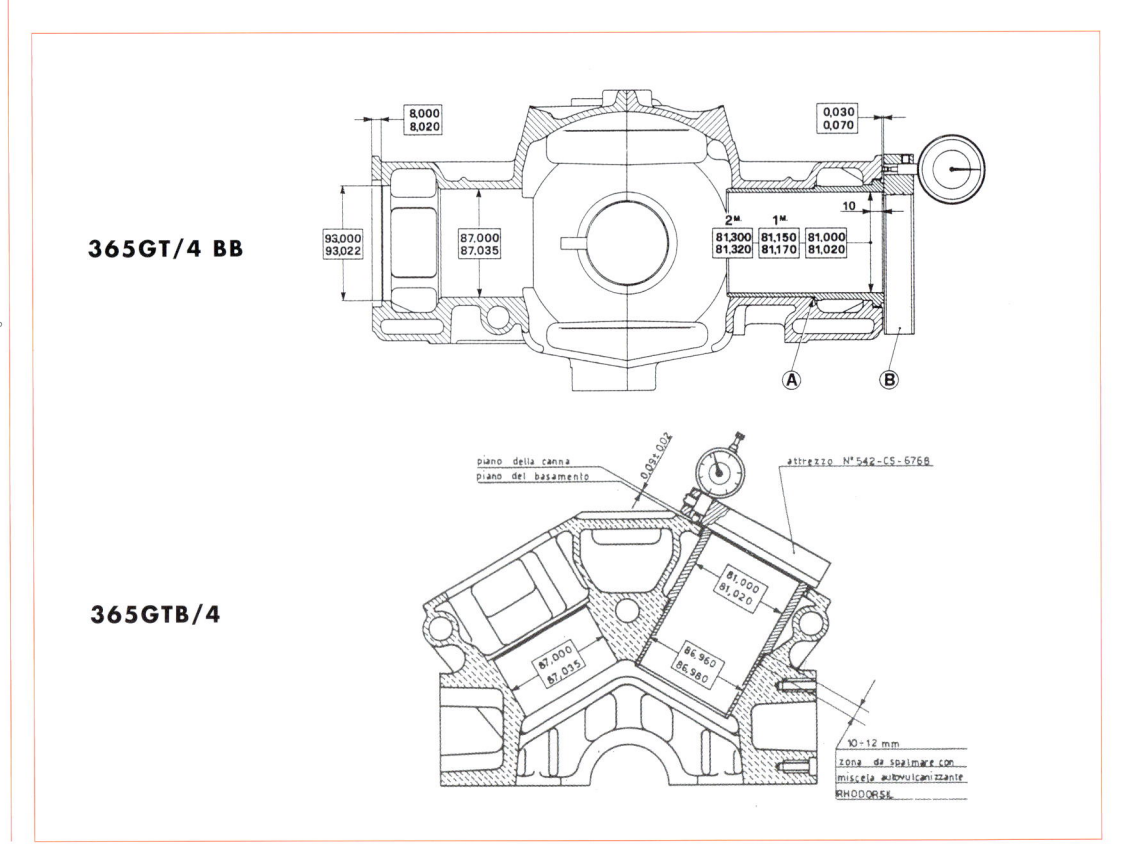

コスメティックレストアの一例。クランクケースは切削部すべてをマスキングしてガラスビーズ・ブラストを施したのち切削部を耐水ペーパー等による手作業で研磨した。当時の純正ガスケットは製紙の段階でアスベストに金属を混入させたもので、ガスケット部金属面の腐食を誘発しており、分解後にガスケットの固着を剥離するのも非常にやっかいである。通常であってもエンジンのオーバーホール作業時間の多くは部品の洗浄の手間に費やされるが、とりわけこの時代のフェラーリの場合ガスケット面を整えるのに多大の労力を強いられる。今回スタッドボルトをすべて抜いたのはその作業の便のためもある。

【このページ図版】シリンダスリーブ挿入部の寸法公差を示す。上が本機のもの、下はデイトナ用251型のもの。断面で明らかなように251型のモノブロック構造はいかにも肉厚で剛性が高そうだが、本機は非常にきゃしゃである。にもかかわらず図に示されている通りシリンダスリーブにまったく同一の製造公差（＝クリアランス設定）を適用していたことが分かる。本機におけるサイドウォータギャラリーの構造にも注目（シリンダ下部長方形の冷却水路）。〈上：サービスマニュアルNo.95990807より転載　下：同365GTB/4（デイトナ）用1969年発行版より転載〉

【右ページ上図版および写真】エンジンとトランスアクスルの構造的干渉を示す。図版は本機サービスマニュアルNo.95990807記載のエンジン断面図（本書76ページに所載）と同記載トランスアクスル・デファレンシャルギヤ収納部付近の断面図とを同縮尺で重ね合わせ、6番ジャーナル付近の断面を示したもの。ご覧の通り外縁の締結部分が完全に干渉する。断面形の印象も前掲のものとは大きく異なることに気づかれるだろう。512BB用F102B型ではトランスアクスルケース後半部を主に下方に寸法拡大してデフギヤ径を増加、テスタロッサ用F113A型ではクランクケース側設計を変更して6番ジャーナル部も締結できるよう改めた。

【右ページ下写真】左右クランクケースを合わせフロントカバーをつけトランスアクスルケース上に載せてみた。V12エンジン一基分の空間にパワートレーン構造のすべてを収めようとした本機設計の意図がよく伺われる。

365GT/4 BB

365GTB/4

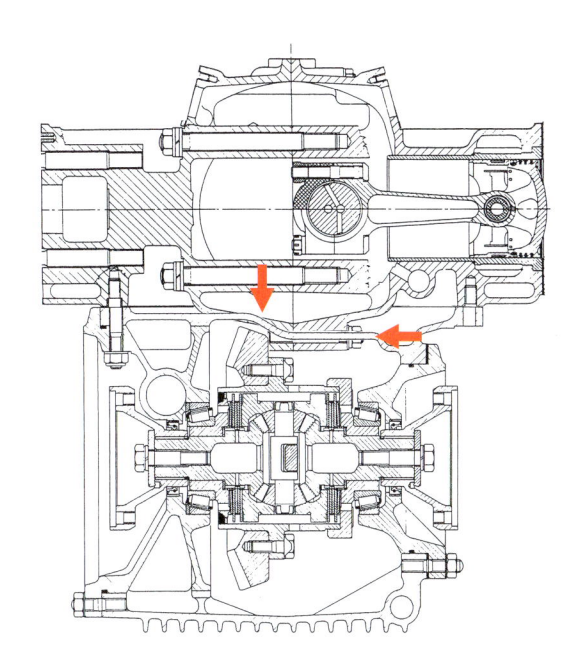

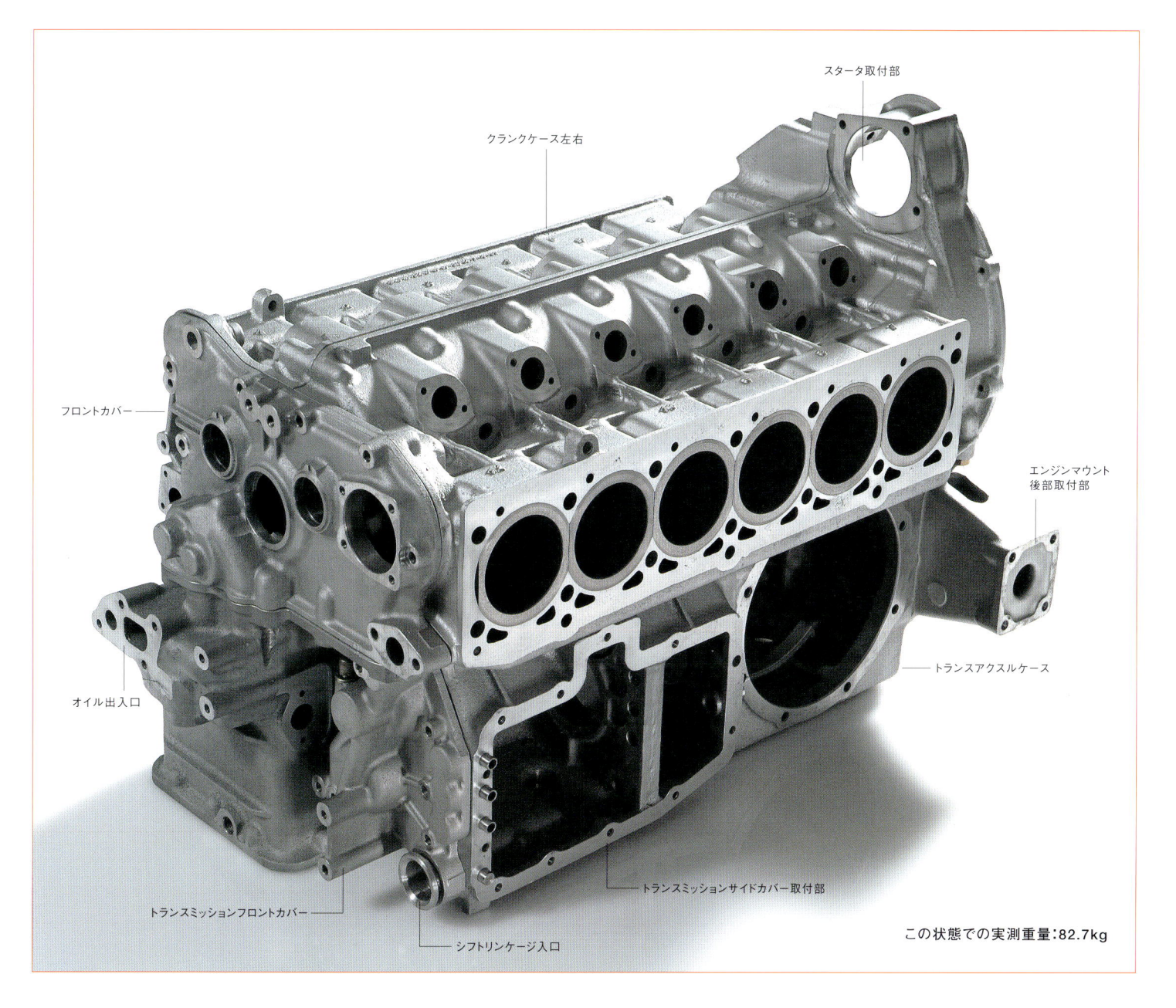

スタータ取付部

クランクケース左右

フロントカバー

エンジンマウント後部取付部

トランスアクスルケース

オイル出入口

トランスミッションフロントカバー

シフトリンケージ入口

トランスミッションサイドカバー取付部

この状態での実測重量：82.7kg

クランクシャフトの設計・生産仕様

Design and Production Specifications of the Crankshaft

本機構成部品の中で最も壮大かつ印象的なパーツである。単体重量は実測値24.7kg。プーリ（同4.2kg）、フライホイル（同7.5kg）、カム駆動出力ギヤ（同362g）装着状態で36.6kg、12セットのピストン／コンロッドを加えた往復／回転運動部の総質量は49.1kgに達する。これを毎分7000回転させようというのであるから前項におけるクランクシャフト保持剛性云々のクランクシャフト指摘も杞憂とは言えまい。

基本設計は2スローのクランクピンを持つフルカウンターウエイト型で、カム駆動出力部（ギヤ⇔スプロケット）およびプーリ固定方式（Tスロット⇔スプライン）を除けば、寸法／製造公差指定ともにデイトナ用251型のものとまったく同一である。

よく知られているようにフェラーリはクランクシャフトを形鋼（丸棒材）からの切削加工によって製造していた。Michael Dregniの"INSIDE Ferrari"にも"The unworked solid steel billet weighed in 149kg"とある。しかし切削加工品の物性が鍛造加工品に比べて劣るというのは工業界一般の通常の認識であり、この製造法は投下コスト低減のためのやむを得ない措置と考えるのが妥当である。材質はクロムモリブデン鋼と言われているが、完成したクランクシャフトから確認することは出来ない。素材形鋼の製造方法には鍛造、圧延、連鋳などがあり完成品の品質を左右するが、これも定かではない。製品カウンターウエイト部の薄緑褐色は軟窒化処理を行なったことを示唆している。

Among all of the items comprising this engine, the crankshaft is the grandest and the most impressive component. Unit weight according to actual measurement is 24.7 kg. When the pulley (4.2 kg), flywheel (7.5 kg), and cam output driveline gear (362 g) are installed, the weight becomes 36.6 kg. Furthermore, with 12 sets of piston/conrod added, the total mass of the reciprocating and revolving components reaches 49.1 kg. To think that this mass will turn at 7000 revolutions per minute, the points raised in the previous paragraph can not be said to be groundless. The basic design is of the full counterweight type with two-throw crank pins, and if the cam driveline part (gear ⇔ sprocket) and the fixing of the pulley (T-slot ⇔ splined) are excluded, dimensions as well as specified production tolerances are identical to those of Daytona's Type 251. As is well known, Ferrari produced crankshafts by milling steel billet. In Michael Dregni's "INSIDE Ferrari", it is described as "The un-worked solid steel billet weighed in 149 kg". However, it is established common understanding within the industrial circles that the characteristics of cutting/machining product is inferior to that of items made by forging. Therefore, it will be appropriate to conjecture that this production process was an unavoidable step to reduce invested costs. While it is said that the material is chrome molybdenum steel, this can not be confirmed from the finished crankshaft. It is unclear what method used in producing steel billets, namely, forging, rolling or continuous casting, will best influence the quality of finished product. The light greenish-brown color of the counterweight is indicative of low nitrogen treatment.

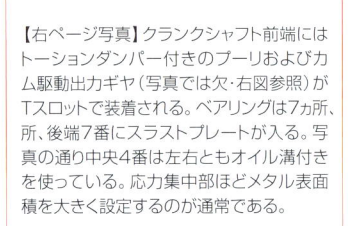

【右ページ写真】クランクシャフト前端にはトーションダンパー付きのプーリおよびカム駆動出力ギヤ（写真では欠・右参照）がTスロットで装着される。ベアリングは7ヵ所、所、後端7番にスラストプレートが入る。写真の通り中央4番は左右ともオイル溝付きを使っている。応力集中部ほどメタル表面積を大きく設定するのが通常である。

【右パーツ図】クランクシャフト／クランクケースジャーナル部の寸法を示す。主要な寸法数値／製造公差指定値は確認してみたところデイトナ用251型のものとまったく同一だった。251型の場合、より小型のプーリをスプライン結合、シャフト部にカム駆動出力用スプロケットを一体加工している。〈パーツカタログNo.95990216およびサービスマニュアルNo.95990807より転載〉

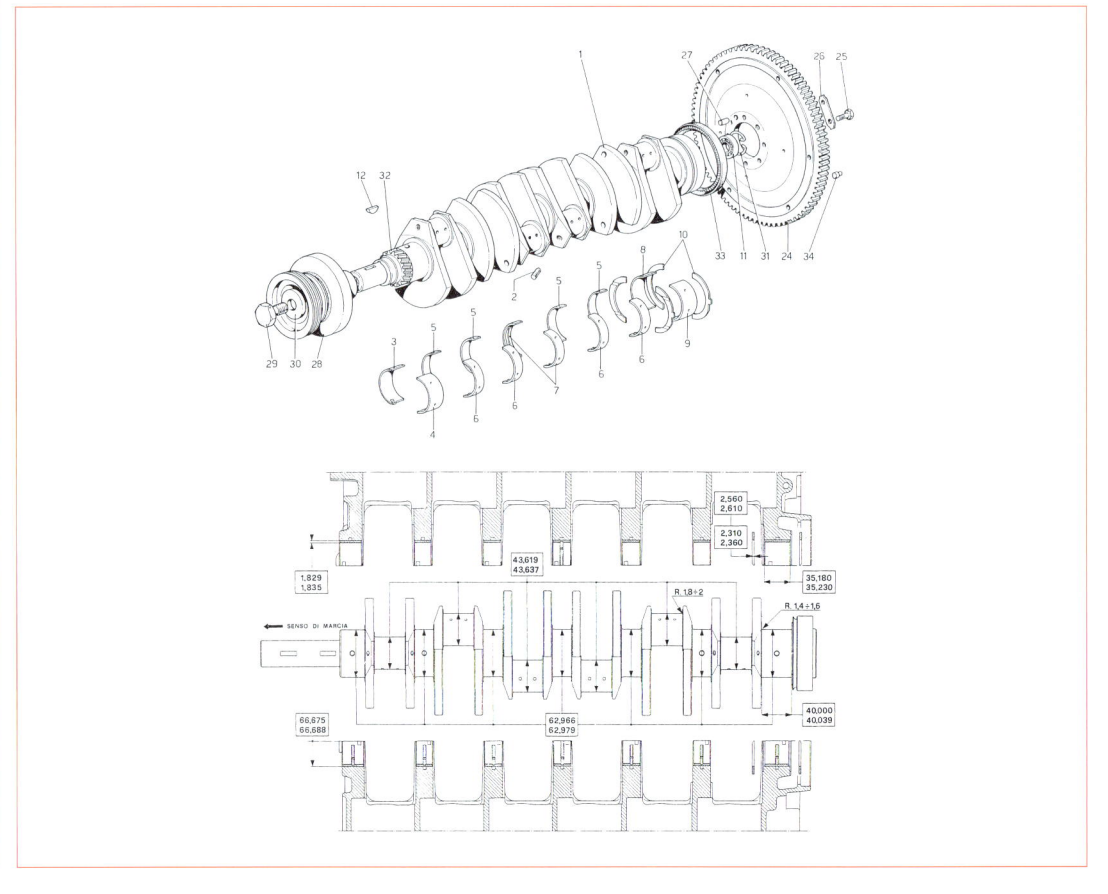

クランクシャフトのレストア / Restoration of the Crankshaft

前述のように本機のクランクシャフトには中心線上で約0.1mmに達する湾曲が発生していた。

原因は不明だが、エンジン各部の状況からは過負荷／過回転運転等の異常運転の兆候・痕跡は一切看取できず、本書ではクランクケースの基本設計に起因する自然発生的な湾曲と類推した。ただし製造時から曲がっていた可能性もある。製造工程の熱処理等でクランクシャフトに湾曲が生じるのは通常のことであり、湾曲の修正は一般に行なわれている。レーシングエンジン整備の世界でも同様である。

修正は基本的には湾曲部を山側から油圧で押して行なう。一度押し、応力が抜けるのを待って再修正する。繰り返すほど修正精度は向上する。

本機では加圧－放置－再測定－再加圧の工程繰り返しに約1ヵ月半を要した。修正後のクランクシャフトは垂直に立てて保管するようアドバイスされた。オリジナルのメインベアリングの軸受金属はアルミ合金（通常アルミニウム－錫－シリコン合金）で当然オーバーレイはしていない。水平対向エンジンではくさび膜圧が左右メタル分割線をまたいで発生するため条件的に厳しくなるが、本機では通常直列／V型と同様片側にプレーン、片側にオイル溝付きのものを組み合わせて使用している。これはすべて純正新品に交換した。いずれにしろクランクシャフトの湾曲を修正せずにメタルの状態やクリアランスを云々しても無意味である。

As mentioned before, there was a curve of as much as 0.1mm along the centerline of the crankshaft of this engine. Although the reason is not known, based on the fact that no signs of abnormal operation, such as over-loading or excessive revolution were evident in any part of the engine, I analogize in this book that the curve is apparently a natural development stemming from the basic design of the crankcase. However, there also is a possibility that the crankshaft was bent from the time of production. It is quite normal that crankshafts tend to curve due to heat treatment during manufacturing, etc., and corrections of such curves are common procedure. This is no exception in maintaining a racing engine. Basically, correction is carried out by pushing the protruded side by hydraulic power. After the initial push, another corrective step is taken after the stress is gone. By repeating these processes, the accuracy of corrective work will increase. In this engine, about one and a half month was required for the work cycle of pressurizing - resting - re-measuring - next pressurizing, and we were advised to keep the corrected crankshaft in an upright position. The original main bearing was made of aluminum alloy (normally Aluminum/Tin/Silicon alloy) and as a matter of course, not overlaid. In case of horizontally-opposed engine, the condition is extreme as the wedge membrane pressure develops over the dividing line of left and right metals, but in this unit, combination of plain and oil-grooved bearings are used as in case of normal in-line or V-shaped engines. All of those were exchanged with brand new genuine parts. At any rate, it is meaningless to comment on the condition of metals and clearances without correcting the curved crankshaft.

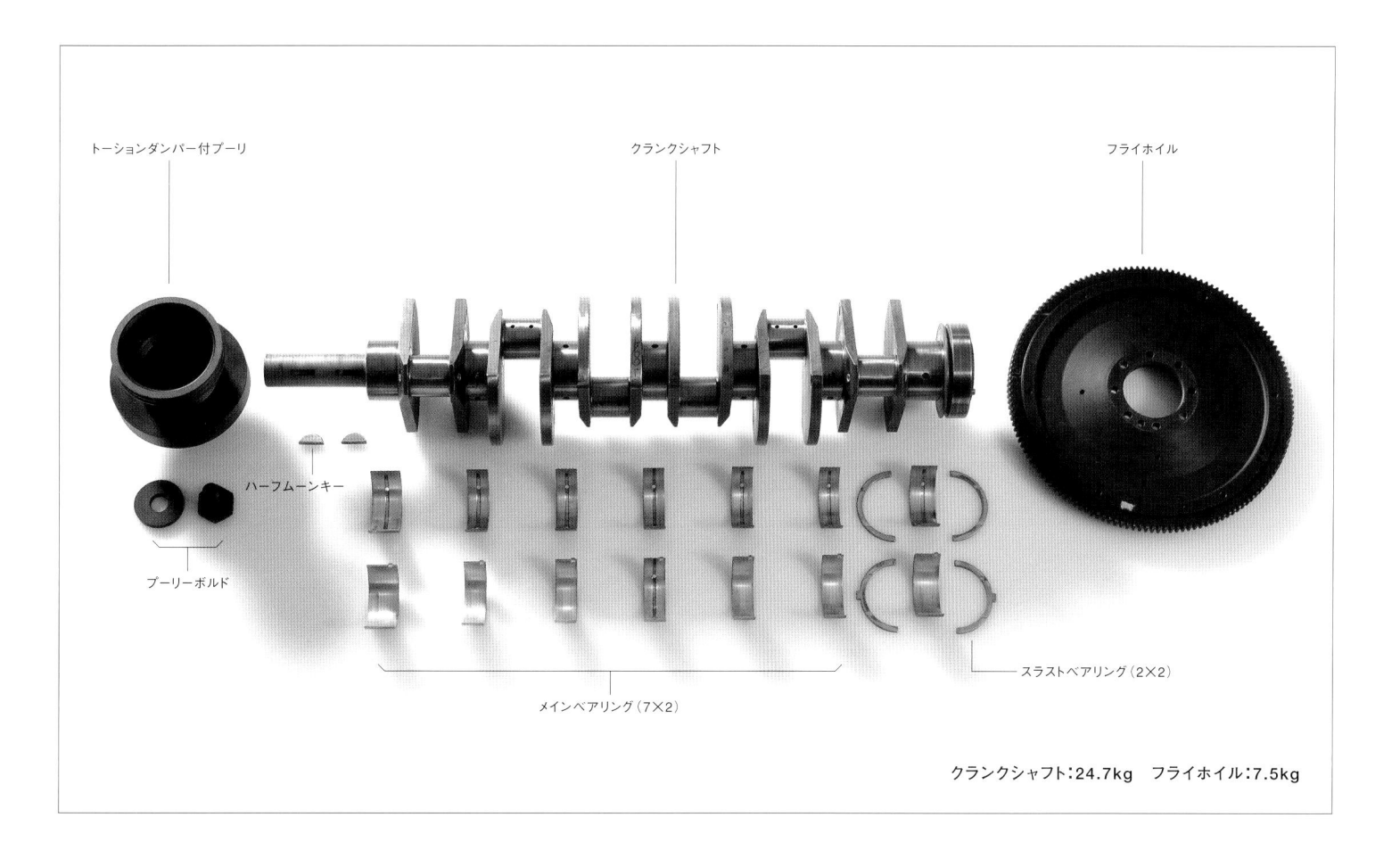

トーションダンパー付プーリ　クランクシャフト　フライホイル

ハーフムーンキー

プーリーボルト

メインベアリング（7×2）

スラストベアリング（2×2）

クランクシャフト：24.7kg　フライホイル：7.5kg

ピストンおよびコンロッド / Pistons and Conrods

本機のピストンストロークは71mmで、7000rpm時のピストン速度は16.57m/sと比較的高く、往復運動部質量がピストンの変位／加速度／上限速度に及ぼす影響もそれだけ大きいが、3本の圧縮リングおよびダブルタイプのオイルリングを備えたピストンのコンプレッションハイト（ピストンピン中心⇔ピストン頂部までの寸法的指標）は非常に大きく、結果ピストン単体重量は実測398g（±1g）もある。

ピストン重量とボアとの関係を示す設計的指標をK値というが（K値＝ピストン重量g／ボア値の三乗cm³）本機K値は一昔前のディーゼルトラック並の1.35である。重量増加の不利を承知の上でデイトナの2本リングからあえて3本圧縮リングとしたのはシリンダの水平配置という特殊性への配慮であったのかもしれないが、後年のテスタロッサ用F113A型であっさり2本リングに戻していることからも設計的な錯誤があったことは明らかである。

ピストンの材質はアルミ合金で、Y合金かLO-EXの高圧凝固鋳造製と思われる。

内部には熱膨張抑制対策として鋼板製ストラットが入っている（スロットなし）。トップランドにはスカッフ（焼付き）対策のV溝が8本刻まれている。リングトレーガや陽極電解処理などのリング溝補強、オイルジェットやクーリングチャンネルなどの冷却措置、ショートスカートやコーティングなどの低μ化対策などは一切ない。

本機のピストンがかくも古くさく見えるのは、それだけこの30年間のピストン設計の進歩が著しかったという証拠だろう。

The piston stroke of this engine is 71mm, which makes the piston speed at engine speed of 7000rpm relatively high at 16.57m/s. Accordingly, the influence of the piston mass on change of piston alignment, acceleration rate and upper limit of the piston's motional speed is correspondingly greater. The compression height (the dimensional index between the center of piston pin ⇔ top of piston) of the piston having three compression rings and double-type oil ring is extremely large, resulting in the unit weight of the piston, according to actual measurement, of as much as 398g (±1g). The design index denoting piston weight and bore is called K-Value (K-Value = piston weight g / cube of bore value cm³), and the K-Value of this engine is 1.35, similar to that of diesel truck engines of a generation ago. The reason why the numbers of rings were increased from Daytona's two to three compression rings, a bold measure in spite of the apparent disadvantage of increased weight, may have been in consideration of the particularity of the horizontal cylinder layout. However, looking from the fact that two rings were used in Type F113A engine for Testarossa of the later years, it is quite evident that there was a design error. The material of the piston is aluminum alloy, presumably of high-pressure Squeeze-casting of Y-alloy or LO-EX. As a countermeasure against heat expansion, struts made of steel plate are installed on the inside (without slots). At the top-land, eight V-grooves are cut as preventive measure against scuffing. There are no wear resistance ring grooves, cooling steps such as oil jet and cooling channel, and measures to attain low μ, like short skirt or coating. The pistons of this engine look so old-fashioned, which, on the other hand, is an eloquent proof of the magnitude of progress in piston design in the past thirty years.

ピストン/コンロッドAssy.×12：12.7kg

番号はピストン番号（シリンダ番号と同じ）

V溝（8）
L字断面圧縮リング
圧縮リング
オイルリング

87

前記の通り本機シリンダスリーブ内壁の上死点付近には深さ100分の3〜4ミリのやや異常な段つき摩耗が発生していた。状況は12本のシリンダについてほぼ同じであった。

エンジン作動中のピストンは、ピストンピンを中心にシリンダとの寸法クリアランスのぶん傾きながら複雑な水平および2次の回転運動をしており、シリンダ壁との摺動はピストンリング部だけでなくスカート部においても発生している。スカート部で生じる摩耗抵抗はリング部の摺動によるものと同等と言われており、近年ピストンのショートスカート化やスカート部への固体潤滑皮膜の付与などが行なわれているのもそのためである。しかしこれらのこととシリンダ壁の摩耗とは実はあまり関連がない。

シリンダ壁の摩耗を引き起こすのは一般に吸入空気やオイル中に含まれている塵埃などの異物、燃焼生成物や水などの腐食物質である。前者によるものを「ざらつき摩耗」、後者を「腐食摩耗」という。いずれも一番圧縮リング（トップリング）上死点付近の摩耗が最も大きくなるのが特徴である（オイル中に塵埃等が混入していた場合はシリンダ全面に摩耗が分布）。

本機のシリンダの状況は上記いずれと仮定しても摩耗が大きく、複合要因であると思われた。第一に本機特有のL字断面のトップリングである。L字リングは60年代にケンブリッジ大学のポール・ダイクス博士が提唱したピストンリングの潤滑理論に基づいて考案され「ダイクスリング」として知られるようになったものだが、ねじれ力などが加わった時の摺動面の変位が一般のI断面リングより大きくなることは明らかだ。512BB用F102B型ではトップリングを通常I断面に戻しており、古谷氏の経験では本機に見られるような異常摩耗が認められたことは一度もないという。シリンダ内面にはめっき等の表面処理はされておらず、これが摩耗を増大させたことも確かだろう。その他クロスハッチ不適正（やや浅い）や前記シリンダスリーブの固定不良（ガタ）も原因として考えうる。いずれにせよ状況が示唆しているのは本現象が設計仕様に起因した本機F102A型固有のものに違いないということである。

As mentioned already, the inner wall of cylinder sleeve of this engine had a somewhat abnormal stepped wear of 3/100mm-4/100mm near Top Dead Center. The situation is almost identical in all twelve cylinders. While the engine is operating, the pistons, with the piston pin as the center, are engaged in complicated inclined, horizontal and secondary revolving motion within the dimensional clearance to the cylinder. This rubbing with the cylinder wall occurs not only at piston rings, but also in the skirt area. It is said that the frictional resistance in the skirt area is equal to rubbing at the rings, and for this reason shorter skirts and provision of solid lubrication membrane at the skirt are now the norm. The above are not predominant causes of cylinder wall wear. Generally speaking, cylinder wall wear is caused by foreign substances such as dust in intake air or oil, as well as corroding substances like combustion product and water. The former is called "abrasive wear," while the latter is referred to as "corrosive wear." In either case, the characteristic is that the wear will be greatest near Top Dead Center of the first compression ring (top ring). In case dust, etc., are intermixed with oil, the wear will be distributed all over the cylinder surface. Looking at the condition of this engine's cylinder on assumption of either of the above, the wear is quite extensive and hinted multiple factors. First cause is the top ring with L-shaped cross section, a peculiarity of this engine. This L-shaped ring was designed based on the lubrication theory for piston rings advocated in the '60s by Dr. Paul Dykes of Cambridge University, and is known as the "Dykes Ring." However, it is clear that when torsion force is applied, the change of rubbing surface is bigger than in case of the normal ring with I-shaped cross section. In the 512BB, the top ring was returned to the normal I-shaped cross section, and according to Mr. Furuya's experience, there was not a single case when abnormal wear such as the one seen in this engine was found in the cylinder of 512BB. There are no surface treatments such as plating on the inner surface of the cylinders, certainly a factor for excessive wear. Other reasons could be inadequate crosshatch (a bit shallow), and inferior securing (cluttering) of the cylinder sleeve as mentioned previously. At any rate, the enumerated conditions are suggesting that the phenomena are caused by design specifications peculiar to 365GT/4 BB.

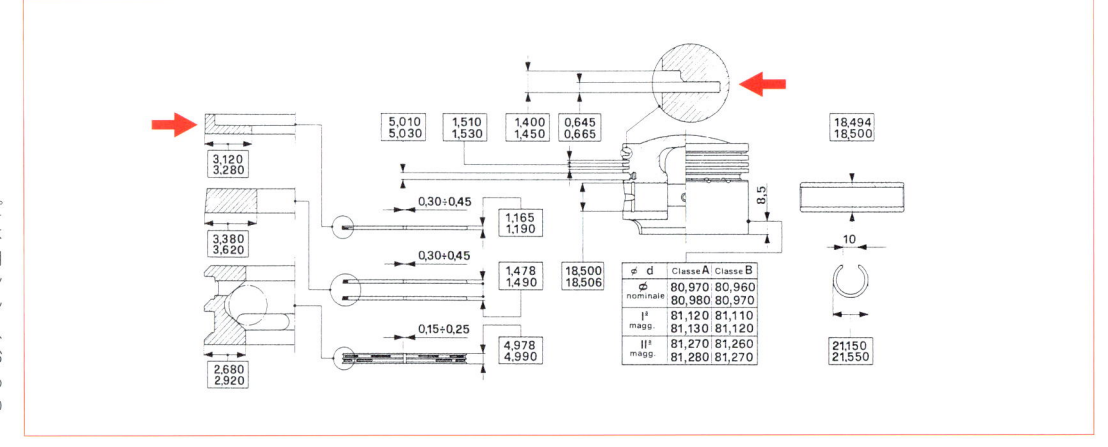

サービスマニュアルNo.95990807記載のピストンおよびピストンリング寸法図。基本設計は各部寸法および製造公差値も含めデイトナ用251型のものをそっくり踏襲しているが、コンプレッションハイトをわずかに高くして圧縮リングを3本としている。他の条件が一定ならピストン重量はコンプレッションハイトによっておおむね左右される。L字形のトップリングを収めるトップリング溝もL字断面であることがお分かりいただけるだろう（矢印）。

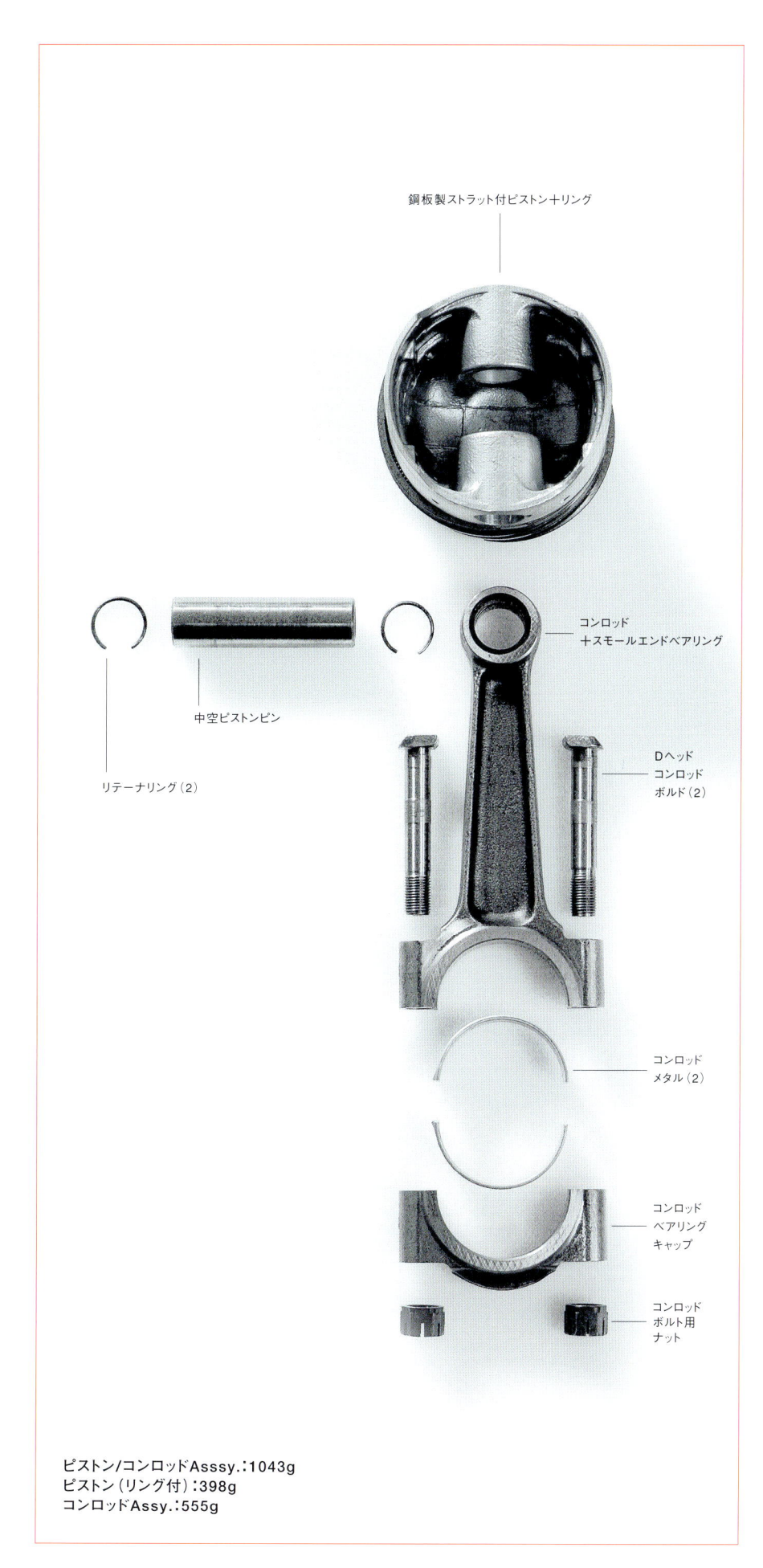

コンロッドは通常のいわゆるⅠ断面形状で、おそらく鍛造製である。

コンロッドは大きな引っ張り応力／圧縮応力／曲げ応力を反復して受けるため設計が難しく、高出力型エンジンではSCM材（クロームモリブデンスチール）などの構造用強靱鋼を使う。

ピストンピン⇔クランクピン間長さは137mm（＋0－0.087mm）で、ストローク／センターディスタンス比は1.93である。

サービスマニュアルによればコンロッドボルトを含めた重量において製造部品は520gから600gまで4g単位20段階に分類され、AからVまでのアルファベット表示が示されている。本機の実測値はコンロッドボルトを含み555g（＋1g－2g）であった。

小端部径／大端部径を含めこれらの寸法値は製造公差指定までデイトナ用251型のものと同じであるが、コンロッドボルト周りの設計はコストダウンのため妥協されている。コンロッドボルトは回り止めのついたDヘッドタイプだが、デイトナ用251型の場合Dヘッド下部を切削して除去するとともにコンロッド側のボルト締結部に側壁を設けてDヘッド上端を壁に当てて回り止めとしていたのに対し、本機では締結部のR面にDヘッドを乗り上げて回り止めとしている。この方式ではボルト締め付け時にコンロッドボルトに初期曲げ応力が生じる。レーシングユースを考慮しない設計に転じたとも言えるだろう。

鋼板製ストラット付ピストン＋リング

中空ピストンピン

リテーナリング（2）

コンロッド＋スモールエンドベアリング

Dヘッドコンロッドボルド（2）

コンロッドメタル（2）

コンロッドベアリングキャップ

コンロッドボルト用ナット

ピストン/コンロッドAsssy.：1043g
ピストン（リング付）：398g
コンロッドAssy.：555g

The connecting rod is a normal, so-called I-cross section type, and probably made by forging. Because the design of the conrod, which is subjected to repeated and extensive pull, compression and torsional stresses, is extremely complex, and constructed toughened steel such as SCM- chrome molybdenum steel- are used in high output engines. The distance between piston pin and crank pin is 137mm (+0 - 0.087mm), and the stroke/center distance ratio is 1.93. According to the service manual, the manufacturing components are categorized in 20 steps of 4g units ranging from 520g to 600g in weight measures including the conrod bolts, and indicated alphabetically from "A" to "V." The actual measurement of this engine, inclusive of the conrod bolts, was 555g (+1g-2g.) Those dimensional values including the small-end and large-end bores of connecting rod, are identical to Daytona's Type 251, although the design around the conrod bolt is compromised for cost saving. The conrod bolt is the rotating stopper type (D-head), but contrary to Daytona's Type 251, where the lower part of the D-head was cut so that the upper part will hit the wall at conrod mounting to stop the rotation, in case of this engine, the rotation is eliminated by running the D-head against the R-surface of the mounting. As this method will cause initial bend stress at the conrod bolt during tightening process, it could be assumed that design policy was changed to exclude racing usage.

ヘッドおよびバルブトレーン

　燃焼効率を決めるヘッド周りにおける設計的パラメータは、弁配置と燃料室形状、弁頭径／弁揚程／弁開閉タイミング、マニホールドとポート形状などである。本機のヘッドはデイトナ用251型の設計を母体としており、上記パラメータの基本の多く、バルブ狭角や燃焼室およびポート形状、バルブトレーンの基本設計などを踏襲している。また各部の基本寸法や製造公差値も251型用と同一と考えてよい。

　バルブ狭角はシリンダ鉛直線から左右23度の46度で、この時代のDOHC2弁ヘッドとしては非常に狭い値である。バルブ狭角を小さくするとヘッド高は大きくなるが、燃焼室が偏平となってピストン頭部を大きく盛り上げなくても高圧縮比が実現できるため、同じ燃焼室容積なら燃焼室表面積が小さくなって熱効率が向上する。

　点火プラグは251型のように2本のカムシャフトの間からではなく、インテークマニホールドの横から燃焼室に対し斜めに、かつ燃焼室頂部から横方向にオフセットした位置にねじ込まれている。この配置では燃焼室各部への火炎伝播距離が不均等になり、燃焼に要する時間が結果的に長くなってパワーが出ない。燃焼室の吸気ポート出口部を3次曲面に切削しているのは燃焼室内のガス気流速度を上げて燃焼を安定させようという設計意図も含まれているかもしれないが、この程度の形状では十分なスワールが発生するとは考えにくく、逆に燃料室の表面積を増加し、ホットスポットも作っている。S/V比（燃焼室の表面積／容積比）はバルブ狭角のより広い同時代のポルシェやランボルギーニよりは小さいものの、デイトナのものに比べるとS/V比、メカニカルオクタン価ともども低下している。

　弁頭径は吸気42.5φ、排気36.8φで、それぞれ251型の101.2%、98.4%である。弁揚程は吸気9.26mm、排気8.64mmとほぼ同じだが、開弁時間は吸排気ともわずかに短く、とくに排気弁を早閉じ（ATDC26度）している。オーバーラップは251型の83度に対して66度と短い。

　ポート形状は吸気側はデイトナのものとほぼ同様だが、排気側は排気マニホールド形状との兼ね合いで内側壁面が大きく屈曲しており、デイトナより効率は低下している。同じ水平対向レイアウトのポルシェは、より広いバルブ狭角を持つため排気ポート形状は本機より優れている。大雑把に言って吸気側はキャブレターを含めたインテーク全体として考えるとデイトナよりやや優位でポルシェと同等だが排気は両車より不利、総合的に言って当時の最新鋭車としてはヘッド周り設計レベルは高度とは言い難い。

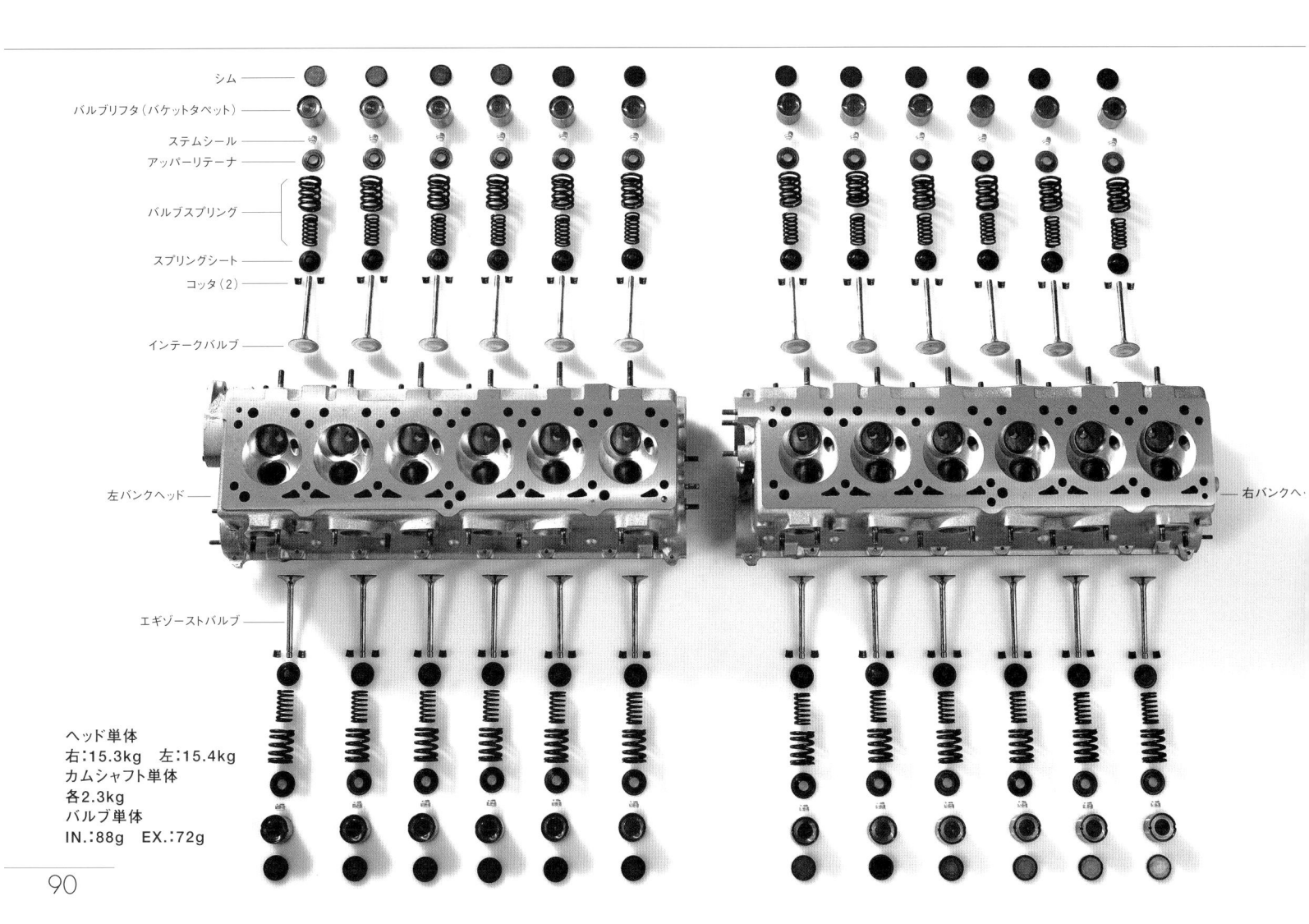

ヘッド単体
右：15.3kg　左：15.4kg
カムシャフト単体
各2.3kg
バルブ単体
IN.：88g　EX.：72g

Heads and Valve-Train

The design parameters around the head area to determine combustion efficiency are; valve arrangement and shape of combustion chamber, diameter of the valve head/valve lift/timing of valve opening and closure, shapes of manifold and port, etc. The head of this engine is derived from design of the Type 251 for Daytona. Many of the above-mentioned parameters, such as valve angle, shapes of combustion chamber and port, basic design of valve train, etc., are inherited therefrom. Furthermore, it is safe to say that basic dimensions and manufacturing tolerances are identical to Type 251. The valve angles are 46 degrees or 23 degrees left and right from the vertical line of the cylinder, an extremely narrow value for DOHC 2-valve heads of the times. The smaller valve angle results in higher head height, but as the combustion chamber becomes flat, higher compression ratio is achieved without making a large hump on the piston head, thus resulting in improved heat efficiency due to smaller surface area of combustion chamber in case of similar combustion chamber volume. In case of this engine's head, the spark plug, unlike the Type 251 in which the plug is located between the two camshafts, is screwed into the combustion chamber from the side of intake manifolds at an angle and offset sideways from the top of the combustion chamber. This layout results in an uneven spark travel distance to the various areas in the combustion chamber, which means lengthening of combustion time and therefore lower power output. Assuming from the fact that intake port outlet of the combustion chamber is cut in three dimensionally curved surfaces; there may be a design intention to stabilize combustion by speeding up gas/air flow within the combustion chamber. However, it is hard to believe that sufficient swirl generation is possible with this sort of shape, because the surface area of the combustion chamber is increased and a hotspot is formed. In terms of the S/V ratio (surface area of combustion chamber/volume ratio), while it is smaller than Porsche or Lamborghini of those days which had larger valve angles, it is inferior in this engine when compared with the Daytona's also in terms of designed anti-knock index. As for valve head diameters, the intake is 42.5ϕ, while exhaust is 36.8ϕ, 101.2% and 98.4%, respectively, of the Type 251. Valve lift is almost same, at 9.26mm for intake and 8.64mm for exhaust, but the valve opening time is a bit shorter for both intake and exhaust, especially the exhaust closure is earlier (ATDC 26 degrees). Overlap is 66 degrees, shorter than Type 251's 83 degrees. Shape of the port is almost the same as Daytona's on the intake side, but on the exhaust side, the inner wall is curved extensively due to delicate relation with the shape of exhaust manifold, resulting in lower efficiency than Daytona. In comparison, Porsche, having the same horizontally-opposed configuration, has a wider valve angle and therefore is superior to this engine as far as the exhaust port is concerned. Roughly speaking, on the intake side including the carburetors, this engine is a bit superior to Daytona and on the same level as the Porsche, while inferior to both cars on the exhaust side. So, on overall evaluation, the design level around the head is by no means high considering this was one of the newest cars at that time.

ヘッドはクランクケース等と同様アルミ合金の砂型鋳造製で、ポートや冷却水路などは中子で抜いている。カムカバーを左右一体としたためカムシャフトホルダー部の構造はデイトナ用ヘッドより簡略／軽量化できているが、実測重量は右バンク側15.3kg、左バンク側15.4kgと依然としてかなり大きい。カムカバーも砂型鋳造アルミ合金製だが、材質自体は本体とは異なるようだ。

　カムシャフトは中空の切削加工品である。当時のフェラーリの製造工程ではカムローブ部だけでなく、カムシャフト全体を熱処理していた。カムシャフト前方側にはベルトドライブ用のプーリをボルト結合している。左バンク吸気側カムシャフト後端ではディストリビュータをダイレクト駆動、右バンク吸気側カムシャフト後端はブレーキの真空倍力装置の負圧をアシストするための機械式負圧ポンプを減速ギヤを介さず直接駆動している。カムプロフィールはおそらくマルチサイン形状だと思われる。リフト量に対し開閉時間が比較的短いためバルブの加速度は高めである。

　ヘッド周りを完全分解して点検したところ燃焼室に多量のカーボンが溜まっていたことを除けば、カムシャフト／バルブトレーン系を含めよいコンディションであった。カムホルダー部には潤滑油切れと思われるひきずり傷が見られたが、エンジンが冷えている状態でブリッピングを反復すると起こりやすい現象である。

　ヘッド周りについては念のため以下のメカニカルレストレーションを行なった。①ヘッド接触面の切削（面研）②バルブガイドの新規製作および打ちかえ（24本）③バルブシートの新規製作および打ちかえ（24枚）④ポートとシートの段付き部研磨⑤バルブステム部の鏡面研磨。④についてはポート内面のフェラーリ工場における研磨作業が非常に乱雑でシートとの間に大きな段差が生じていたため、シートの打ちかえにともなってポート部を若干削り込み、段付きを修正した作業である。当時のフェラーリは鋳造時の中子のバリ取りを兼ねて吸排気ポートおよび吸気マニホールド内面を手作業で研磨していたが、他車の例を参照しても研磨技術は決して高いとは言えず、この結果設計的な狙いが十分製品に反映されているとは言い難い場合が多い。前ページでポルシェとの設計的な比較を行なったが、実際のパーツ各部を見る限り当時のポルシェの生産技術はフェラーリのそれを大きく凌駕しており、実際の製品の性能という観点に立つなら、その差はむしろ設計的差異より大きく製品に影響しているのではないかという印象である。

　ヘッド周りには以下のコスメティックレストレーションも行なった。①ヘッド外装部分のガラスビーズブラスト②カムカバー内外面のガラスビーズブラストおよび外面の結晶塗装。①についてはカーボン等を洗浄したのち完全に脱脂し、切削加工部分のすべてを入念にマスキングした後に施行した。脱脂が十分であるなら、細部に入り込んだガラス粉は洗剤を併用した高水圧洗浄で容易に除去することができる。カムカバーのオリジナルの塗装のクオリティは非常に低い。下地処理を入念に行なったうえ塗装を行なった。塗装部と非塗装部の塗り分けについてはオリジナルを忠実に再現した。

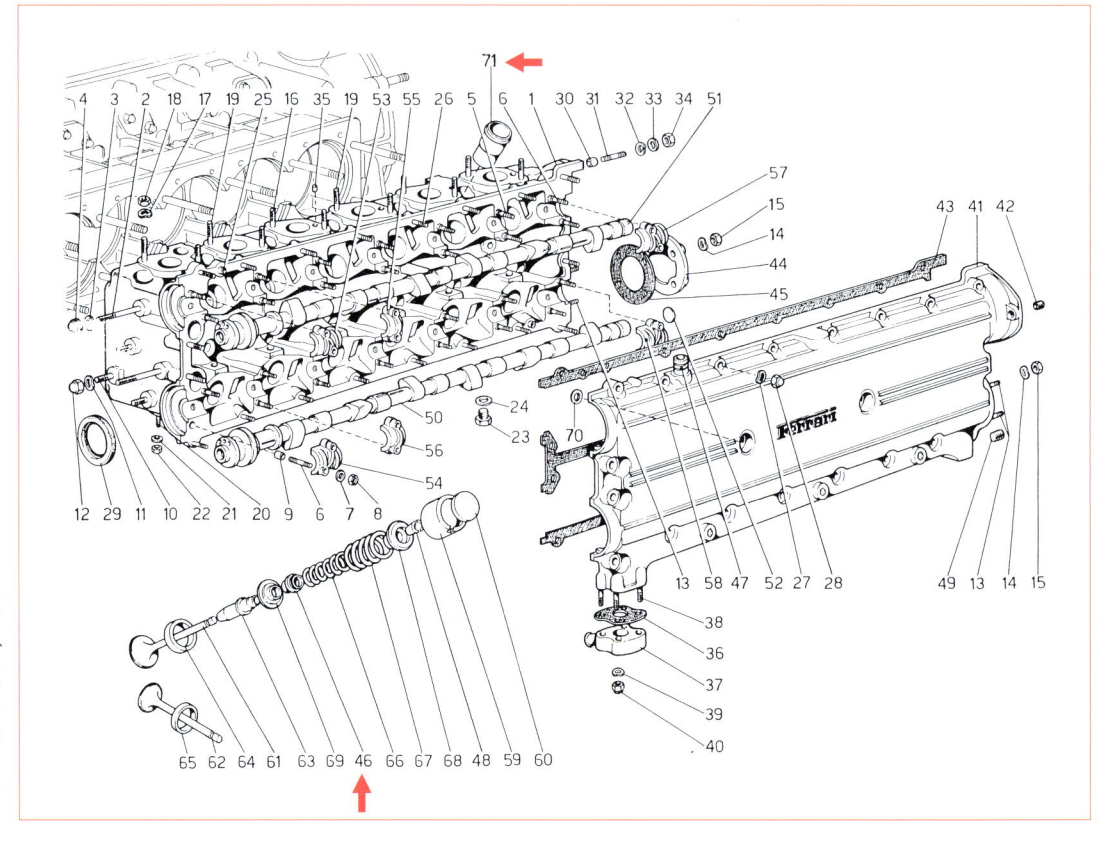

パーツカタログNo.95990216記載のヘッド周り部品構成図。左バンクのものである。バルブは直動式で図中46番はバルブガイド末端につくPTFE樹脂製のステムシールである。スプリングはダブル式、クリアランス調整用シムはバルブリフタ（バケットタペット）の外側につく。これらのパーツ構成はバルブスプリングのばね定数も含め弁頭径以外はほぼデイトナ用と同一である（デイトナ用251型は吸気弁頭径42.0φ、排気弁頭径37.4φ）。バルブ重量は吸気側の単体で実測88g、排気側の単体が72g、バルブスプリングやリフタを含めたバルブムービングパーツAssyの重量は吸気286g（±2g）、排気270g。図中71番は後期型（#18237以降）に装備された点火プラグの防水用カバーである（本機未整備）。

365GTB/4　　　　　　　　　　　　**365GT/4 BB**

本機ヘッドとデイトナ用251型ヘッドの比較。共にサービスマニュアルから転載したものである。両者とも図の左が吸気側。バルブ狭角、バルブシートとバルブステムの寸法／構造／製造公差、ポート形状（吸気側）、冷却水路などの設計的パラメータが同一なことが分かる。ただし本機の排気ポートは排気マニホールドとの取り回しの関係で大きく屈曲しており、レイアウトは改悪された。

The head, same as the crankcase, etc., is made by sand mold casting of aluminum alloy, with the ports and cooling water channels punched out by cores. By making left and right cam covers into a single unit, the construction of cam shaft holder part is simpler and lighter, but according to actual measurement, the right and left side banks were 15.3kg, 15.4kg, respectively, still relatively heavy. Cam cover is also made of aluminum alloy sand mold casting process, but the quality of the material seems to be different from the main unit. Camshaft is of hollow cut-machined construction, and it is assumed that in Ferrari's production processes of those days, heat-treatment was applied not only to the cam area, but to the entire camshaft. Pulley for belt drive is bolted on at the front side of camshaft. At the rear of the intake side camshaft on the left bank, distributor is driven directly, while at the rear of the intake side on the right bank, a mechanical vacuum pump to assist the vacuum brake booster is bolted directly onto the camshaft, also without a reduction gear. The cam profile is assumed to be of the multi-sine theory by multi-sine cam design. As the opening/closing time is relatively short in relation to lift amount, valve acceleration is on the high side. Thorough inspection after complete dismantling of the head area revealed that except for an extensive carbon accumulation in the combustion chamber, all components including the camshaft and valve train were found to be in favorable condition. While some drag scar was noticed in cam holder area, probably caused by lack of lubrication, such phenomena could well be caused by repeated blipping of the cold engine. Just to be on the safe side, the following mechanical restoration were made around the head area; ① milling of head contact surfaces; ② valve guides newly produced and implanted (24 pcs); ③ new production and implanting of valve seats (24 pcs); ④ polishing of stepped areas of port and seat and ⑤ mirror polishing of valve stem areas. Regarding ④, as the polishing of inner surface of the ports at Ferrari factory was very sloppy causing large steps in between, the port section was slightly cut during implanting to correct the steps. In those times, Ferrari was hand-polishing the inner surfaces of intake/exhaust pots and intake manifold in order to remove burrs in the core formed during casting process. This technique is unsatisfactory when compared to that of other car manufactures. Consequently, it is difficult to say that the designed targets were adequately reflected in the finished products. In the previous page, I compared designs with Porsche, but from looking at various actual parts, the production technique of Porsche in those days exceeded Ferrari's by far. From the standpoint of performances of actual products, my impression is that the disparities are much more than designed differences and affecting the products. Around the head, following cosmetic restorations were also made; ① glass-beads blasting of exterior parts of the head and ② glass-beads blasting of inner and outer surfaces of cam cover, as well as crystal painting of the outer surface. In case of ①, the job was carried out after washing the carbon, etc., and degreasing completely and carefully masking all of the milled areas. If degreasing is sufficient, the glass particles which went into narrow areas can be easily removed by high pressure detergents. As the quality of original paint on cam cover was extremely poor, it was repainted after careful primer treatment. In defining the painted and non-painted areas, extreme care was taken to faithfully reproduce the original finish.

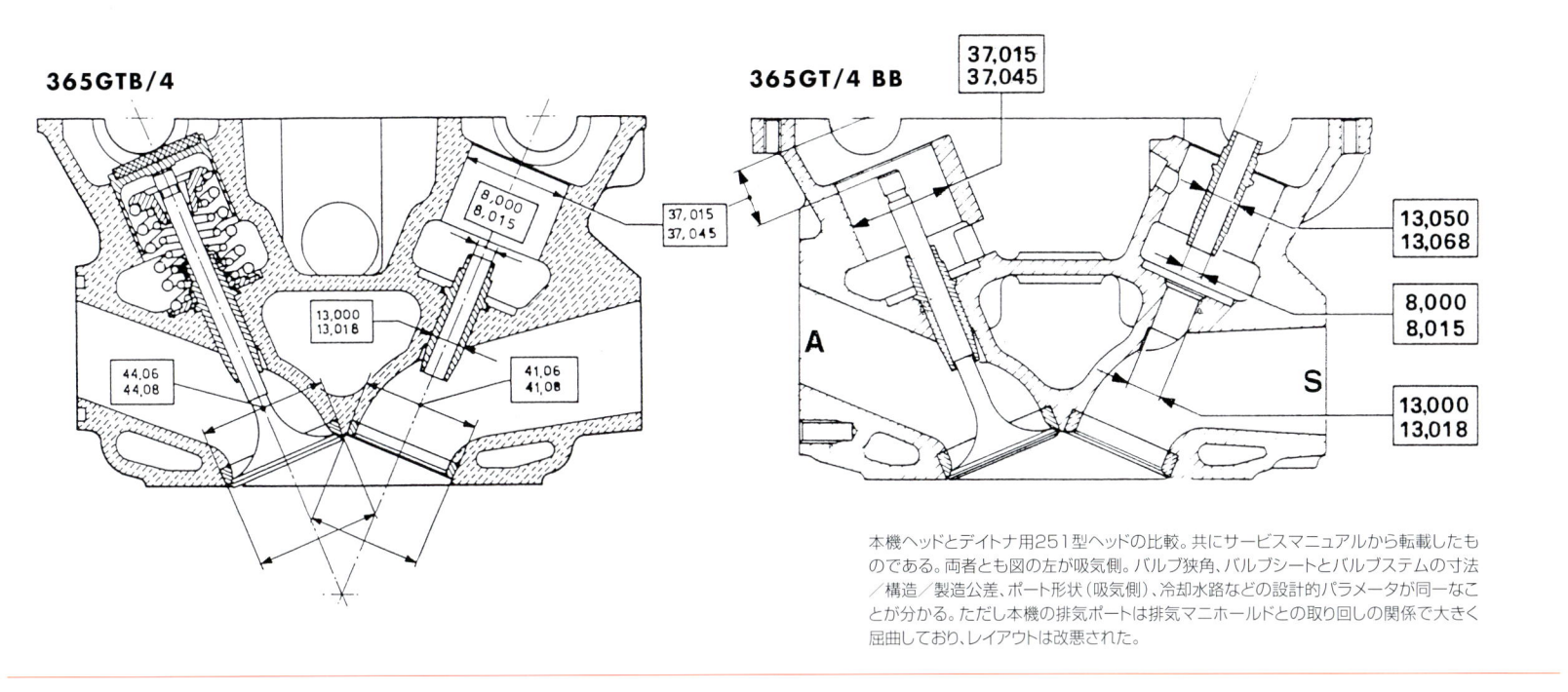

【写真上】分解直後のヘッドの状態。濃いガスセッティングのせいでカーボンが蓄積していた。シートの当たりも不良で、そのせいで何本かのバルブステムにも湾曲が発生していた。写真は左12番である

【写真下】カーボンを除去し、面研とバルブシートの打ち変えを行った後のヘッド。上側がインテーク。燃焼室を切削しインテークバルブ面積を最大限に確保しているプラグ位置は燃焼室中心から大きくオフセットしている。バルブシステム挿入前の状況である（写真は左10番）。

カムドライブ

　70年代以降に設計・開発されたフェラーリの量産車用エンジンはF50とエンツォフェラーリを除き一貫してカム駆動にベルトを用いてきたが、本機はその先鞭を告げたモデルである。

　カムシャフトの回転数はクランクシャフトの1/2だから、クランクから直接カムを駆動するとカム側のスプロケット／プーリはクランク側の倍径になってヘッド周りのマスが大きくなると共にバルブ挟角を狭く設定することが難しくなる。デイトナ用251型の場合（正確には前身の275GTB／4用226型から）クランクスプロケットからチェーンを使ってアイドラースプロケットを駆動し、2本のカムはそこから一段減速してギヤ駆動する二段減速方式を採用していた。ベルト駆動を導入するに際して本機ではクランクシャフト末端のギヤで減速してタイミングプーリを回し、カムドライブプーリ部のベルト歯数でさらに減速する二段減速方式を採用した。このとき左バンク側のタイミングプーリ駆動ギヤでウォーターポンプ駆動ギヤを（増速）、右バンク側タイミングプーリ駆動ギヤでオイルポンプ駆動ギヤを（こちらも増速）回している。下の写真はそれらの位置関係を示しており、破線で示したのがタイミングベルトである。

　ベルトテンショナーは手動調整式である。コイルばねが内蔵されており、ばねによって押されるアイドラプーリの押し出し位置とベルトのテンションとが釣り合った場所でボルトを締め込んでアイドラプーリを固定する。サービスマニュアルおよび車載オーナーズマニュアルではこの調整を2万kmごとにエンジン冷間時に行なうよう指定しているが、古谷氏によると本機は水平対向レイアウトの関係からか温間時のエンジン横方向への膨張が非常に大きく、冷間時調整では温間時にベルトの張りが強くなりすぎてアイドラプーリ・ベアリングからの異音やベルトの伸びなどが発生する傾向があるという。古谷氏は温間時のベルトの張り具合も併せて確認することを強く勧めている。

　本機はトランスアクスルケース内にオイルタンクを備え各部を潤滑したオイルを再びオイルタンク内に戻すウエットサンプ式である。オイルタンクは内側でトランスミッションと、また外側で排気マニホールドと隣接しており、油温が上昇しやすい傾向がある。このため512BB用F102B型では外部オイルタンクを設置し、油量を増やしてドライサンプ方式に改めた。

Cam Drive System

Ferrari's production car engines designed and developed after 1970's, with the exception of the F50 and Enzo Ferrari, all had cams driven by belts, and this engine was the forerunner of this trend. As the revolution of the camshafts is 1/2 of the crankshaft, if the cam is driven directly by the crankshaft, the sprocket/pulley on the cam side becomes double the diameter of the crank side, resulting in larger mass around the head and making it difficult to set narrow valve angle. In Daytona's Type 251 engine (or, to be exact, from the predecessor Type 226 for 275GTB/4,) two-stage reduction method, in which idler sprockets were driven by chain from the crank sprocket, with the two cams driven from there after another reduction, was adopted. In introducing the belt drive in this engine, two-stage reduction, first by gear at the end of crankshaft to reduce the speed before turning the timing pulley, and then further reduction by toothed belt at cam drive pulley, was employed. At the same time, the timing pulley drive gear on the left bank side drives the water pump drive gear at increased speed, while the timing pulley drive gear on the right bank side powers the oil pump drive gear (also at increased speed). The picture at left page shows the respective arrangements, and the broken line indicates the timing belt. The belt tension is adjusted manually. The idler pulley with integral coil spring is secured by tightening the bolt at the point where the idler pulley pushed out by belt tension and spring power is balanced. The service manual as well as the owner's manual supplied with the car stipulates that this adjustment should be carried out every 20,000km with the cold engine, but according to Mr. Furuya, this engine, probably from its horizontally-opposed layout, had excessive lateral expansion when the engine is warm. Therefore, if the adjustment is made while the engine is cold, the belt tension may become too tight with warm engine and cause abnormal noise from idler pulley bearing or stretched belt. Mr. Furuya strongly recommends belt tension be checked when the engine is hot. This engine is of the wet sump lubrication type. From the oil tank located in the transaxle case, after lubricating the various areas, the oil is again returned to the tank. As the oil tank is located in close proximity to the transmission on the inside and exhaust manifold on the outside, there is a tendency to raise the oil temperature. Therefore, in the 512BB, lubrication was modified to the dry-sump system by installing an external oil tank and increasing oil capacity.

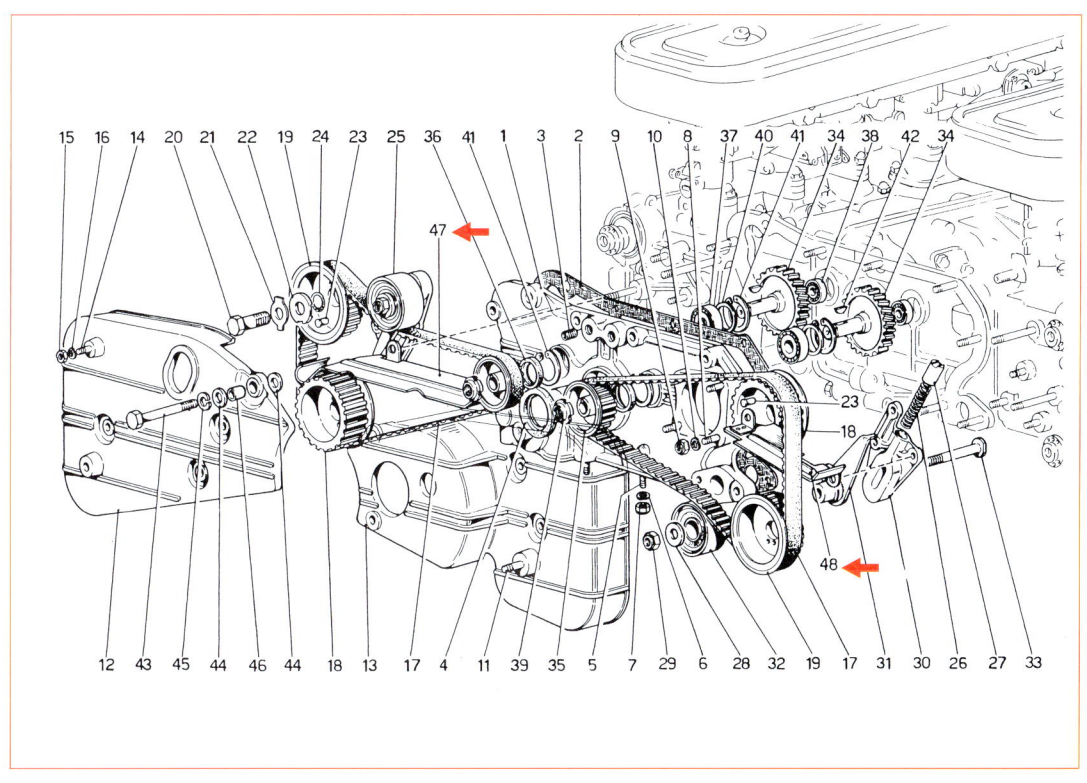

パーツカタログNo.95990216記載のカムドライブトレーンパーツ図。左の写真と合わせてご覧になると各部品のレイアウトがお分かりになりやすいと思う。本車は購入前に「タイミングベルトの交換およびテンショナー交換整備」と称する有料の整備を受けたが、エンジンを分解してみたところテンショナーは外側から見える左バンク側のみ交換、ベルトは中古品という手抜き整備であった。図中の47および48番は#17993以降に装着されたベルトの跳ね止めのスラックガイドで、本機には装備されていない。

95

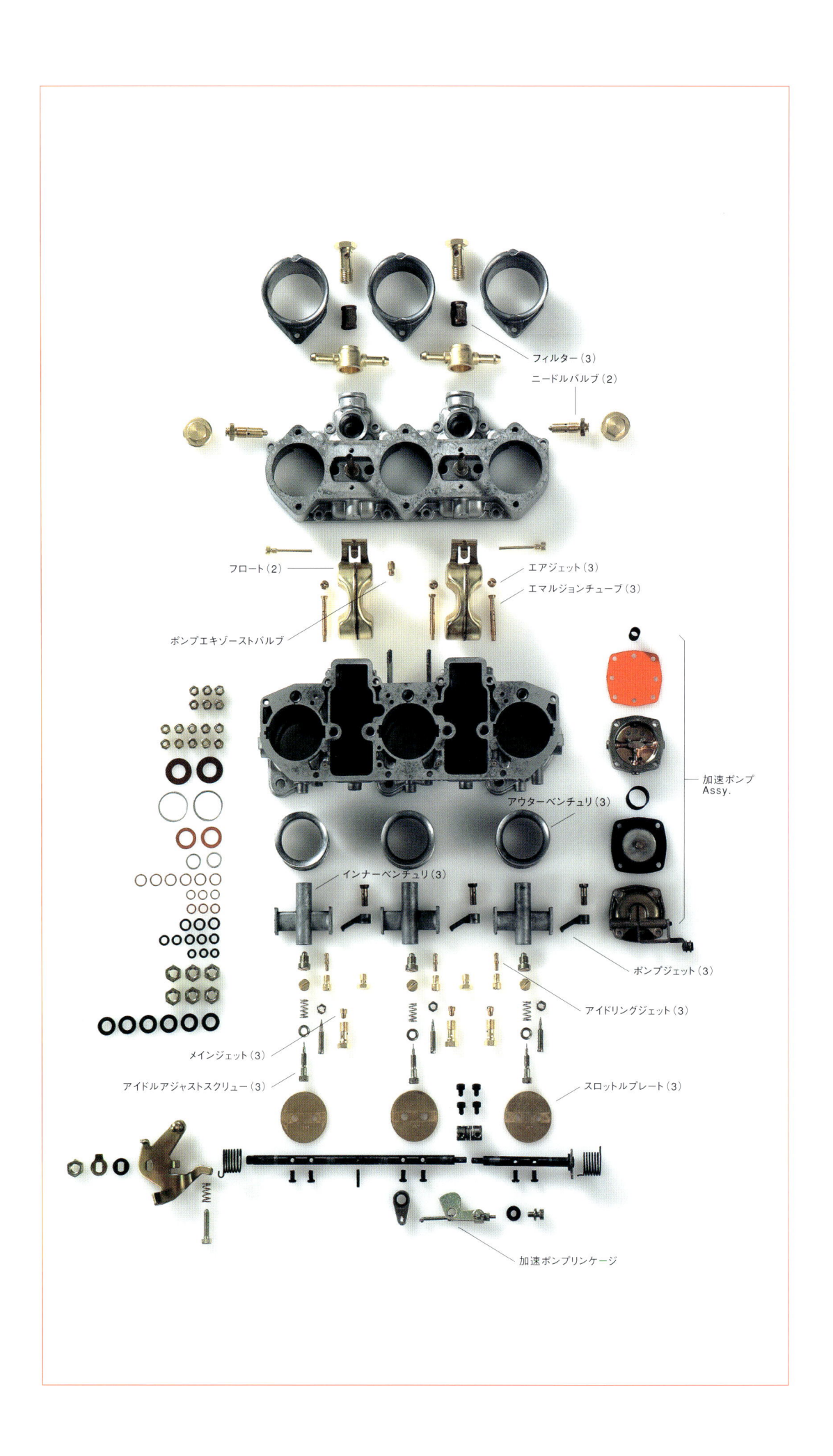

- フィルター（3）
- ニードルバルブ（2）
- フロート（2）
- エアジェット（3）
- エマルジョンチューブ（3）
- ポンプエキゾーストバルブ
- 加速ポンプAssy.
- アウターベンチュリ（3）
- インナーベンチュリ（3）
- ポンプジェット（3）
- アイドリングジェット（3）
- メインジェット（3）
- スロットルプレート（3）
- アイドルアジャストスクリュー（3）
- 加速ポンプリンケージ

キャブレター

Carburetors

　燃料供給はウェーバー製40IF3C型気化器で行なっている。固定ベンチュリ（チョーク）式／ダウンドラフト型／シングルバレルタイプの気化器を3つまとめて1つのケースの中に収め、左右気化器でフロート室を兼用するという設計構造で、本機ではこれを4基装着する。すなわち各気筒ごとに一基ずつ独立した気化器を備えているのと同様である。

　ウェーバーのトリプルチョーク型気化器は1960年初頭にランチア・フラミニア用V6エンジンの高性能版用として設計・開発された。通常IDA3C型と呼ばれている。ランチアに続き1966年春にはポルシェ911がソレックス製の同タイプ気化器に換えて導入、またランボルギーニもミウラ用V型12気筒に採用（65年10月発表）した。60年代後期に開発されたダウンドラフト／2チョーク型のIDA型やIDF型とは構造が異なり、交換用のジェット類やエマルジョンチューブなどの設計仕様には50年代に設計されたDGV/DFV型のものを流用している。また本機に使用しているタイプには特別に40IF3C型という名称が与えられており本体にもその旨刻印が打刻されているが、トップカバー部とリンケージ部を除けばフラミニア－911－ミウラが使用し広く市販もされていた40IDA3C型と同一である。

　燃料はフロート室に溜められたのち交換式の大小ベンチュリで発生した負圧によってメインジェットを通って吸い出され、エアジェットからの空気と混合されてからスモールベンチュリ内部に供給されるが、この主系統とは別に低速供給系統および加速ポンプ系統を備える。低速系の燃料供給量はバイパスポートで発生する負圧、アイドリングジェット口径、アイドルアジャストスクリュー締め込み量によって決定される。低速系から主系統への移行はエンジン回転数で3000rpm付近である。本キャブレター固有の設計的問題点は①磨耗してガタが出やすいスロットルシャフトのスリーブ式軸受け②液面で揺動しやすいフロートの保持構造③ガタつきが出やすいインナベンチュリ固定法④フロート室内にオフセット配置した燃料供給穴による燃料吐出追従性不良⑤設計起因による低速系の微調整能力不足などである。

Fuel supply is by WEBER Type 40 I F3C carburetors. Three carburetors consisting of fixed venturi or choke/down draft/single barrel type are bundled together and contained in one casing, with the left and right carburetors sharing the same float chamber. In this engine, four of those are used, having the same effect as each of the cylinders is equipped with one independent carburetor. The WEBER's triple choke type carburetor was designed and developed in the early 1960 for the high-performance version of the V-6 engine for Lancia Flaminia, and is generally known as the Type IDA 3C. After the Lancia, this unit was used by Porsche from the spring of 1966 replacing a similar carburetor made by SOLEX, and also by Lamborghini for the Miura's V-12 engine announced in October 1965. The construction differs from down draft 2-choke Type IDA or Type IDF developed in the late 1960's, and basic design specifications such as exchangeable jets and emulsion tubes, were inherited from the Type DGV/DFV designed in the 1950's. The type used in this engine was specially given the designation Type 40 IF3C, and this is stamped on the carburetor body. However, except for the top cover part and the linkages, it is identical to the Type 40 IDA3C widely marketed and used in Flaminia, 911 and Miura. The fuel, after accumulating in the float chamber, is sucked out through the main jet by vacuum generated by the interchangeable large and small jets, mixed with the air from the air jet and supplied into the small venturi. In addition to this main system, there is a separate low speed supply system and the acceleration pump system. The amount of fuel supplied via the low speed system is determined by the vacuum generated at the by-pass port, diameter of the idling jet and degree of tightening of the idling adjust screw. The transition from the low speed system to the main system occurs at an engine speed of around 3000rpm. The inherent design problems of this carburetor are; ① the sleeve-type bearing of the throttle shaft is susceptible to cause play due to wear; ② the construction of the float could cause the fuel level to sway; ③ the support method of the inner venturi may cause play; ④ poor fuel output due to fuel supply hole located in offset position within the float chamber and ⑤ lack of fine-tuning capability of the lower range due to a design problem.

【左および下右写真】フェラーリ用40IF3C型はリンケージのタイプによって装着位置が決まるため、本体およびトップカバーに1番～4番の打刻が打たれている。メインジェット挿入口（メインジェットは3つのチョークに対し各ひとつで、4つの挿入口のうちひとつは空孔である）の位置以外外観は同一なので、オーバーホール時に番号位置が入れ替わりやすい。新車時は左バンク前方が1番、後方が2番、右バンク前方が3番、後方が4番である（下写真は1番本体）。気化器は完全分解したが、磨耗しやすいスロットルプレート部のポート内面やガタのでやすいシャフト軸受部等を含め各部の状態は非常に良好だったため、オーバーホールキットを利用してガスケット／ワッシャ類を交換し、内外のコスメティックレストアを施すに留めた。アルミ合金ダイキャスト製の本体とトップカバー、および各パーツはガラスビーズブラスト、ねじ類および加速ポンプカバー等は亜鉛クロメートめっき、黒染め部は再処理を行なった。真鍮製パーツについてはりん酸－硝酸－氷酢酸浴に浸漬して化学研磨した（キリンス）。同処理をしておくと酸化変色しにくくなる。

【下左写真】本機スロットルリンケージ機構。砂型アルミ鋳物製のブラケット、鋳鉄製亜鉛めっきのアーム、鋼製りん酸塩皮膜処理のシャフトなどから構成された凝ったもので、ブラケットの取付アライメント如何によらず作動を補償するためスフェリカルブッシュが圧入されている。

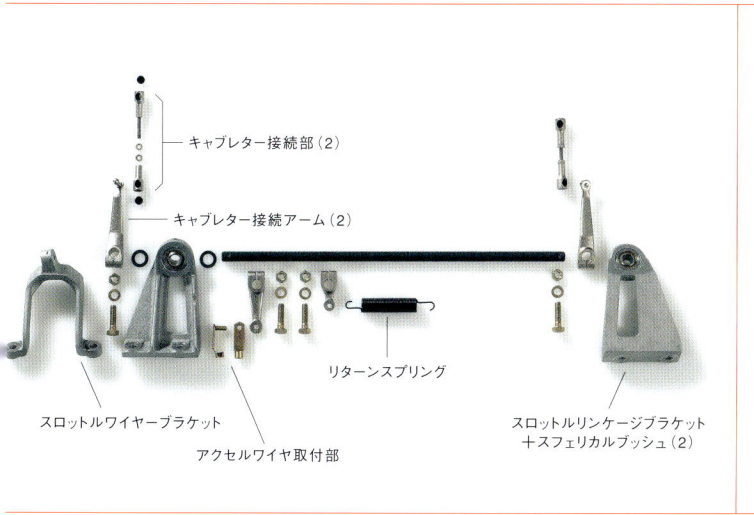

- キャブレター接続部（2）
- キャブレター接続アーム（2）
- リターンスプリング
- スロットルワイヤーブラケット
- アクセルワイヤ取付部
- スロットルリンケージブラケット＋スフェリカルブッシュ（2）

下記は本機と365GTB/4（デイトナ）および2ℓ時代のポルシェ911各車とのエンジン/気化器仕様比較である。ウェーバー気化器では量産車の場合メインジェット口径に対しエアジェット口径を0.40〜1.00mm太くするのが通常だが、本機は911でいうT〜E相当の低中速仕様エンジンにアイドル1.10、メイン1.55、エア1.60という、低速/主系統共に非常に濃い空燃費を設定している。始動困難やプラグのくすぶり、低速から主系統への移行時の息つき発生など本機固有の不調も自明の理だ。エンジン仕様を考えると少なくともメイン1.55に対しエア2.20〜2.40、アイドル0.60前後というセッティングが妥当なところだろう。

Below is a comparison of engine/carburetor specifications between this engine, 365GTB/4 (Daytona), and the various Porsche models of the 2 liter era. In case of WEBER carburetors, it is customary to make the air jet diameter 0.40~1.00mm larger than that of the main jet. However, in this engine, an extremely high air density is set at both low speed/main system by settings of idle 1.10, main 1.55 and air 1.60 on a low/medium speed specification engine corresponding to T~E in terms of the 911. The inherent problems of this engine such as difficulty in starting, wet plugs, and the lag during transition from low speed to main system, are all self-evident. Conjecturing from the engine specifications, settings of air 2.20~2.40 against main 1.55 should be appropriate.

	365GTB/4	365GT/4 BB	911T (2.0ℓ)	911E (2.0ℓ)	911S (2.0ℓ)	911R (2.0ℓ)
Bore (mm)	81	→	80	→	→	→
Stroke (mm)	71	→	66	→	→	→
Displacement/cylinder (cc)	365.86	→	331.75	→	→	→
Compression ratio	8.8	→	8.6	9.1	9.8	10.5
Valve						
Intake	42.0φ	42.5φ	42φ	→	→	45φ
Exhaust	37.4φ	36.8φ	38φ	→	→	39φ
Intake opening (BTDC)	45°	40°	40°	52°	64°	104°
Intake closing (ABDC)	46°	48°	56°	62°	76°	104°
Exhaust opening (BBDC)	46°	54°	66°	64°	64°	100°
Exhaust closing (ATDC)	38°	26°	22°	44°	44°	80°
Operating angle, intake	271°	268°	276°	294°	320°	388°
Operating angle, exhaust	264°	260°	268°	288°	288°	360°
Overlap	83°	66°	62°	96°	108°	184°
Carburetor						
Outer venturi	32	34	27	—	32	42
Inner venturi	4.5	3.5	4.5	—	4.5	4.5
Main jet	1.35	1.55	1.10	—	1.30	1.70
Air jet	1.90	1.60	1.45	—	1.10	0.70
Idle jet	1.60	1.10	0.45	—	0.55	0.80
Pump jet	0.40	0.40	0.50	—	0.50	0.50
Emulsion Tube	F25	F26	F1	—	F3	F24
Needle	1.75	→	→	—	→	→
Rated Maximum power (bhp/rpm)	352/7500	344/7200	110/5800	140/6500	170/6800	210/8000
Rated Maximum torque (kg-m/rpm)	44.0/5500	41.7/3900	16.0/4500	18.2/4500	18.5/5500	—

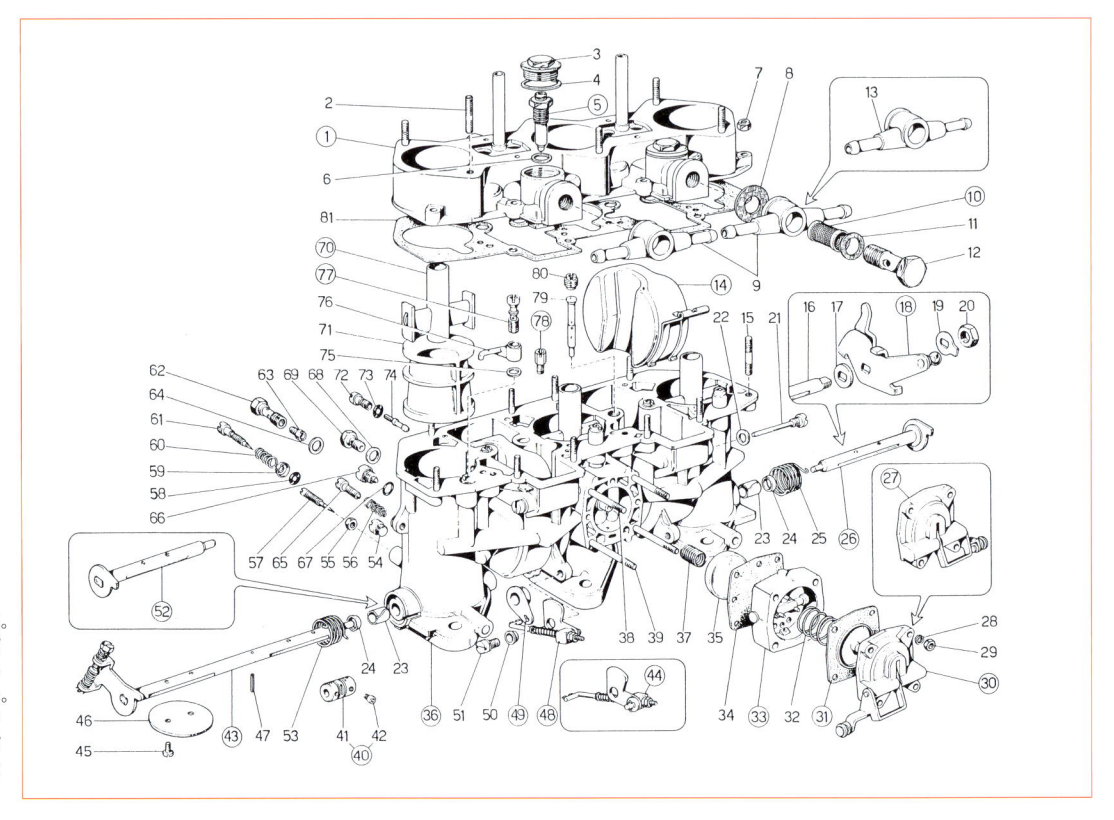

本機パーツカタログNo.95990216より転載。ウェーバー社が公表しているIDA3C型とほぼ同じ図版である。図中（ ）内のパーツは1番〜4番によって変わるリンケージ用パーツである。63:メインジェット、80:エアジェット、79:エマルジョンチューブ、74:アイドルジェット、77:ポンプジェット、78:ポンプエギゾーストバルブ、61:アイドルアジャストスクリュー。

分解直後の燃料ポンプ。本体、ステーなどの外装部品をレストアし、そのまま組み立てた。モーター部カバーのシールは専用溶剤を使って剥離し、本体再めっき後に再び貼付した。完成状態は右の写真を参照。

　二連装の燃料ポンプおよび燃料フィルタユニットは鋼板製のブラケットにマウントされ、ノイズコンデンサとともにエンジン前方の車体バルクヘッド壁面に固定されている。
　60ℓ入り2基の燃料タンクから吸い出された燃料はパイプ出口に設けられたストレーナを通って燃料フィルタに入り、二又に分かれて並列の燃料ポンプから気化器列へ送られる。未使用燃料は気化器列から直接燃料タンク注入口へ戻る。
　FISPA製燃料フィルタは交換式ろ紙製エレメントを内蔵する旧式のもので、エレメントは下部のばねによってケース上部に押し上げられ、ゴミ/さび/水分などの重量物はケース下部に沈殿する。ケースはダイス成形の鋼板塗装仕上げ、カバーはアルミ合金ダイキャスト製である。
　燃料ポンプはAPG/BCD製の電動モータ式ベーンタイプで、本体下部のアルミ合金製ケースの内部に放射状に配置された5枚のベーンを持つ偏心回転ロータが収められている。吐出量は2基で100ℓ／時である。
　各ユニットはすべて分解し点検したが状態は非常に良好であったためコスメティックレストアのみ施した。燃料フィルタのカバーはブラストし防錆のため半ツヤのクリアウレタン塗料を薄くスプレーした。燃料ポンプはケース本体をブラストしアロジン処理、モータのケースは同じくブラスト後に亜鉛ユニクロめっき、ステーおよびボルト類は亜鉛クロメートめっきを施した。装着部ブラケットはブラストし防錆塗装後ウレタン塗装をした。燃料量センダユニット本体は亜鉛クロメートめっきを施した。

The twin fuel pumps and the fuel filter units are mounted onto a steel bracket and affixed to the bulkhead wall of the body at front of the engine together with the noise condenser. The fuel supplied from the twin 60 liter fuel tanks goes through the strainer at the pipe exit, fuel filter, and then divides into two branches and delivered to the carburetor row by the parallel fuel pumps. The unused fuel is returned directly from the carburetor row to the filler port of the fuel tank. The fuel filter made by FISPA is an old type having an exchangeable paper element, in which the element is forced toward the upper part of the case by the spring located below, and heavy substances such as dirt, rust and water will settle at the bottom of the case. The case is made of steel by forming die, and is painted. The cover is made of aluminum alloy die cast. The fuel pump is the vane type driven by an electric motor, with an eccentrically revolving rotor with five radial vanes contained within a box made of aluminum alloy located below the engine. The output is 100 liters/hour with two units. After dismantling everything for inspection, all units were found to be in an excellent condition. Therefore, only cosmetic restorations were carried out as follows; the cover of the fuel filter was blasted and sprayed lightly with a semi-gloss clear urethane finish. For the fuel pump, the main unit was blasted and treated with zinc chromate plating. Similarly, the motor case was zinc uni-chromate plated after blasting, and the stays as well as bolts were treated with zinc chromate plating. Mounting brackets were blasted and then painted with urethane paint after anti-rust treatment. The main part of the fuel level sender unit was treated with zinc chromate plating.

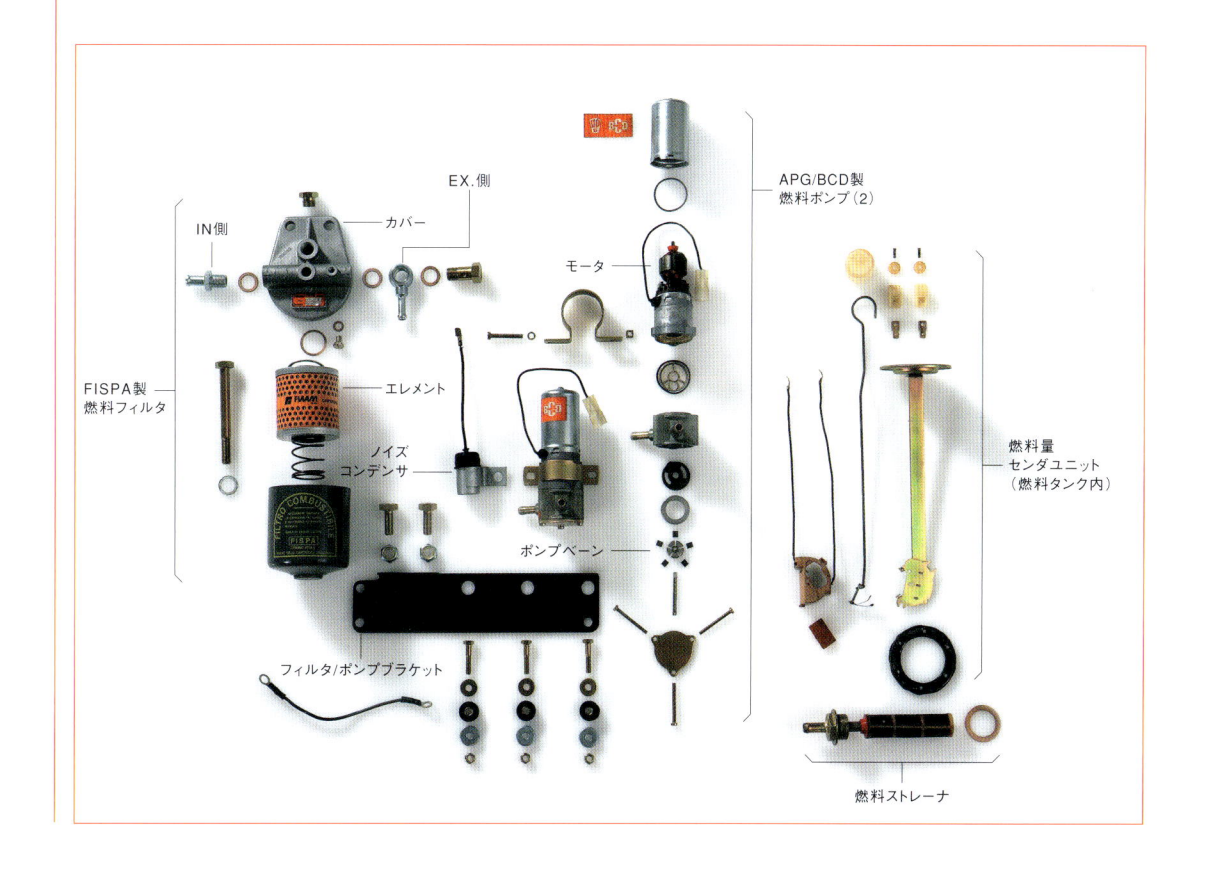

冷却系

本車はフロントラジエータ方式を採用しており、冷却水はフロア中央の2本のアルミ管を通じてエンジンルームとの間を循環する。冷却水量はサブタンク分も含め22ℓである。

遠心式ウォータポンプはエンジン左バンク・フロントカバー部に外装されており、クランクシャフトからギヤ駆動する（94ページ参照）。駆動ギヤと羽根車（ロータ）は背中合わせにレイアウトされており、中間に冷却水で潤滑されながら同時に冷却水をシーリングするメカニカルシールがつく。メカニカルシールはいわゆるバランス形で、シールリングとメイティングリングはカーボン／超硬材の組み合わせと思われる。主軸支持は単列式ボールベアリングをメカニカルシール近くとドリブンギヤの近くにそれぞれ配置している。

ウォータポンプの能力は他の条件一定ならケーシング内部の冷却水通路（吸込流路／ボリュート／ディフューザ）形状とロータ形状で決まるが、本機は長方形ボリュートと前向き／後向き角度のついていない平面放射状ロータの組み合わせという60年代的設計である。こうした旧式のロータ形状では冷却水温が高い状態で高回転運転を行なうとキャビテーションが発生して著しく効率が低下しやすいし、ボリュートやディフューザ部の壁面が衝撃圧のために侵食されることもある。いずれにせよ275GTBの時代からほとんど進化していない設計は、22ℓもの冷却水を循環させなくてはいけないフロントラジエータ式ミッドシップという本車レイアウトに十分な能力を持つとは言い難い。さすがにメーカーも認識していたらしく、テスタロッサ用F113A型エンジン以降はロータに後向き角タイプのものを採用している。

サーモスタットはエンジン上部の冷却水出口に設ける出口液温制御（インライン）タイプである。ラジエータおよび配管内の冷却水容量が大きいフロントラジエータ式ミッドシップカーで冷却水のインライン制御を行なうと、サーモスタットが開いた瞬間に冷たい冷却水が一気に流れ込んでサーモスタットが閉じてしまうため、全部の冷却水の温度が安定するまでサーモスタットが何度も開閉をくり返す現象（ハンチング）が起こりやすい。1977年発行のサービスマニュアルではサーモスタットにドリルで直径3.5～4.0mmほどの穴を開けることを勧めているが、おそらくこのハンチング対策であると思われる。

Cooling System

サブタンクは設計仕様当初エンジン横に設置されていたが#17847以降は本機のようにエンジン上部に置かれるようになった。またこのとき水冷式のエンジンオイルクーラーも廃止された。本機のサブタンクはさびも少なくよい状態だったので内外をブラストし入念に防錆処理を施してからウレタン塗装を施した。キャップは当時と同じ2つ瓜タイプの新品を入手して交換、タンク上のシールはアメリカ製のレストア用既製品を使用した。写真はブラスト中の状況である。

This vehicle has radiators at the front. Cooling water is circulated between radiator and engine room via two aluminum tubes which run through the floor center. Including the sub-tank, the cooling water capacity is 22 liters. The centrifugal water pump is situated externally on the front cover of the engine's left bank and is driven via a gear from the crankshaft. (See Page 94). The layout of the drive system and the rotor is back-to-back, and the mechanical seal which is lubricated by the cooling water and also seals the coolant is situated in the middle. This "mechanical seal" is the so-called balance type. The material of seal ring and mating ring are believed to be a combination of carbon and cemented carbide alloy. The main shaft is supported by single row ball bearings located close to the mechanical seal and the driven gear. The water pump capacity is dependant on the type of water channel within the casing (intake channel/volute/diffuser) as well as the type of the rotor, provided that other preconditions are the same. But in case of this engine, it is more or less a 1960's design having a volute with rectangular cross section and plane radial rotor without frontal or rearward angles. In such an old-fashioned rotor type, excessive deterioration of efficiency is caused by formation of cavitation when driven at high speed with high water temperature. Also, the walls of the volute or diffuser may be corroded due to impact pressure. At any rate, the design which made almost no progress from the days of 275 GTB can not be regarded as being sufficient for this vehicle having the mid-ship layout with front radiator which must circulate cooling water of as much as 22 liters. Apparently, the manufacturer was aware of the problem, as from the F113A engine for the Testarossa, a rotor with rearward angle was adopted. The thermostat is the type which detects and regulates the temperature at the cooling water outlet located at the top of the engine, or the so-called in-line type. When the inline regulation of the cooling water is made in a mid-ship vehicle with front radiator having a large cooling water volume in the radiator and tubes, cold water flows in at once when the thermostat opens, thus closing the thermostat. This is likely to cause repeated opening/closing of the thermostat until the temperature of the cooling water becomes stable. In the service manual issued in 1977, it is recommended to drill a hole with a diameter of 3.5~4.0mm at the thermostat, apparently a countermeasure against this phenomena.

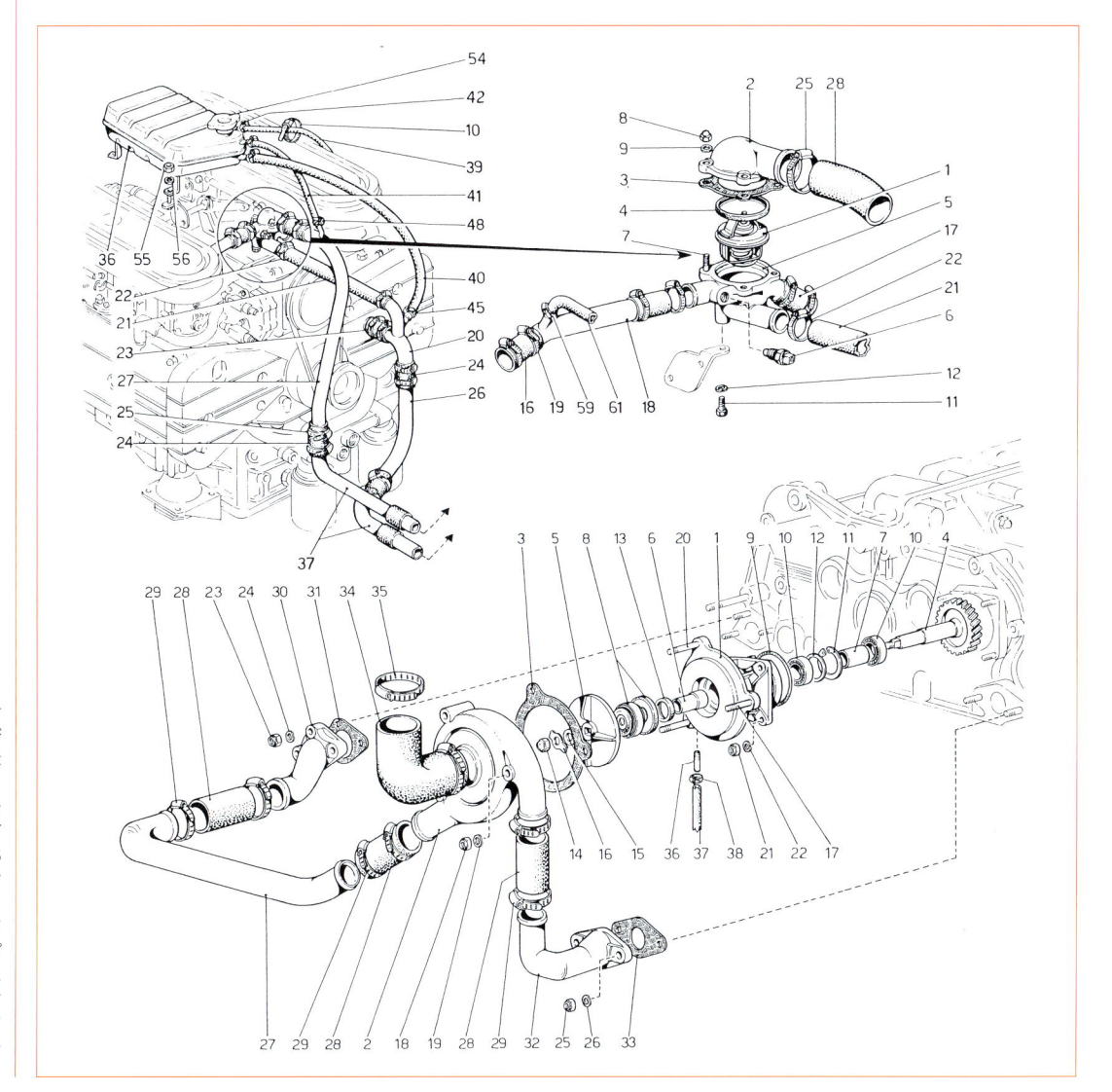

パーツカタログNo.95990216記載のサーモスタット周りの構成図（上半分）およびウォータポンプ構成図（下半分）。冷却水は図中パイプ18からサーモスタットに入り、サーモスタット開弁状態ではパイプ27を通ってフロントのラジエータへ送られ、パイプ26→20と戻ってホース23の内部にあるウォータポンプからエンジン左右バンクへ還流する（下図のパイプ30および32）。サーモスタット閉時はホース21から出てパイプ20内部でUターンしウォータポンプへ戻る。#17845以前の車両ではラジエータから戻ってきた冷却水がウォータポンプに入る手前、上図中のパイプ26に相当する部分に筒形の水冷式エンジンオイルクーラーが設置されていた。

101

点火系

ディストリビュータキャップの点火分配順を示す。シールの番号はエンジン点火順を7時間ずつずらしていったものである（ロータ前後分配式）。番号シールは分解・洗浄時に剥がれ落ちやすいが、1番点火場所が判明していればエンジン点火順から容易にハイテンションコード接続位置を割り出すことができる。本機ディストリビュータキャップおよびロータはよい状態だったので、洗浄/点検後、表面のクリア塗装のみ剥離しウレタンクリアで再塗装した。番号シールは新規製作して貼り直した。

　点火装置はMAGNETI-MARELLI製のDinoplexと呼ばれるレーシングタイプのバッテリー点火CDI方式（容量放電式点火装置）で、シグナルジェネレータ内蔵のS158A型ディストリビュータ、トランス付AEC104BK型CDI、BAE202型点火コイル（開磁路型）によって構成されている。

　12Vのバッテリー直流を発振器でパルス電流にしてからトランスで約400Vの交流に昇圧し、ダイオードで整流して約400Vの直流に換え、これをコンデンサに蓄える。ディストリビュータ内部にはシグナルロータとピックアップコイルからなる発電機（シグナルジェネレータ）があり、これによって作られたスイッチング信号電流でサイリスタをONにし、コンデンサに放電をうながす。

　サイリスタのゲートの作動電圧は一定だが、ピックアップコイルの発生電圧は回転の上昇と共に高くなるので、サイリスタのONタイミングは高回転時ほど早くなる。すなわち点火タイミングはエンジンの回転の上昇にともなって進角する（電気進角）。

　ディストリビュータ内には機械式遠心進角装置も内蔵されており、シグナルロータに進角度を与える。バキューム式進角装備は備えていない。本機の最大進角度は5000rpm時36〜38度である。

　高電圧の各プラグへの分配はディストリビュータキャップ内に収められたロータと12本のサイドエレクトロードによって行なわれる。ロータのアーム部は2ヵ所備えられており上下装着位置が異なる。またサイドエレクトロードもそれに合わせ6本は高位置、6本は低位置にある。分配はロータ前後で交互に行なわれる。

　いまキャップ12時の位置でロータ片側のアームからサイドエレクトロードへ分配されたとすると、次の分配はロータ反対側のアームから反対側のサイドエレクトロードへと行なわれる。ディストリビュータを時計に見立てると、次の分配点は常に文字盤の180°反対側のさらに12分の1回転後の位置、つまり「7時間後」の場所になる。本機の点火順は1-9-5-12-3-8-6-10-2-7-4-11だが、これが12時-7時-2時-9時-4時-11時-6時-1時-8時-3時-10時-5時の位置に相当するようハイテンションコードを接続しなければエンジンは始動しない。

　ハイテンションコードは白いシリコン製のブーツに通され、エンジンへの装着用のマウントブラケットがラバーを介して装着されている。

　点火プラグの標準指定はチャンピオンN63Yというコールドタイプ（BP8ES相当）だが、濃い空燃費設定と相まってこれが始動性や低速走行性、メンテナンス性をさらに低下させている要因である。本機の性格を考えるとBP7ES相当の熱価が妥当であると思われる。

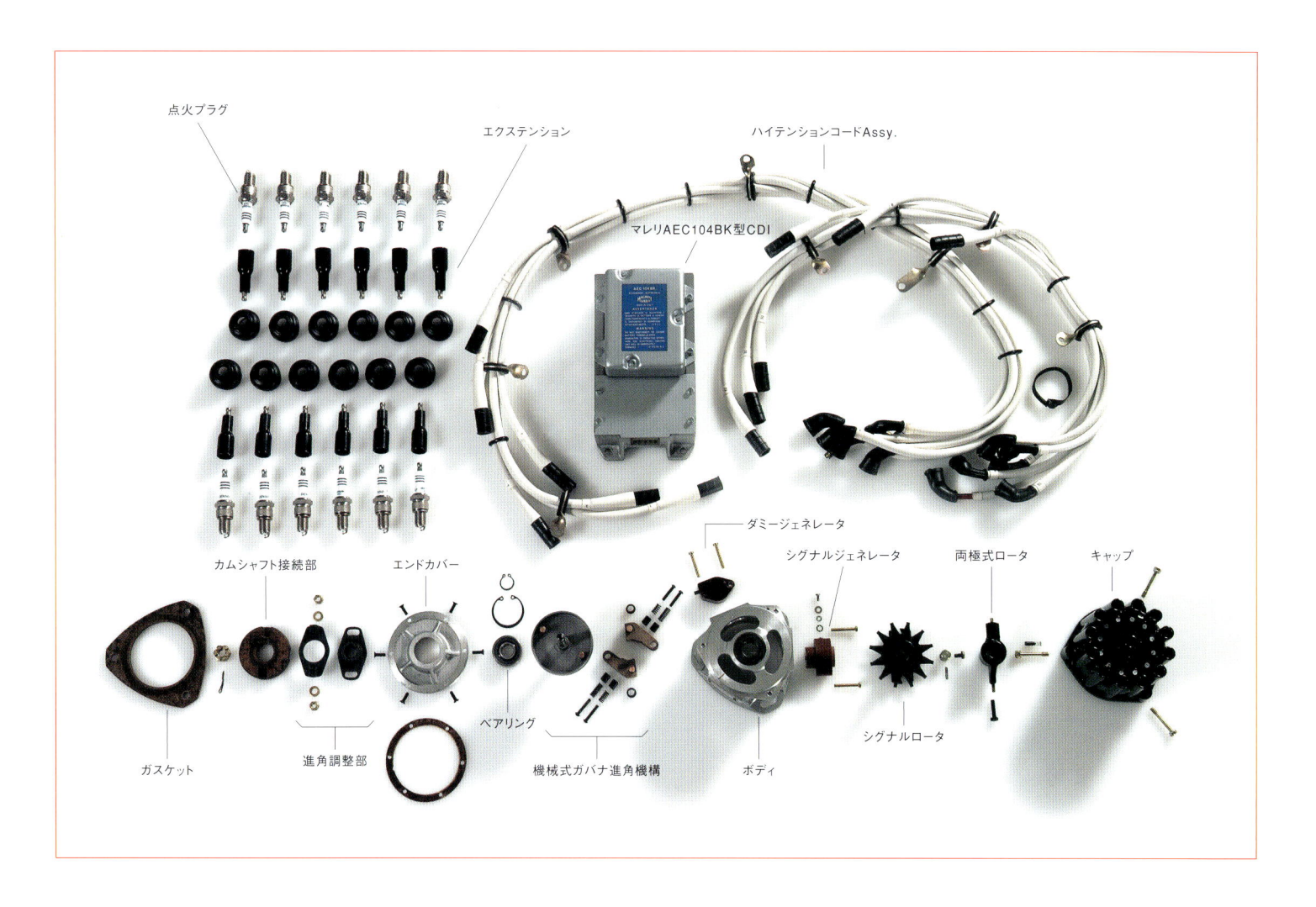

Ignition System

The ignition system is a racing-type battery ignition CDI type (Capacitor discharge ignition system) called Dinoplex made by MAGNETI-MARELLI, and is comprised of Type S158A distributor with integrated signal generator, AEC104BK CDI with transformer and Type BAE202 ignition coil (open end type). The 12 volt direct current supplied by the battery is changed to pulse current by an oscillator, and then stepped-up to an alternating current of approximately 400V by a transformer, rectified by a diode into a direct current of 400V and stored in the condenser. In the distributor, there is a signal generator made up of a signal rotor and pick up coil, and the switching signal current generated by this will put the thyristor "ON", forcing the condenser to discharge. The operating voltage of thyristor's gate is constant, but as the voltage generated by the pick up coil will increase in direct proportion to engine revolution, the "ON", timing of the thyristor will become quicker at higher speed. That is to say that the ignition timing is advanced correspondingly with the increase of distributor shaft speed (electric spark advance). Within the distributor, the mechanical centrifugal advance system is also integrated to give the advance angle to the signal rotor. However, a vacuum advance system is not adopted. The maximum advance angle of this engine is 36-38 degrees at 5000rpm. Distribution of high tension electricity is carried out by the rotor located in the distributor cap and 12 side electrodes. The rotor has two arms, the upper and the lower. Correspondingly, the 6 side electrodes are at upper level, while another 6 is located at low level. Distribution is made alternately by upper and lower arms. Supposing the distribution is made from one arm of the rotor to side electrode at the cap in 12 o'clock position, the next distribution will be from the arm at opposite side of rotor to the side electrode on the opposite side. Looking at the distributor as if it were a clock, the next distribution point is always at 180° opposite side with another 1/12 turns added, meaning a "7 hours later" position. The ignition order of this engine is; 1-9-5-12-3-8-6-10-2-7-4-11, and the engine will not start unless the high tension cords are connected to relative locations of 12o'clock - 7o'clock - 2o'clock - 9o'clock - 4o'clock - 11o'clock - 6o'clock - 1 o'clock - 8o'clock - 3o'clock - 10o'clock - 5o'clock. The high tension cord is covered by boots made of white colored silicon, and attached via rubber ring to the mounting bracket to the engine. The standard specification spark plug is Champion N63Y, a cold type corresponding to BP8ES. However, this specification, coupled with the rich air/fuel mixture setting, is the reason for poor starting performance and low speed driving as well as poor maintenance serviceability. Judging from the characteristics of this engine, I believe spark plug with heat value corresponding to BP7ES will be more appropriate.

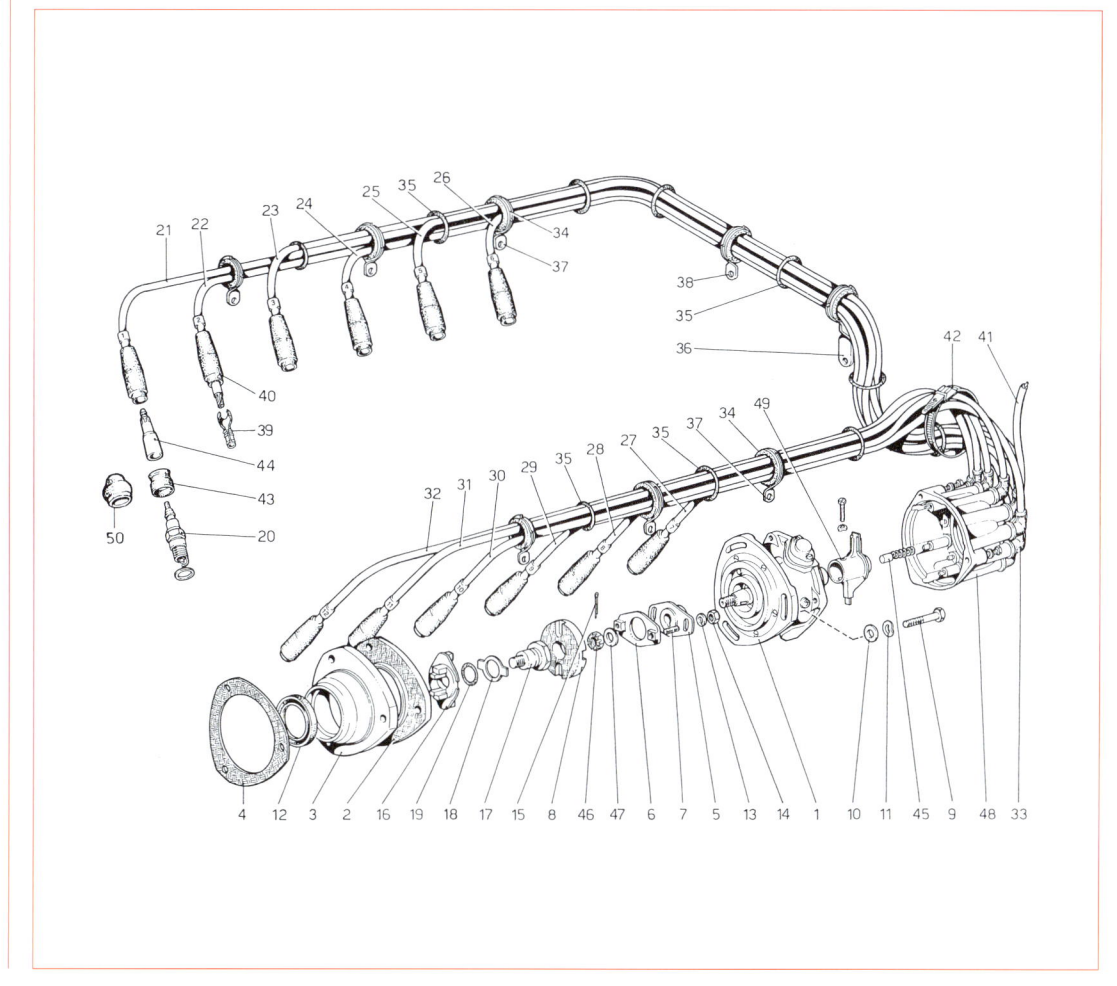

MARELLI製AEC104BK型CDI。発振器とトランスがCDIに結合されている。非常に高価なシステムで、熱害などで故障も起こりやすいため一般市販に交換しているケースが多い。本機では作動正常であったため、外観部のレストアを行なってそのまま使用することにした。

MARELLI製S158A型ディストリビュータ。本機から取りはずして分解した状態。内部の防水措置がまったく施されていないため、遠心式進角装置やシグナルロータは真っ赤にさびていた。このため全部品を分解し、ブラストしてさびを除去したのち黒染め、亜鉛クロメートめっきなどオリジナルと同じ表面処理を施した。シャフト一体式の進角装置ボディはシャフト部をマスキングしてから無電解ニッケルめっきを施した。

ディストリビュータおよびハイテンションコード、プラグの配置図。パーツカタログNo.95990216より転載。44はプラグの樹脂製エクステンションである。コネクタ部（40）にはノイズコンデンサを内蔵している。本機には当初プラグブーツ（50）が装着されていたが、この部品は#18237以降に新型の防水カバー（91ページの図中71番）と共に採用されたもので、単独で使うとプラグホールの中に容易に水が進入してしまう。本機は防水カバーのない旧タイプのため、旧型のプラグパーツ（43）を入手して使用した。本機レストアではハイテンションコードは新品に交換したが、樹脂製の特殊形状のタイラップ（42）は入手できなかったため、オリジナルコード付属のものを慎重に取り外して再使用した。

スタータモータ

Starter Motor

　本機搭載のスタータモータはFIAT製E100-1.5／12Var.1型で、リダクションギヤを持たない旧式の直動式マグネティックシフトタイプである。定格出力1.5kwの直動直巻モータはフィールドコイルとアーマチュアコイルが直列に結線され、鋳鉄製のヨークの中に収められている。モータ先端にはローラー式オーバーランニングクラッチと摺動式ピニオンが装着され、ピニオンを前後に動かすシフトレバーが噛み込んでいる。シフトレバーは万一の誤作動の際のフューズ代わりを意図した樹脂製である。ポリフェニレンエーテルなどの高強度耐熱樹脂だと思われるが定かではない。シフトレバーを作動させるマグネティックスイッチ部はヨークの上部に置かれ、高圧結線部を防水するためのゴムブーツで包み込まれている。高圧線自体もシリコンチューブの中を通してからエンジン上部に固定されている。スタータモータの定格回転数は300A時1300rpmである。

　他の補器類同様完全に分解し点検したが、アーマチュアおよびブラシ部、シフトレバー部等よい状態であったため、パーツの洗浄およびねじ類の再めっき、外装部の再塗装などのみを行なった。鋳鉄型のギヤケースはシルバーに塗装されていたが、一切の下地処理が施されておらず発錆していたので、ショットブラスト後防錆下地を施しウレタン塗装した。

The starter motor mounted on this engine is E100-1.5/12 Var. Type 1 made by FIAT, an old direct acting magnetic shift type without reduction gears. In this direct acting series motor with a rated output of 1.5kw, field coils and armature coils are connected in series and installed in cast iron yoke. At the tip of the motor, a roller-type overrunning clutch and sliding pinion are attached, in which the shift lever to move the pinion back and forth is engaged. The shift lever is made of resin material to act as a fuse in the unlikely case of operational error. The material is assumed to be a high strength heat resisting resin such as polyphenylene ether, but is not clearly known. The magnetic switch to activate shift lever is located on top of the yoke, and surrounded by rubber boots to protect the high tension connector from water. The high tension wiring itself is also run through silicon tubes before they are secured at top of the engine. The rated revolution of the starter motor is 1300rpm at 300A. As in cases of all other accessories of the engine, the starter motor was fully overhauled and inspected. However, as the armature, brush as well as the shift lever were all found to be in good condition, the only work carried out were cleaning of all parts, re-plating of screws, etc., and repainting of the exterior. The gear case made of cast iron was painted in silver, but had no primer coating whatsoever and rust formation was noticed. Therefore, it was urethane painted after shot blasting and anti-rust primer treatment.

オルタネータ / Alternator

発電機はMAGNETI-MARELLI製GCA113A-55A型オルタネータおよび同社製RTT101-C型接点式ボルテージレギュレータで構成される。いずれも1967年に275GTB/4用226型で採用されたものと基本的に同一である。

オルタネータは直流発電式のダイナモに代わる三相交流発電機で、性能／耐久性／コストの各面においてダイナモより優れる。直流への整流は不過逆式の性質を持つシリコンダイオードを使う。6個のダイオードはヒートシンクに装着されモータ後部に配置される。本機のダイオードは旧式の圧入型である。

オルタネータは永久磁石ではなく電磁石によって磁界を作る。ロータコイルに流れる電流を制御しオルタネータの出力電圧を一定範囲に保つのがボルテージレギュレータである。当時すでに本体一体型ICレギュレータも登場していたが、本機は旧式の別体型接点式である（#18625以降BOSCHトランジスタ型に変更）。

オルタネータは回転数が高くなると出力飽和して効率が低下し、最高回転数が高いと耐久性が低下する。また雰囲気温度が高いとやはり出力低下する。このため冷却ファンの効率とプーリ比が性能と耐久性を左右するが、本機冷却ファンは旧式の閉鎖式であり、最大定格12000rpmに対しプーリ比約1.62（増速）なのでエンジン高回転を多用すると耐久性に劣ることは明らかである。

The generator is comprised of a GCA 113A-55A type alternator, made by MAGNETI-MARELLI, and a RTT 101-C type voltage regulator with contact points also made by the same manufacturer. Both are basically the same as the ones adopted in 1967 for the 275GTB/4's Type 226. The alternator is a three phase alternating current generator in lieu of direct current generator type dynamo, and is superior to a dynamo in performance, durability as well as cost. Rectification to direct current is by silicon diode having irreversible characteristics. Six diodes are affixed to a heat sink, located at the rear of the alternator. The diodes used in this engine are the old-fashioned press-in type. In the alternator, magnetic field is generated by an electromagnet, not by a permanent magnet. A voltage regulator regulates the current flowing through the rotor coil in order to maintain the output voltage within a prescribed range. Although a unitized IC regulator was already available then, an old separate regulator with contact points is used in this engine. (Changed to BOSCH transistor type from #18625). As the revolution speed increases, the efficiency of the alternator deteriorates due to saturation of output, and if the maximum revolution is too high, the durability is impaired. The decrease of output is also caused by high ambient temperature. Therefore, performance and durability depends largely on the efficiency of the cooling fan and ratio of the pulley. In this engine, the cooling fan is an old closed type, with the pulley ratio approximately 1.62 (increased speed) against a rated maximum of 12000rpm. Therefore operating the engine at high speed will result in lowering durability.

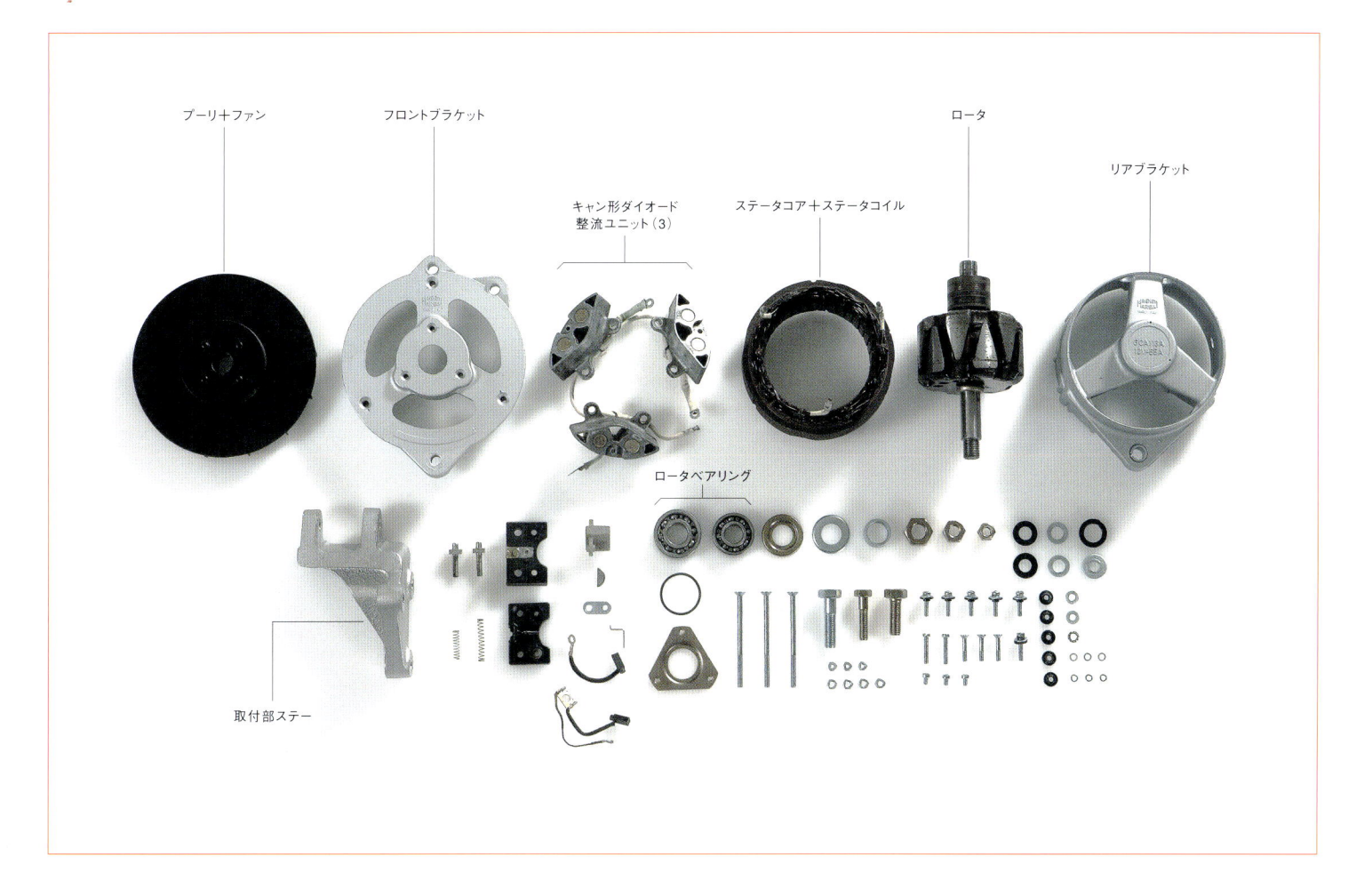

完全分解して点検したが、ブラシ／スリップリングとも状態は良好でダイオードも機能正常であったため、コスメティックレストアのみを施した。プーリ／ファンは劣化した塗装を剥離しショットブラストを打ってから防錆塗装したのちウレタン塗装した。ブラケット（本体）はアルミ合金ダイキャスト製で元々表面のみ塗装が施してあった。これもブラストしてからジンククロメート塗料で下塗りし（写真の状態）ウレタン塗装をした。

プーリ＋ファン　フロントブラケット　キャン形ダイオード整流ユニット(3)　ステータコア＋ステータコイル　ロータ　リアブラケット

ロータベアリング

取付部ステー

ACコンプレッサ   Air Conditioner

エアコンは標準装備であった。システムは冷房装置とヒータ装置から成り、コンプレッサ以外は車体前部に配置されている。室内気はダッシュボード下部に水平に設置されたファンユニットによって助手席足元から吸い込まれエバポレータを通って冷却され、ダッシュボード上部中央吹出口から吐出する。ヒータシステムはこれとは別系統で、フロントグリル奥に設置した左右一対の電動ファンから外気を導入し、ラジエタの温水を還流させている小型のヒータコアを通して温風にしたのち、ダクトで室内に導入する。温風出口はダッシュボード下部左右、上部中央部および左右部で、これをワイヤによる手動操作式フラップで方向選別する。ダッシュ上部中央のみは冷気とエアミックスできることになる。

冷媒はサイドシルに這わせた左右2本のラバーホースでエンジン部に設置されたコンプレッサに導かれる。Borletti製Aspera FrigoHG 700AP型コンプレッサはピストンおよびクランクシャフトを持つ旧式の往復列形（クランク式）である。クランクプーリからVベルトで電磁クラッチ付プーリを直動するが、プーリの減速比は約1.34と大きくない。クランク式コンプレッサは高速回転向きではなく、エンジン高回転を多用していると耐久性は低下する。

The air conditioner was standard equipment. The system comprises a cooler and a heater, located at the front of the body except for the compressor. Interior air is sucked from co-driver's leg room by a fan unit located horizontally below the dashboard, cooled by going through an evaporator and delivered to the room via central ducts on the top of the dashboard. The heater is a separate system. The outside air is taken in by a pair of electric fans located at left and right sides behind the front grille, heated by passing through a small heater core where hot radiator water is circulated, and then delivered via ducts. The warm air ducts are located at lower left and right as well as top center and left/right of the dashboard. The air direction is selected by manually operated flaps. Only the duct at the top of dashboard can mix both cool and hot air. The refrigerant is supplied to the compressor located at the engine via two rubber hoses left and right along the side sill. The Aspera Frigo HG700 Type AP compressor made by Borletti is an old-fashioned in-line reciprocating model (crank type). The pulley with an electromagnetic clutch is driven directly from the crank pulley by a V-belt, but the reduction ratio is not large at approximately the 1.34. As the crank type compressor is not suited for high revolutions, durability will probably suffer if high engine speed is frequently used.

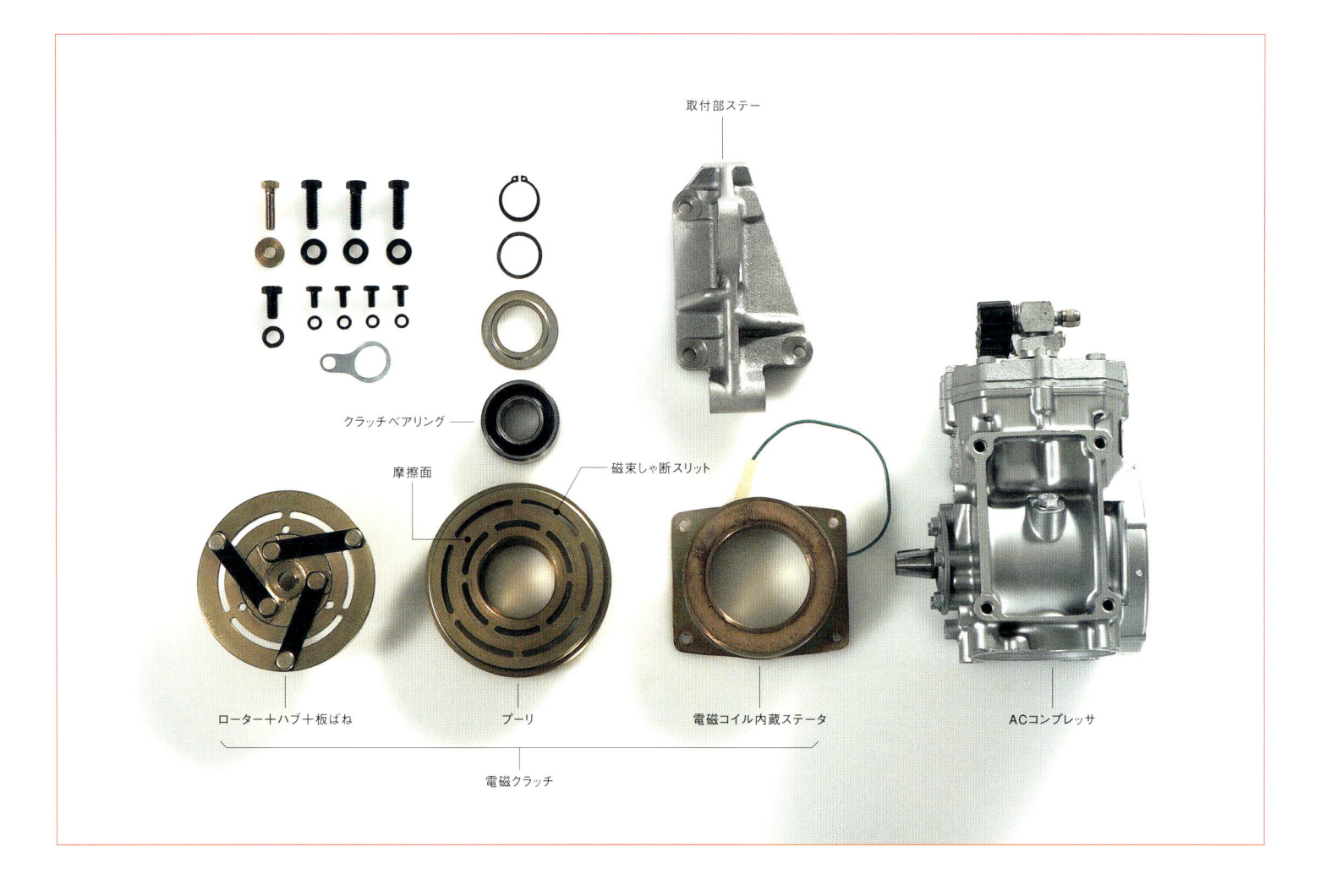

コンプレッサ本体はアルミダイキャスト製だがピストンヘッドとクランク軸カバーは鋳鉄製で、シルバーで共色塗装してある。本例ではアルミ部と鉄部にそれぞれ最適の防錆下地塗装を施したのちウレタン塗装した。写真灰色部が鋳鉄製部品。

電磁クラッチ部は分解しブラストしてから亜鉛クロメートめっきを施した。ロータ部は非分解式のため、めっき後にマスキングを施して板ばね部のめっきをブラストで除去したのち黒染めした。ベアリングは念のため新品に交換した。ねじ類もすべて再仕上げした。

取付部ステー
クラッチベアリング
摩擦面
磁束しゃ断スリット
ローター＋ハブ＋板ばね
プーリ
電磁コイル内蔵ステータ
ACコンプレッサ
電磁クラッチ

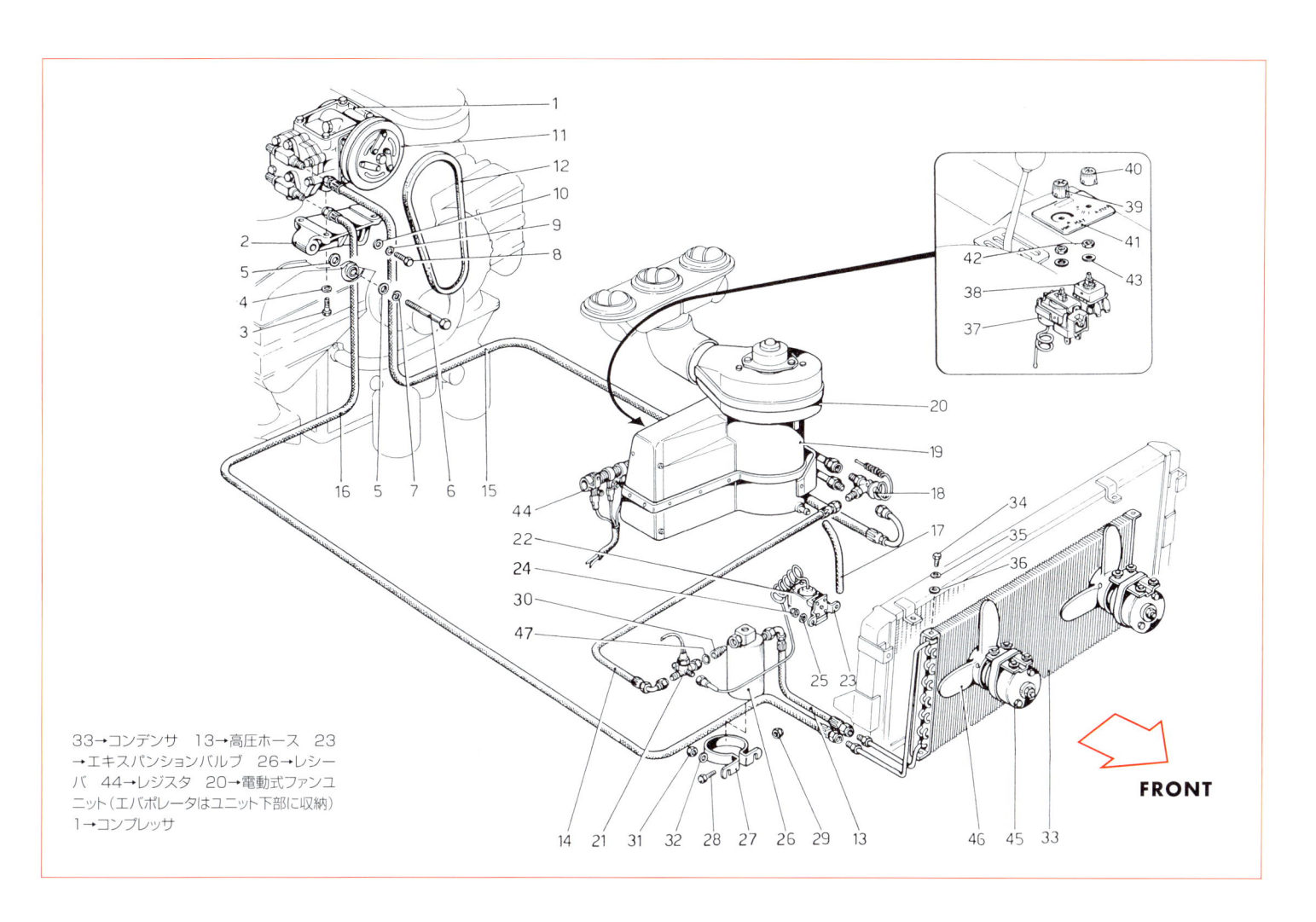

33→コンデンサ 13→高圧ホース 23→エキスパンションバルブ 26→レシーバ 44→レジスタ 20→電動式ファンユニット(エバポレータはユニット下部に収納) 1→コンプレッサ

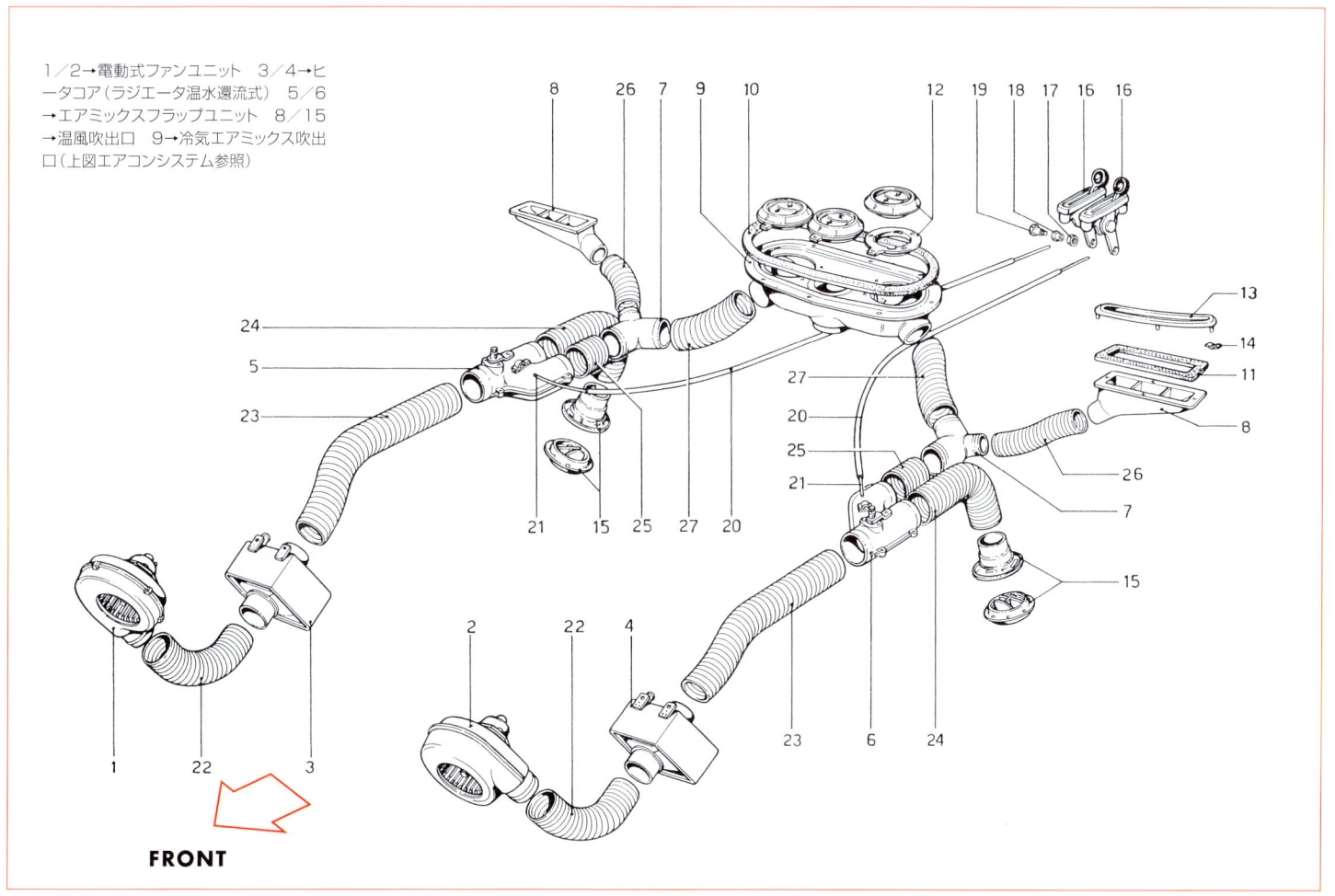

FRONT

1/2→電動式ファンユニット 3/4→ヒータコア(ラジエータ温水還流式) 5/6→エアミックスフラップユニット 8/15→温風吹出口 9→冷気エアミックス吹出口(上図エアコンシステム参照)

FRONT

クラッチ

外径241.3mmのクラッチは乾燥単板式でコイルばねを使ってディスクプレート自体にクッションスプリング機能を持たせた回転緩衝機構付である。フェーシングは当時一般的だった有機系材料製と思われ、強度と熱伝導性を向上させる目的で黄銅線が混入されている。メーカー公表のフェーシング摩擦係数は0.8である。

クラッチカバーは平滑なフライホイルに装着するフラット形で、プレッシャプレートとクラッチカバーを薄板鋼板のストラップで結合したストラップドライブ式である。コントロールはワイヤ式で自動調整機構はついていない。ペダル踏力を軽減するため操作系レバー比を大きく設定すると共にレリースアームにターンオーバーばね機構を組み込んでいる（右図6と74の二重コイルばね）。

動力はクラッチをへてベルハウジング外側に取り付けられた3列のヘリカルギヤによって下部のトランスアクスル部へ伝達される。基本的にはアレック・イシゴニスが考案しミニに採用したアイディアと同一である。ヘリカルギヤの比は28:29:28で等速同回転となる。アイドラギヤの歯数を変えているのはギヤの当り位置を一回転毎にずらすためである。ヘリカルギヤの支持にはボールベアリングとローラベアリングを部位によって使い分けている。本機ではクラッチとクラッチカバーを交換し、さらにコスメティックレストアを行なった。

Clutch

The clutch having an outer diameter of 241.3mm is of the dry-type single plate, with a rotation absorbing mechanism in which the disk plate itself has a cushion spring function utilizing coil springs. The facing is assumed to be the organic friction material which was common in those days, and brass wires were intermixed with the purpose of enhancing strength and thermal conductivity. The facing's coefficient of friction announced by the manufacturer is 0.8. The clutch cover is a flat type attached to a flat and smooth flywheel, a strap drive system combining the pressure plate and clutch cover with a strap made of thin steel sheet. Control is by wire without an automatic adjusting mechanism. In order to achieve lighter pedal disengagement load, the ratio of the operating lever was set at a high value with a turnover spring function combined in the release arm. (See the right diagram and the double coil springs in 6 and 74). Power is transmitted via clutch and a set of three helical gears located on the outside of the bell housing to the transaxle located below. Basically, this is the same design as the one invented by Alec Issigonis and adopted to the Mini. The ratios of the helical gears are 28:29:28, operating at uniform revolutions. The reason why the number of teeth of the idler gear is different is to change the meshing point of the gear with each revolution. To support the helical gear, ball bearings and roller bearings are located as required. In this engine, both clutch disc and cover were exchanged before overall cosmetic restoration was made.

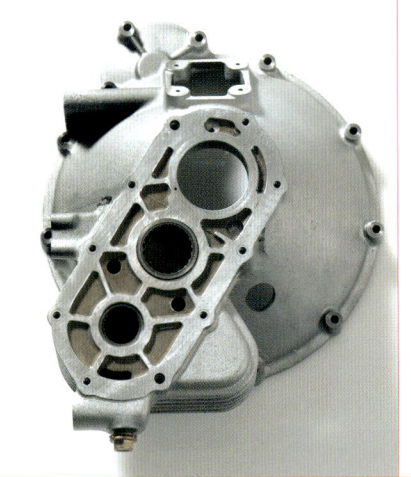

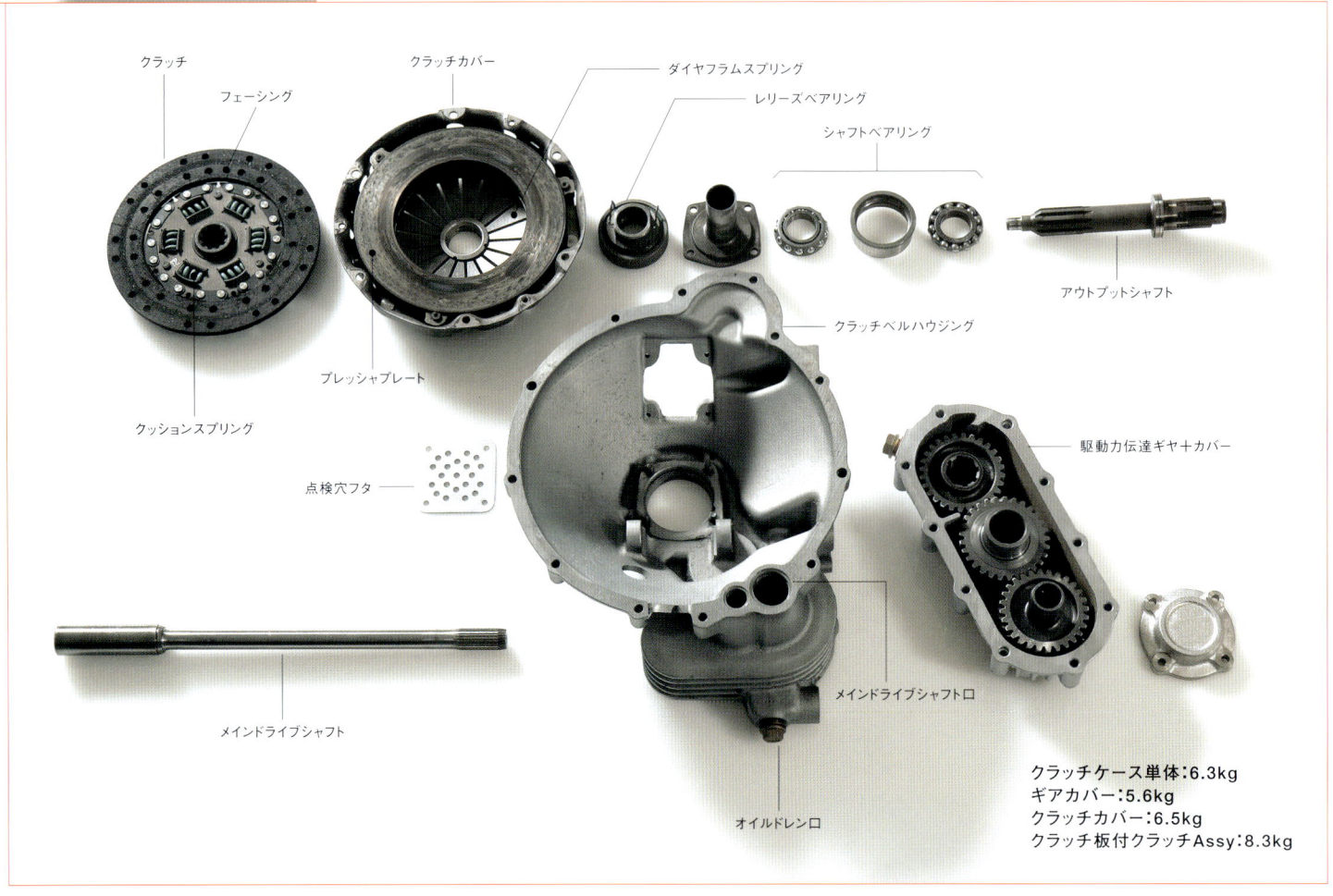

クラッチケース単体：6.3kg
ギアカバー：5.6kg
クラッチカバー：6.5kg
クラッチ板付クラッチAssy：8.3kg

レリーズベアリング
レリーズレバー
ターンオーバスプリング(2)
レリーズシャフト
調整機構付プルロッド
コントロールアーム
ターンオーバ機構
コントロールアーム
コントロールワイヤ取付部

【右写真】動力伝達用ギヤ。はすば歯車(ヘリカルギヤ)を使う。写真左側がトランスアクスル側である。

【左写真】クラッチレリーズアームおよびコントロールアーム。206／246GTでは横置き搭載のためFF車のようなテコ式のレリーズフォークを使っていたが、本機ではアームとシャフトを使いターンオーバー機構を組み込んだ複雑な設計に変更した。本機では写真の全部品についてコスメティックレストアを施した。

パーツカタログNo.95990216記載のクラッチおよび駆動力伝達ギア部。上図69がクランク出力軸、下図13が等速同回転で動力伝達されるギヤ列への入力軸(メインドライブシャフト)である。本機系列エンジンにおいてメインドライブシャフトは動力伝達系のウィークポイントのひとつであり、トラクションを上げたりパワーアップした車両の場合、図右端セレーション部根元付近で破断することがあった。本機のターンオーバー機構の設計ではターンオーバーばねに曲げ応力がかかるため、使用しているうちにばね軸(図中12)がわん曲し、クラッチ踏力が重くなったり、クラッチが切れたまま復帰しなくなったりする(CAR GRAPHIC／1976年4月号、ポール・フレールによる試乗記参照)。そのためターンオーバーばねのアシスト用ステー(図中75)が採用され、いわゆるリコール装着された。本機にはその対策は施されておらず、今回のレストアにおいても装着しなかった。

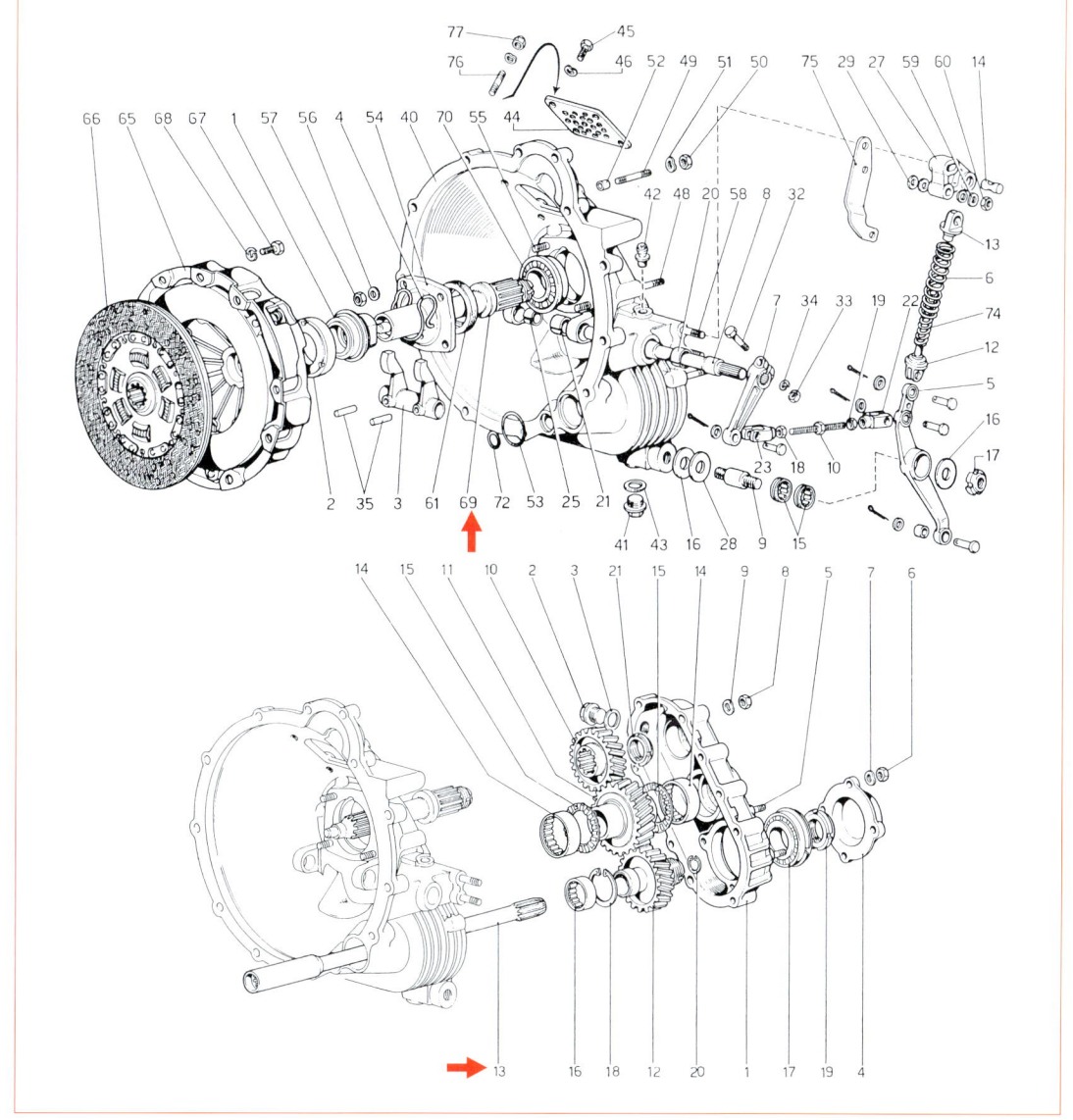

109

トランスアクスルおよびギアトレーン　Transaxle and Gear-Train

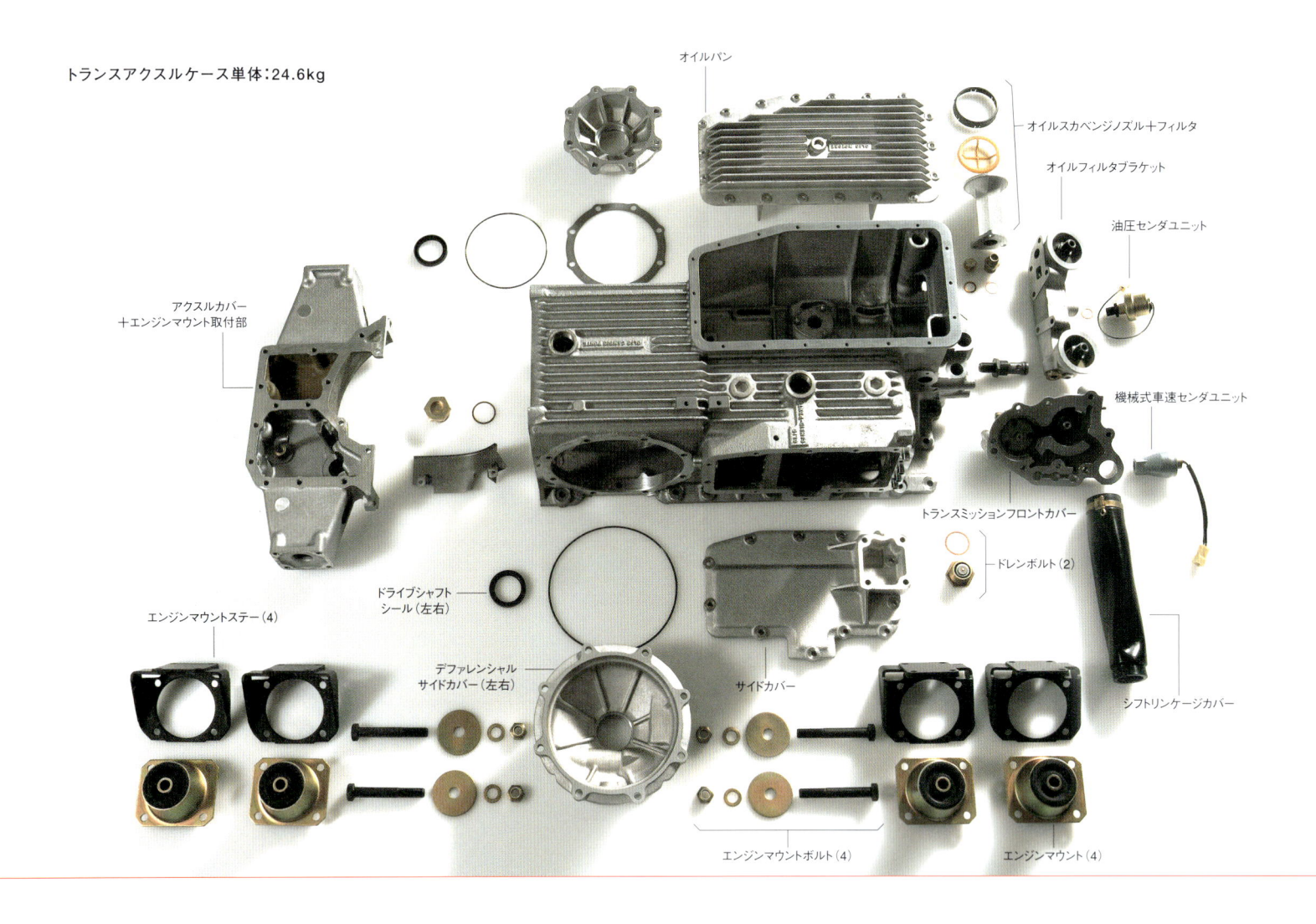

トランスアクスルケース単体：24.6kg

（図中ラベル）
- オイルパン
- オイルスカベンジノズル＋フィルタ
- オイルフィルタブラケット
- 油圧センダユニット
- アクスルカバー＋エンジンマウント取付部
- 機械式車速センダユニット
- トランスミッションフロントカバー
- ドレンボルト（2）
- エンジンマウントステー（4）
- ドライブシャフトシール（左右）
- デファレンシャルサイドカバー（左右）
- サイドカバー
- シフトリンケージカバー
- エンジンマウントボルト（4）
- エンジンマウント（4）

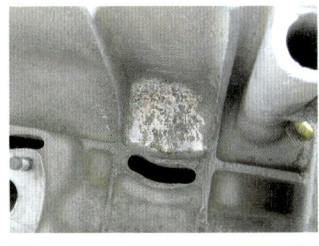

ケースを洗浄すると内部のコーティングの下からオイルタンク上部に穴うめ溶接した痕跡が発見された。後年の改造作業を疑ったが、溶接箇所の横に開口しているスリットが円弧状の形状になっていること、512BBでは同位置にドライサンプ用スカベンジノズルが装着されていること、溶接はコーティングの前に行なわれていたこと、同時期に生産された同型車（#18091）にも同じ溶接痕が認められたこと等から、当時の工場での作業であると判定した。オイルクーラ用パイプ等の取付穴加工のためのガイド凹部を埋めたものと思われる。

　本機トランスアクスルは365GT/4 BBの二世代目に当たるF102AB型であり、キータイプの同期機構を持つトランスミッションに対応している（#17543／生産26台目以降採用）。サーボタイプの同期機構の旧トランスミッションとはベアリング位置が異なるためケース内部の仕切り壁位置やサイドカバー形状、フロントカバー形状が変更されており、ケース自体もF102A型トランスアクスルとの互換性はない。
　トランスアクスルケースはエンジンを上部に載せるマウントを兼ねており、肉厚頑強に作られたアルミ合金砂型鋳物製である。ケース単体重量を測定してみると24.6kgもあった。ケース後端にはクラッチベルハウジングと共にクラッチケースの一部を成すよう設計されたエンジンマウントフレームがボルト留めされる。エンジンマウントはマウントフレームの左右および本体、サイドカバーの4ヵ所に装着される。ケース右バンクはエンジンオイルタンク、ケース後部はデファレンシャルギヤのハウジングを兼用している。
　トランスアクスルケースは完全分解し、ガスケット面をマスキングしてからガラスビーズを高圧でブラストした。ガスケット面は研磨した。内部のコーティングは洗浄時にすべて剥離してしまったが、あえて再処理はしなかった。

The transaxle of this engine is the Type F102AB which is the second generation of the 365GT/4 BB, and is matched with the transmission with key-type synchronization mechanism. (Adopted after #17543/26th production unit). As the bearing positions differ from the old transmission with servo-type synchronization mechanism, the location of the dividing wall, shapes of the side cover and front cover are all changed. Therefore, the case itself has no interchangeability with the Type F102A transaxle. The transaxle case acts concurrently as the mount for the engine above, and is made of robust, thick-walled aluminum alloy casting. The unit weight of the case was as much as 24.6kg. The engine mount frame designed to form a part of the clutch case together with the bell housing is bolted on at the rear end of the case. The engine mount is at four points, left and right of the mount frame, transaxle, and side cover. The engine oil tank is housed in the right bank of the case, while the rear of the case is concurrently the housing for the differential gear. The transaxle was completely taken apart, and blasted at high pressure with sand beads after masking the gasket surface. Gasket surface was polished. Although the coating on the inside was totally removed during washing, I did not venture to redo the treatment.

365GTB/4

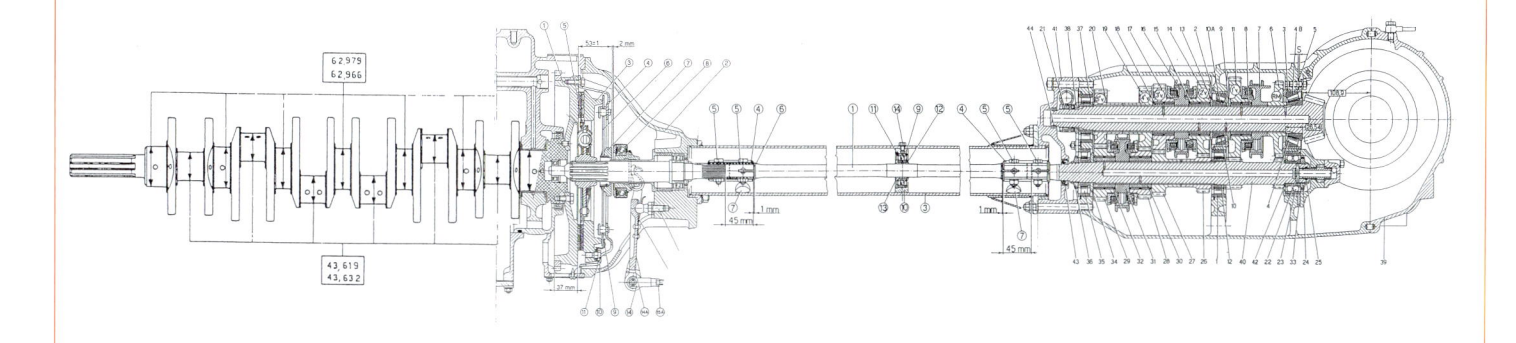

365GT/4 BB

365GT/4 BBおよび365GTB/4のパワートレーンの比較。（上）は365GTB/4のワークショップマニュアル記載のクランクシャフト、クラッチ、ドライブシャフト、トランスアクスルの4図を縮尺を合わせて合成し作製したもの。クラッチより前方は上から見た図である。ドライブシャフトは短縮して描かれている。

（下）本機サービスマニュアルNo.95990807記載のクランクシャフトおよびトランスアクスル2図を縮尺を合わせて合成したもの。長大なデイトナのパワートレーンをジャバラのように折り畳んで、V12一基分＋αのサイズにまとめた本機設計の意図が分かる。なお両図とも構造図のため投影図法では作製されておらず、図中のトランスアクスル高さ/エンジン高さは実際の縮尺になっていない。

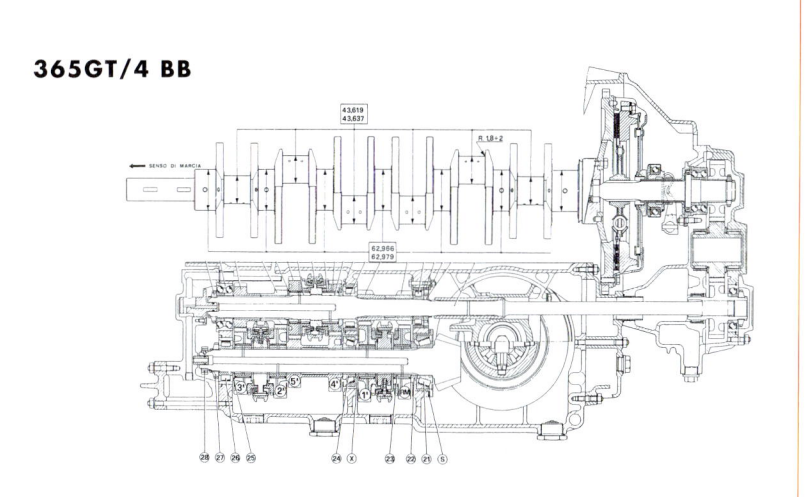

F102AB型トランスアクスルケースの構成図。パーツカタログNo.95990216より転載。＜上図＞36はトランスミッションフロントカバー（10）に装着される機械式車速センサ、34がその駆動ギヤである。512BB後期からはフロントカバーに強制潤滑ポンプが備えられた（74ページ写真参照）。37はギヤオイルのバッフルプレート、41はデファレンシャル用のオイル飛散防止プレートであり、共にF102AB型ケースから採用された。＜下図＞オイルパン1にはバッフルプレートとフラップ(26)が装着されている。15はマウントフレームであり、ギヤオイルのドレン用補助穴もここに装着（23が旧型、50+24+23が#18169以降採用された新型）。湾曲したノズルの上端面が正常なギヤオイルレベル位置であり、旧型タイプの場合ここからギヤオイルを注入するとオイル量をあやまりやすかった（約2ℓ不足する）。正規のギヤオイル注入口はクラッチベルハウジング上部で、新型の湾曲ノズル装着車の場合ここからオイルがもれ出ればオイルレベルは正規（7.75ℓ）ということになる。

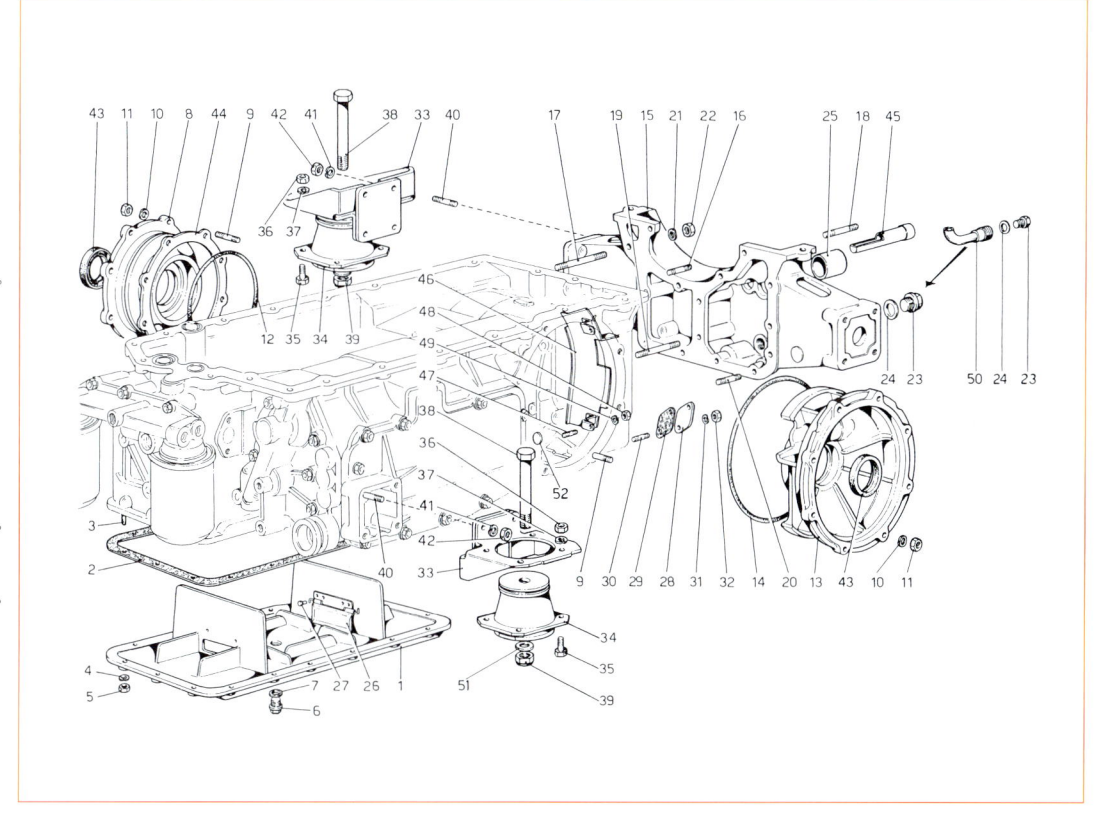

111

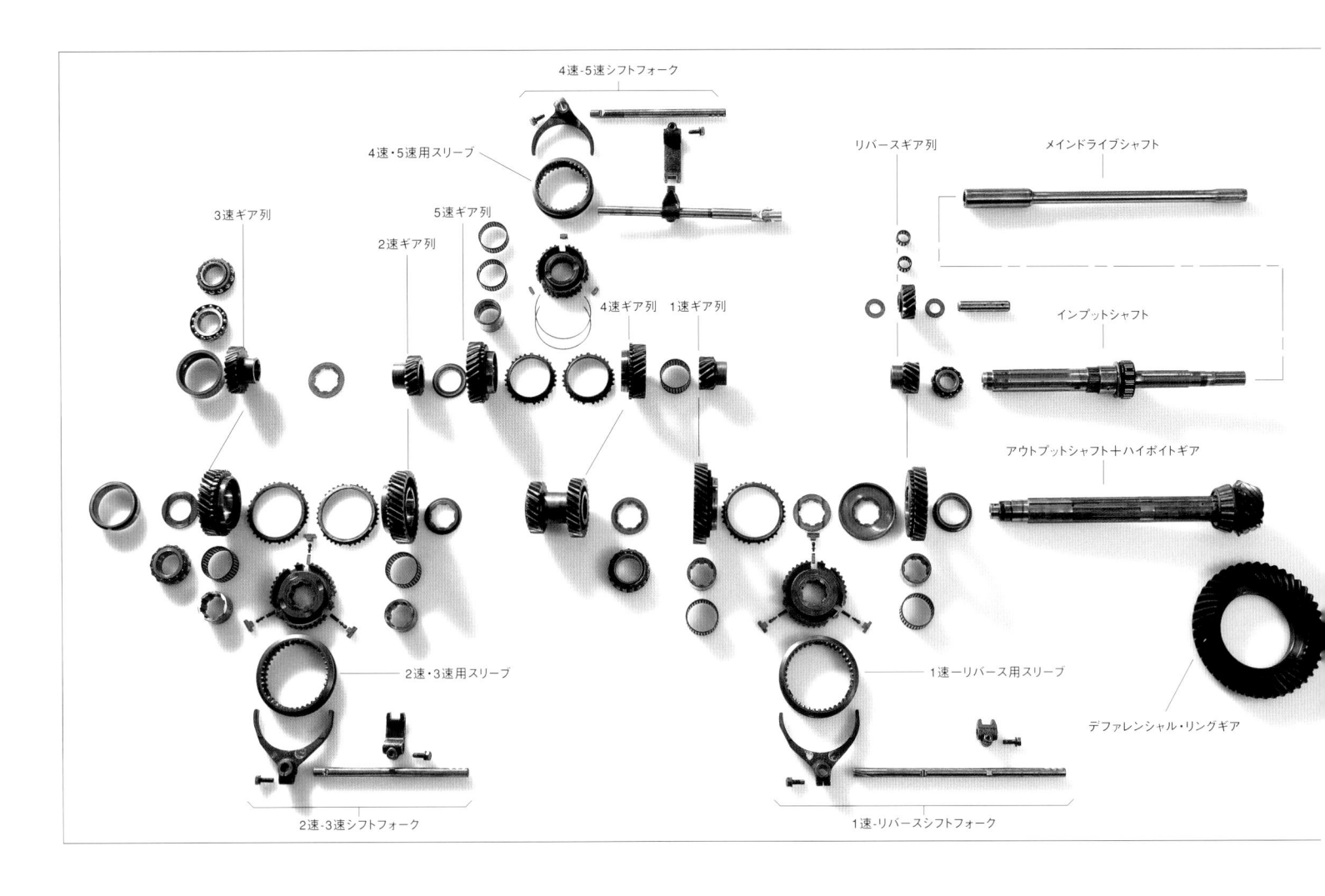

[図中ラベル]
- 4速-5速シフトフォーク
- 4速・5速用スリーブ
- 3速ギア列
- 5速ギア列
- 2速ギア列
- 4速ギア列
- 1速ギア列
- リバースギア列
- メインドライブシャフト
- インプットシャフト
- アウトプットシャフト＋ハイポイドギア
- 2速・3速用スリーブ
- 1速-リバース用スリーブ
- デファレンシャル・リングギア
- 2速-3速シフトフォーク
- 1速-リバースシフトフォーク

トランスミッションはインボリュートはすば歯車を使用した常時結合式5段で、後退ギヤを除く全速にキー式同期機構を備える。動力はギヤ列上段からメインドライブシャフトを通じて入力し、減速されたのちギヤ列下段のアウトプットシャフト後端のハイポイドギヤからデファレンシャルのリングギヤへ伝達する。

シフトパターンから類推できるように中央でスリーブを共用するギヤセットは1速-後退、2速-3速、4速-5速で、回転同期機構は4速-5速のみがインプットシャフト側にある。シンクロナイザリングはシングルタイプで、表面にセレーションを切削加工して同期容量を向上させている。インプット/アウトプットギヤ歯数は1速14/37、2速18/33、3速21/30、

The transmission is a constant-mesh 5 speed using involute helical gears, and has a key type synchronization mechanism on all speeds except the reverse gear. Power is taken in from the upper part of cam gears through the main drive shaft, decelerated and transmitted to the ring gear of the differential via hypoid gear at the rear of output shaft located at lower part of the gear rows. As can be ascertained from the shift pattern, the gear set having a common sleeve at the center is; 1st-Reverse, 2nd-3rd, and 4th-5th. However for the 4th-5th, rotation synchronization mechanism is on the input shaft side. The synchronizer ring is a single type, with serration on the surface to improve synchronization capacity. The number of teeth for input/output gears are; 1st 14/37, 2nd 18/33, 3rd 21/30, 4th 25/27, 5th 28/23 (actual measurement values,) and the reduction ratios are; 1st 2.642, 2nd

本機アウトプットギヤ列を512BB用と比較する。
【左写真】右側が改良型の512BB用。デファレンシャルリングギヤ径を増大し、これにともなってアウトプット・ハイポイドギヤ径も大型化している。両車の円弧歯厚や歯形も改良している。
【右写真】手前が本機で右端の後退ギヤには同期機構がついていない。向こう側512BB用では後退ギヤとスリーブの間にシンクロリングが見えている（後退同期機構付）。

サイドカバー内部。フォークシャフトは上段4-5速列、中段3-4速列、下段1速・後退列用で、ケース前端(写真左端)隔壁部にボール&ばね式のシャフト位置決め機構が、中央隔壁部にプラグ式二重かみ合い防止機構が装着されている。シフトの正確さ/節度/操作力などはこれら機構の正確な組み立てと調整、およびスリーブ/フォークの前後クリアランスによって生じるガタつきとシフトフォークセレクトレバー部のガタつきとの相互調整、同セレクトレバーの相互当たり調整などによってほぼ決まるものであり、同期機構の構造と容量とはあまり関係がない。

トランスアクスルケースの打刻。F102AB ZF No.85と読める。

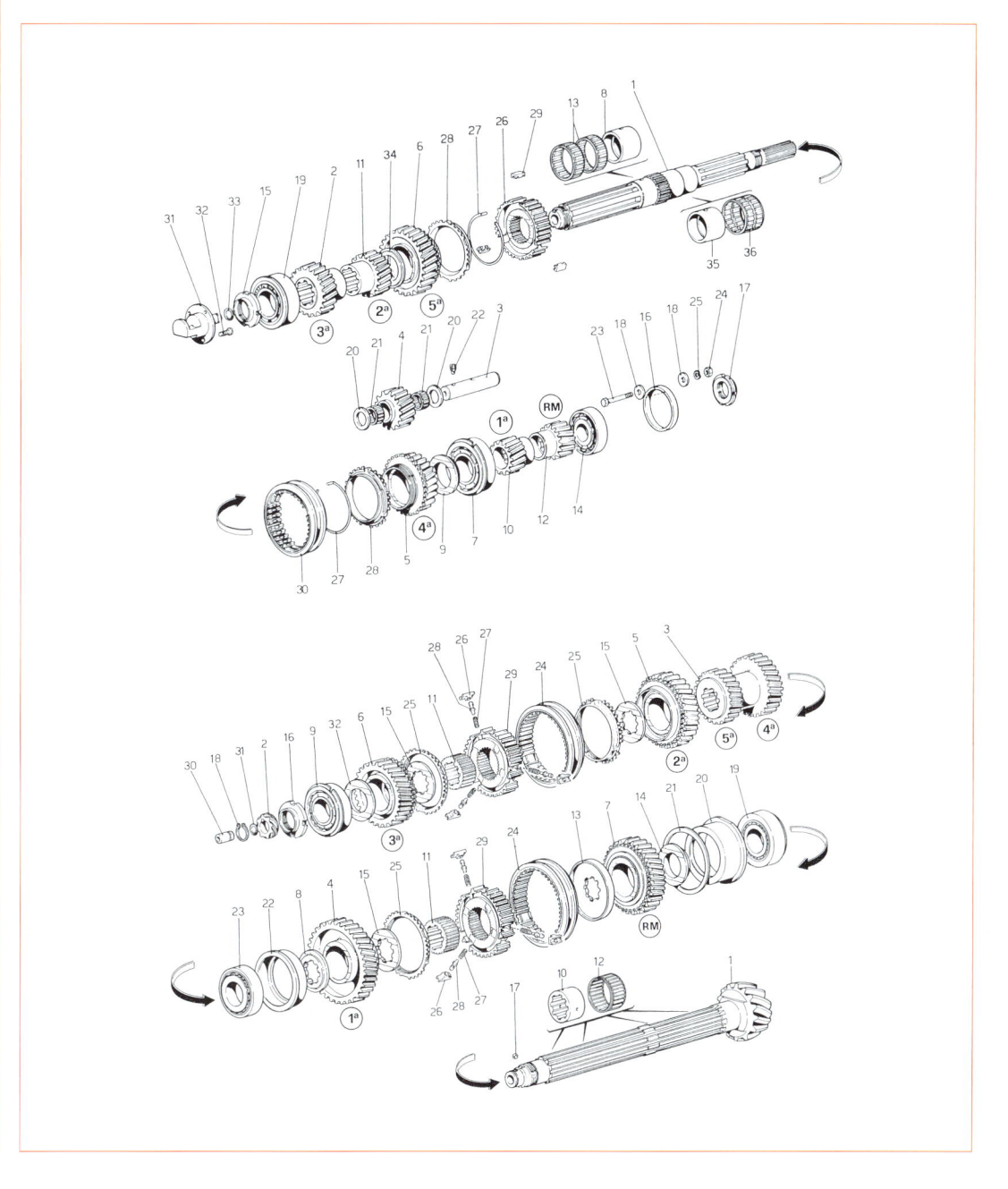

パーツカタログNo.95990216記載のギヤ列部品展開図。上がインプットシャフト・ギヤ列、下がアウトプットシャフト・ギヤ列である。図中○で囲まれaのアルファベットがふられている番号がそのギヤの変速段数である。インプットシャフト(上)は前端のボールベアリング(19)と2つのローラベアリング(7と14)が保持する。アウトプットシャフト(下)は前端をローラベアリング(9)、後端部と中間部をスラストローラベアリング(23と19)が保持する。各ベアリングのアウターレースはケース隔壁に圧入されている。シンクロリング(上図4速/5速用が各28、下図1速/2速/3速用が各25)はギヤのコーン部共々セレーションが切られている。本機のトランスミッションの状態は非常に良く、とりわけ4速5速の同期機構同期面には摺動痕もほとんど見られない状況だったため、洗浄/点検後入念に各部クリアランスを調整しながら組み立てるに留めた。

4速25/27、5速28/23で(各実測値)減速比は1速2.642、2速1.833、3速1.428、4速1.080、5速0.821となる。ハイポイドギヤとリングギヤ歯数は12/45で、最終減速比は3.75である。#18243以降この比は11/43に改められた(3.909)。

前記の通り本機はデファレンシャルとエンジンが干渉するためリングギヤ径に制約を受けており、これがアウトプット・ハイポイドギヤも含めた最終減速機構の耐久性不足となって露呈している。また排気熱の影響を受け易い位置にありながらギヤオイル冷却装置を持たず、そればかりか強制潤滑機構も省略していることは高性能を標榜する機関として十分な設計的配慮をつくしたとは言い難い。本機設計に総じて言えることだが、未完成というより当初から高性能車として設計していない印象である。

1.833, 3rd 1.428, 4th 1.080, 5th 0.821. The number of gear teeth for the hypoid gear and ring gear are 12/45, resulting in a final reduction ratio of 3.75. After #18243, this was changed to 11/43 (3.909). As previously mentioned, in this engine, there is a restriction in the diameter of ring gear due to the problem of intervention between the differential gear and engine. The consequence of this is revealed in a lack of durability of the final reduction mechanism including the output hypoid gear. Similarly, in spite of susceptibility to exhaust heat due to its location, there is no gear oil cooling system, not to speak of the forced lubrication mechanism. From such facts, it is hard to say that sufficient design considerations for an engine professing to be of high-performing nature were exerted. My impression of this engine's design is that it is not unfinished and premature engine, but was never designed from the beginning for a high performance vehicle.

デファレンシャルおよびドライブシャフト

Differential and Driveshaft

本機デファレンシャルはデイナ/サリスベリータイプの摩擦式差動制退装置を備えている。片側4枚のフリクションプレート（クラッチ）にピニオン部のカム機構で発生したスラスト力を与え差動抵抗力を発生させるオーソドックスなタイプで、ばねによる予圧は行なっていない。ピニオン数は4である。リングギヤ・ピッチ円径は206mmだが、車重（1480kg）およびエンジントルクから算出した本車の駆動輪パフォーマンストルクは約252kgf·mであり、曲げ応力基準なら概算262〜263mm径、接触応力基準でも概算250mm前後（いずれもギヤ比3.75のとき）のリングギヤ・ピッチ円径は必要と思われ、本機の能力不足は否めない。ちなみに本機シリーズでは512BB、テスタロッサ、F512Mと時代を下るにつれリングギヤおよびアウトプット・ハイポイドギヤのピッチ円径を増加している。

ドライブシャフトは外径25mmの中実鋼製で両端に等速ジョイントを備える。等速ジョイントはバーフィールド型の発展版といえるクロスグルーブ型（VL型）で、ボール溝を入れた内外輪、ケージに保持した6個のボールで構成する。内外輪のボール溝が逆向きに斜行しているのが命名の由来である。斜行溝のメリットは継手角を確保しながら前後方向へのスライド距離を長く取れることである。

The differential is the friction type limited slip unit of the "Dana" or "Salisbury" type. This is an orthodox type which creates differential resistance by giving thrust power developed by the cam mechanism of the pinion to four friction plates (clutches) on each side. There is no spring pre-loading. There are 4 pinions. The pitch diameter of the ring gear is 206mm. However, considering the vehicle weight of 1480kg and the performance torque value of this car, calculated from the engine torque, of approximately 252kgf·m, it is assumed that a ring gear pitch diameter of approximately 262~263mm on basis of bending stress, and 250mm or so if based on contact stress (both with final gear ratio of 3.75), would be required. Therefore, lack of capability can not be denied. In this connection, in this engine's series, from 512BB, Testarossa, and F512M, the pitch diameters of the ring gear and output hypoid gear were gradually increased. The drive shaft is made of solid steel with the outer diameter of 25mm, and has constant velocity joints at the both ends. The constant velocity joints are of the cross group type (VL type), which could be regarded as the finished version of the Barfield type, and comprises inner and outer wheels and six balls supported by the cage. The name is derived from the fact that the ball grooves of inner and outer wheels are oppositely inclined. The advantage of the inclined groove is that a longer fore/aft sliding distance is possible while maintaining the joint angle.

トランスアクスルケース左右からボルト留めされるサイドカバーが、スラストローラベアリングを介してデファレンシャルを左右から押し付け保持している（プリロード）。365GT/4 BBの場合トランスアクスルケース左側のサイドカバーおよび取付穴が右側より大きく、ここからデファレンシャルユニットを組み込む。このときアウトプット・ハイポイドギヤが干渉するため3次元パズル的な工夫を必要とするが、512BBからはケース後部を大型化し後端開口部を広げて後部から出し入れするように改良した。このためサイドカバーも左右同径になった。

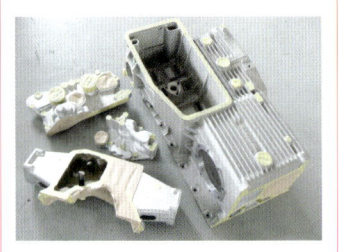

トランスアクスルケースのコスメティックレストア作業。ガスケット部をマスキングしてからガラスビーズブラストした。

- アクスルフランジ
- ボール (6×2)
- 内輪 (2)
- ケージ (2)
- 外輪 (2)
- ラバーブーツ止め (大小各2)
- ラバーブーツ (2)
- ドライブシャフト

スラストワッシャ（2）

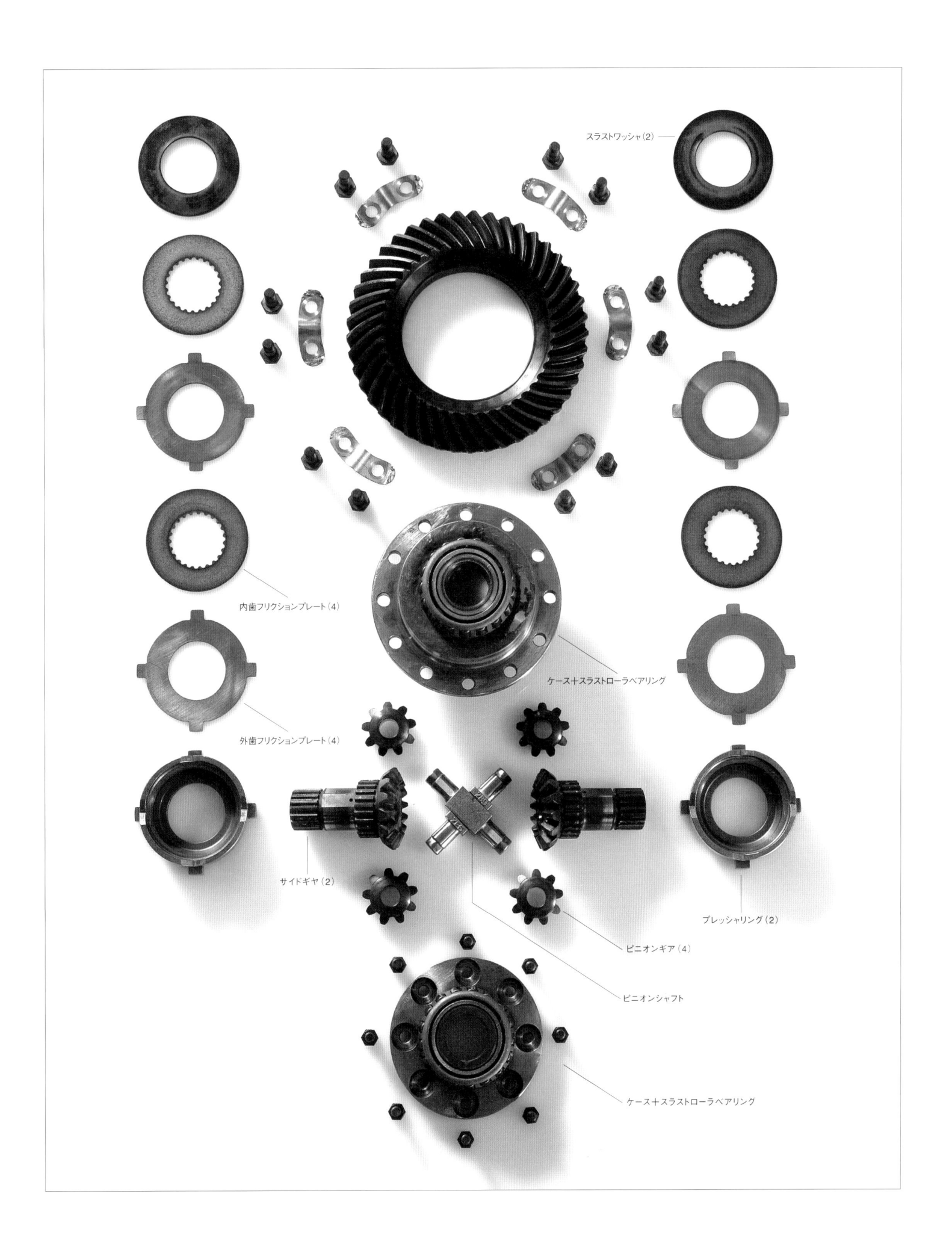

内歯フリクションプレート（4）

外歯フリクションプレート（4）

ケース＋スラストローラベアリング

サイドギヤ（2）

プレッシャリング（2）

ピニオンギヤ（4）

ピニオンシャフト

ケース＋スラストローラベアリング

排気系

　水平対向レイアウトのエンジンは、重心高を低くできるメリットと引き換えに排気系の取り回しに制約を受けるが、本機の場合はトランスアクスル上部にエンジンを配置しているためエンジン前半部の排気マニホールドの設計には比較的自由度が高い。ただしデファレンシャルがエンジン後半4気筒の直下に位置しているため、とくに最後端2気筒（左7番、右6番）の排気マニホールド取り回しがドライブシャフトと干渉する。結果マニホールドはドライブシャフトを包み込むように配置せざるを得ず、ドライブシャフトのデファレシャル側の継手部ゴムブーツが熱で劣化しやすい。これを放置すると内部のグリスが流出して継手の傷損/破損に至る。排気マニホールドには薄板鋼板製のヒートシェラウドが溶接されており内部に断熱用の薄いアスベストシートが挿入されているが、十分な熱害対策とはいえない。

　本機の排気マニホールドは電縫管を曲げて溶接したものだが、パイプの加工/溶接ともに生産技術は低く、元来十分に吟味されているとは言い難い設計仕様すら製品に100%反映されておらず、本機の出力特性/過渡特性に少なからぬ影響を与えていると思われる。

　エンジンポート部への接合部にはアスベストガスケットが、また排気マフラー部パイプとの接合部にはアスベストとアルミと鋼メッシュを混合加圧成形したジョイントが使われている。

Exhaust System

In general, an engine with a horizontally-opposed layout has the advantage of achieving lower center of gravity, which, in turn, limits the arrangement of the exhaust system. But in the case of this engine, there is a relative freedom in designing the exhaust manifold around the front half of the engine due to the fact that the engine is located above the transaxle. However, as the differential is situated right beneath the 4 rearward cylinders, the exhaust manifolds for the 2 rearmost cylinders (No. 7 left & No.6 right) may meddle with the drive shaft. Consequently, it necessitated arranging the manifolds as if they are wrapped around the driveshaft, with a risk that the rubber boots of the joint at driveshaft on the differential side may be deteriorated by the heat. If this is neglected, the grease may flow out and cause damage/breakage of the joint. To prevent this, a heat shroud made of thin steel sheet with a thin asbestos sheet inserted inside is welded onto the exhaust manifold. However, this can not be regarded as an effective countermeasure against heat. The exhaust manifold of this engine is made by bending and welding an electrically welded pipe. But the production technique, both processing and welding are unsatisfactory. Consequently, the design specification, which itself can not be described as being properly planned, is not reflected 100% in the product, and is thought to have considerable negative influence in the output and torque characteristics of the engine. Where the manifold join the engine port, an asbestos gasket is used, and where it unites with the pipe of the exhaust muffler, a joint made by pressurized formation of mixture of asbestos, aluminum and steel mesh is used.

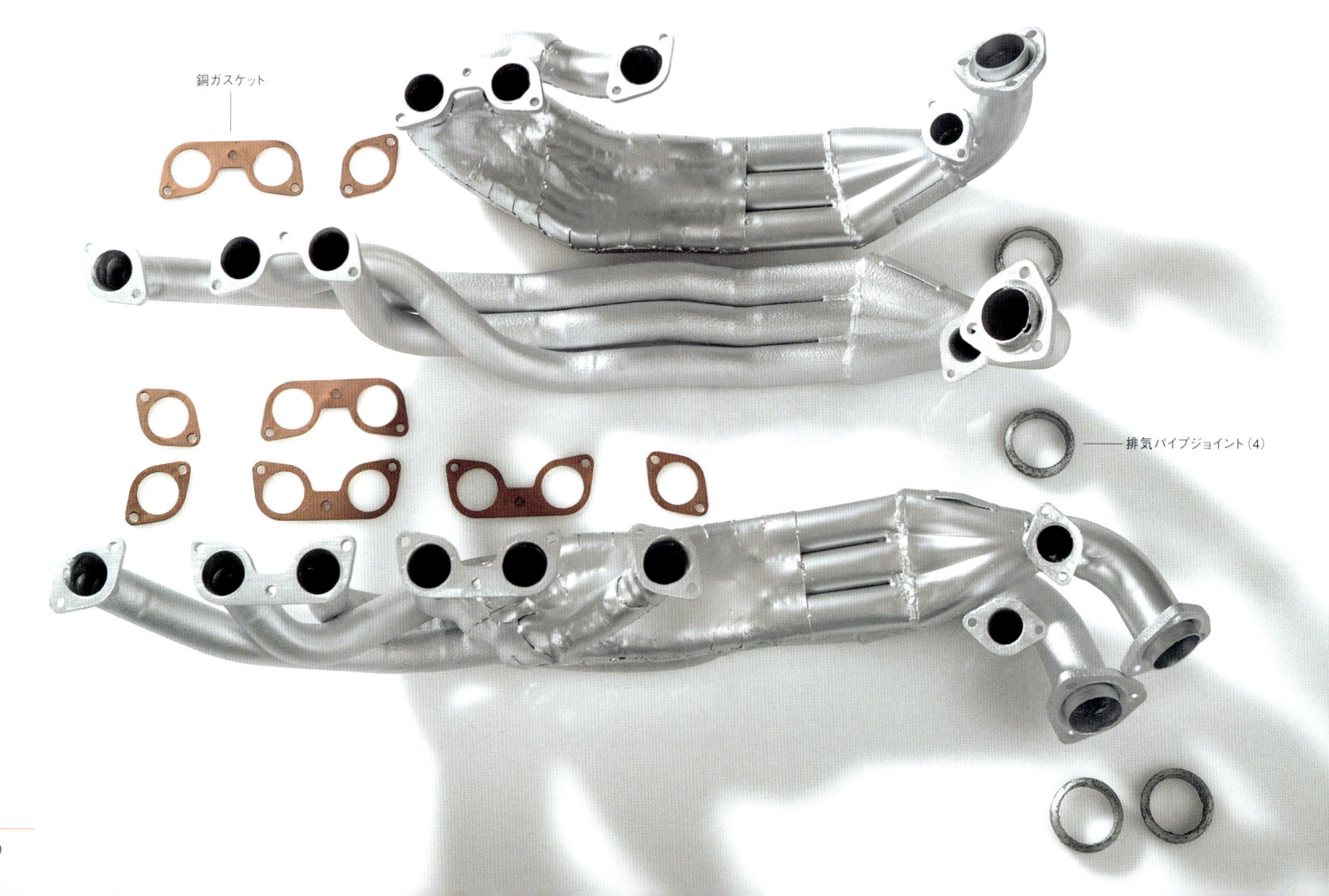

銅ガスケット

排気パイプジョイント（4）

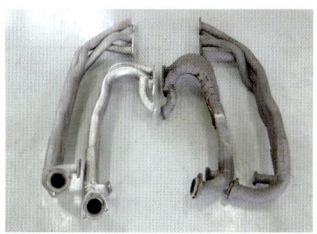

排気系はエンジン左右バンクで完全に独立しており、マニホールド→メインマフラー→サブマフラーの順で排気される。排気系の騒音は排気吐出音と排気系表面放射音の2つに大別される。前者はエンジンから出る脈動圧力波や高速度のガスがパイプ内を通過して出す高周波の気流音、後者はパイプやマフラーの壁を透過して出る透過音や排気脈動が排気系を加振させて出す振動放射音である。

これらを消音する方法は①吸音②共鳴③拡張④干渉だが、本機排気系が行なっているのは①と③である。

①はアスベスト系の吸音材をマフラーの中に入れている。この方法で減衰できる振動エネルギーは一般に200Hz以上の中高周波である。

③では拡張室の容積等で広い周波数帯の排気音を低減できる。本機の排気音は気流音などの高周波成分がよく抑えられている一方、400～500Hzの爆発音は素直に出している印象である（爆発音周波数＝回転数÷60×気筒数÷2）。本機排気系はマニホールドとメインマフラーを細いパイプで結んでいるが、マフラー内部には連通させず二重壁断熱構造マフラーの内層に開口しており、マフラーを余熱するための工夫と思われる。

The exhaust system is completely independent for the left and right banks of the engine. The order of gas exhaust is; manifold → main muffler → sub-muffler. The exhaust noise can be divided roughly into two categories; the exhaust output noise and the radiant surface noise from the exhaust system. The former is caused by pulsation pressure wave from the engine and the high frequency flow noise generated when the high-speed gas flows through the pipe. The latter is the transmission noise transmitted through the walls of pipe and muffler, as well as the vibration radiant noise generated when the exhaust system is vibrated by exhaust pulsation. There are four ways to eliminate those noises, namely; ①absorption, ②resonance, ③expansion and, ④intervention. In case of this engine's exhaust system, ① and ③ are employed. For ①, a kind of an asbestos-like noise absorbing material is installed in the muffler. In general, the vibration energy which could be dampened by this method is mid-high frequencies above 200Hz. For ③, exhaust noise over a wide range could be reduced by capacities, etc. of the expansion chamber. In this engine's exhaust system, high frequency exhaust noise such as air current noise are suppressed well, but I have the impression that the combustion noise of 400~500Hz is emitted as is. (Frequency of Combustion Noise = Engine Revolution ÷ 60 × Number of Cylinders ÷ 2). The exhaust system of this engine has a thin pipe connecting the manifold and main muffler. As this pipe does not extend into the muffler and the opening is at the inner layer of the double-walled heat resisting muffler, it is assumed to be a contrivance to pre-heating the muffler.

排気マニホールドはヒートシェラウドをいったん除去し、さびをブラストしてからシルバーのシリコン耐熱塗料で塗装した。この時代の本車の排気系はすべてシルバー塗装で、メインマフラー外壁のみツヤ消し黒塗装であった（生産185～190台目以降ツヤ有り黒塗装に変更、512BBはマニホールドを除き、りん酸塩皮膜処理）。

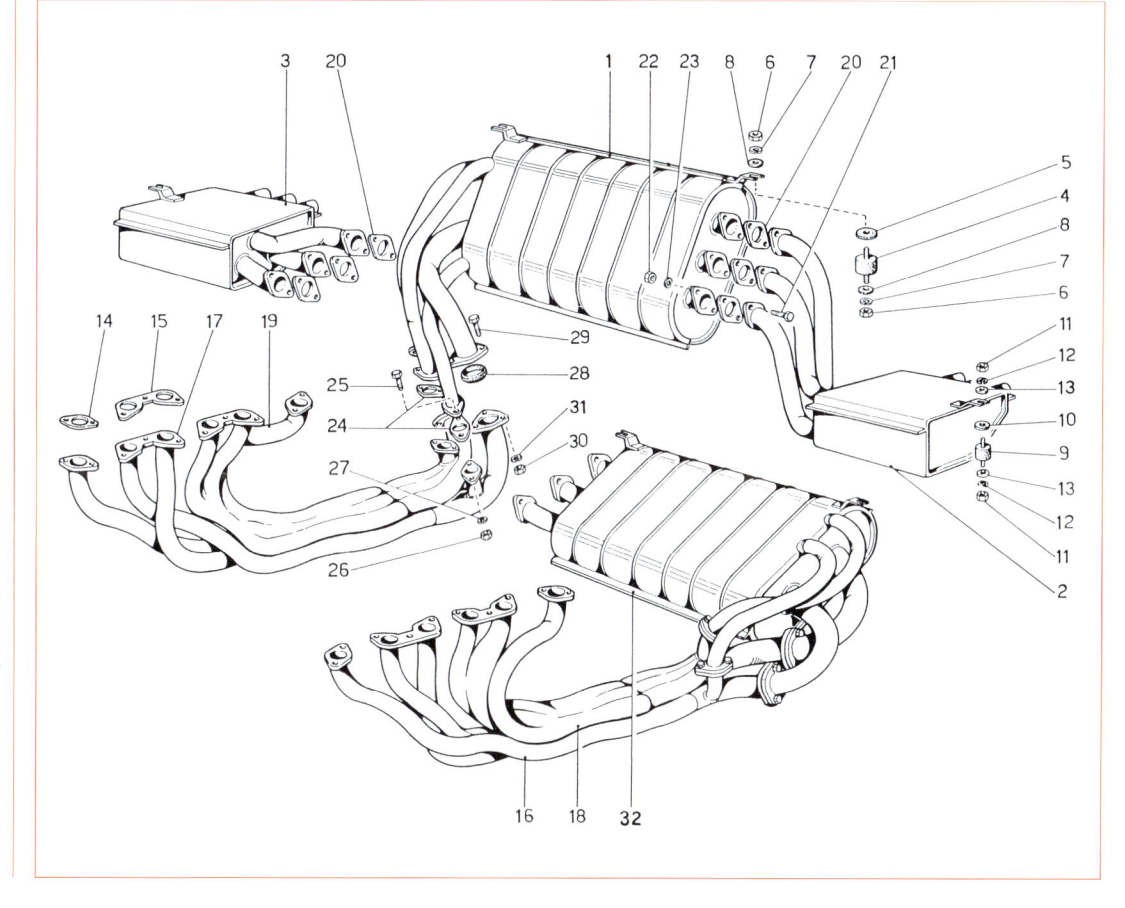

排気系の構成である。左バンク側は車体右側へ、右バンク側は車体左側へそれぞれクロスするように導かれる。左右排気系は連通していない。エキゾーストマニホールドから分岐している2本の細い管は、メインマフラーの余熱用である。メインマフラーでは主に拡張消音、サブマフラーは主に吸音による消音を行なっている。メインマフラーおよびサブマフラーはシャシにゴムマウントされる。フェラーリの排気系は伝統的に銅ナットを使用しており、分解時のねじ固着がほとんどない。

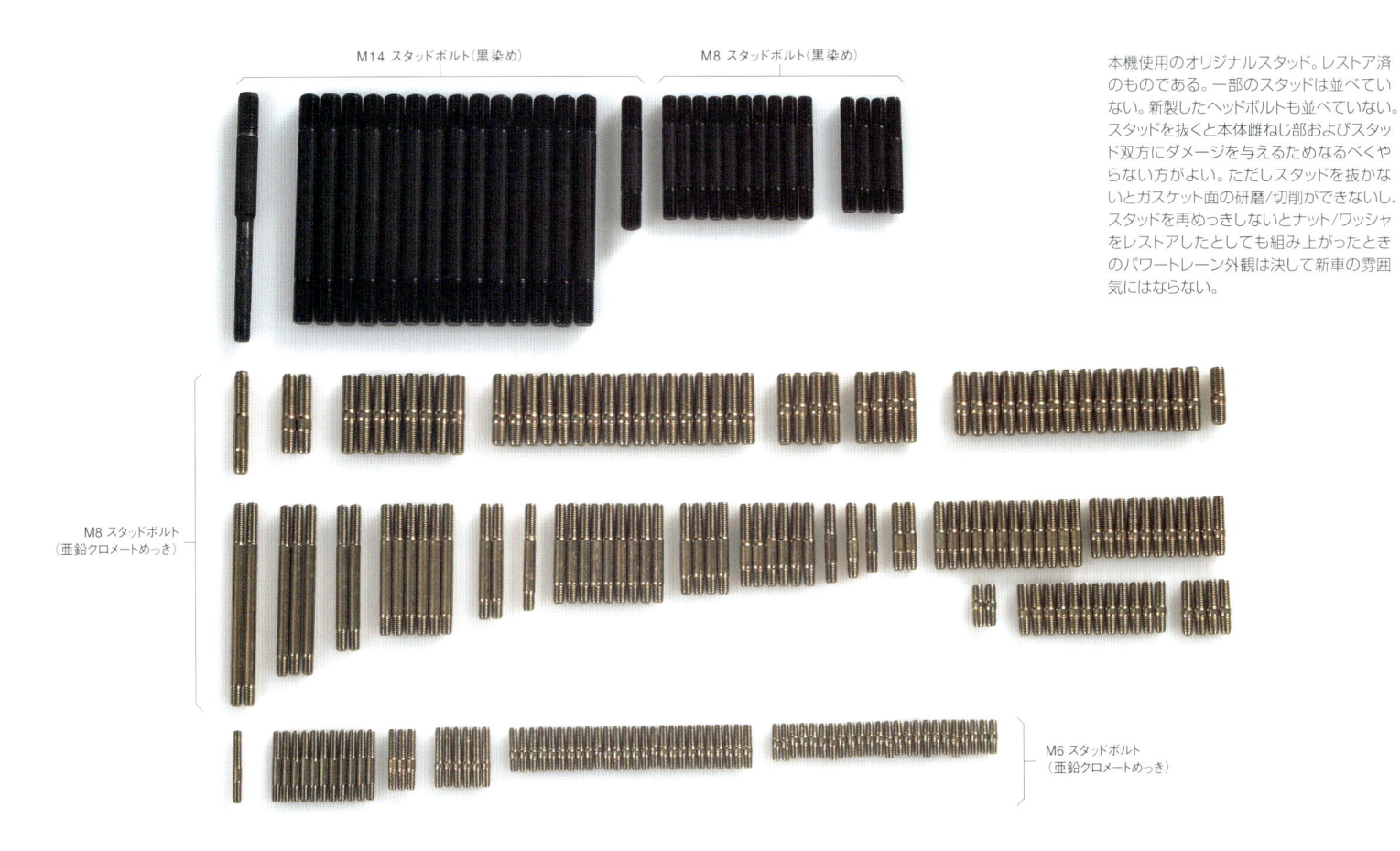

M14 スタッドボルト（黒染め）　　　M8 スタッドボルト（黒染め）

M8 スタッドボルト
（亜鉛クロメートめっき）

M6 スタッドボルト
（亜鉛クロメートめっき）

本機使用のオリジナルスタッド。レストア済のものである。一部のスタッドは並べていない。新製したヘッドボルトも並べていない。スタッドを抜くと本体雌ねじ部およびスタッド双方にダメージを与えるためなるべくやらない方がよい。ただしスタッドを抜かないとガスケット面の研磨/切削ができないし、スタッドを再めっきしないとナット/ワッシャをレストアしたとしても組み上がったときのパワートレーン外観は決して新車の雰囲気にはならない。

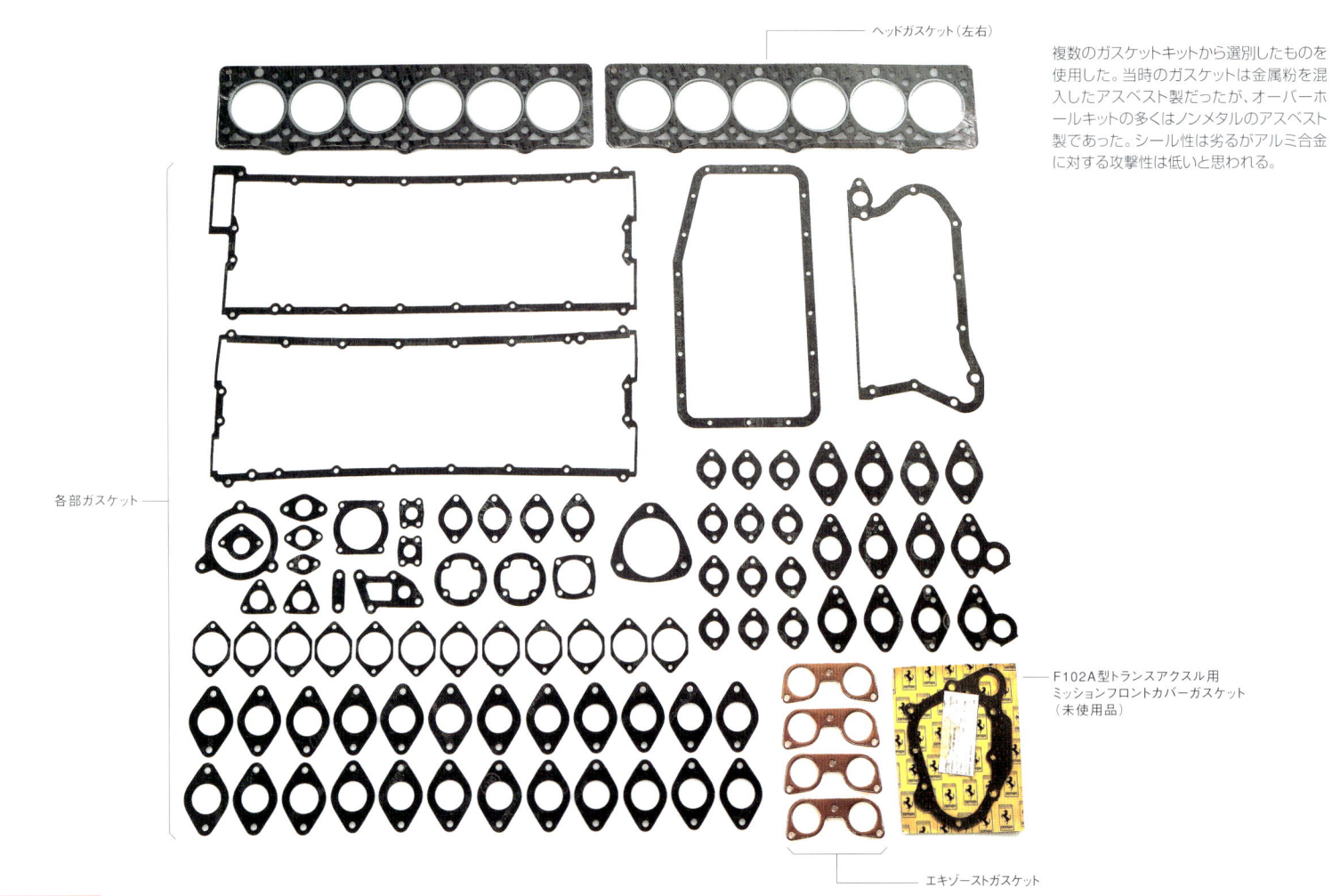

ヘッドガスケット（左右）

各部ガスケット

F102A型トランスアクスル用ミッションフロントカバーガスケット（未使用品）

エキゾーストガスケット

複数のガスケットキットから選別したものを使用した。当時のガスケットは金属粉を混入したアスベスト製だったが、オーバーホールキットの多くはノンメタルのアスベスト製であった。シール性は劣るがアルミ合金に対する攻撃性は低いと思われる。

小部品および消耗部品

Small Parts and Consumption Parts

本機にはM14、M10、M8、M6、M5の各種ボルトおよびスタッドボルトが使われている。エンジン内部のものは黒染め処理、末端が外部に露出するものには亜鉛クロメートめっきが施されている。

外部露出ナットはナイロンの滑り止め付ロックナットを平ワッシャと組み合わせるか、座付ナットをスプリングワッシャと組み合わせて使っている。いずれも亜鉛クロメートめっきが施される。新車装着品のナット/ワッシャはいずれもISO規格外のもので、現在市場に流通している一般製品とは形状が異なる。

すべてのスタッド、ナット、ワッシャを分解したところ、スタッドの100%、ナット/ワッシャのほぼ90%はオリジナルのものであった。いずれも洗浄点検後、ブラストし再表面処理を施した。黒染めにしても亜鉛クロメートめっきにしても当時と現在では浴や処理工程が異なり、現在のものは遥かに品質が良くなっている。亜鉛クロメートめっきは処理プロセスによって色調が変わるため、オリジナルを見本として提示し、なるべく近い色調になるよう留意してもらった。スプリングワッシャの多くは現在の市販品に交換したがナットの不良分/不足分についてはフェラーリのジャンクパーツの中から良品を選びレストアして補充使用した。ホースクランプ/ホース止め金具等も同様の手順でレストアした。

On this engine, various bolts sized M14, M10, M8, M6 and M5, as well as stud bolts are used. Those within the engine are treated with bluing, while those with the ends exposed externally are zinc chromate plated. On the nuts exposed externally, combination of lock nuts with a slip prevention made of nylon, or nuts with seats combined with a spring washer are used. In either case, zinc chromate plating is applied. All of the nuts and washers which were used when the vehicle was produced are not of ISO standards, and differ in shape from the products now on the market. After taking all studs, nuts and washers apart, it was revealed that 100% of the studs and almost 90% of nuts/washers were original items. All were washed, inspected, blasted and given a new surface treatment. Regardless whether bluing or zinc chromate plating, the present day electroplating bath and processes are totally different from the time of the car's production. The current methods are far superior in quality. As the color of zinc chromate plating varies with methods of processing, the original item was given as a color sample with a request to make the color tone as close as possible to the original. Most of the spring washers were exchanged with those on the market, but as for defective or missing nuts, those in good condition were picked from Ferrari's discarded parts, restored and used. Hose clamps and other tightening fixtures of the hoses were restored in a similar manner.

燃料ラインホースを固定するホースクランプ。交換されてしまっている場合が多いが、本機は幸運にもオリジナルがすべて残っていたのでレストアして再使用した。現在のステンレス・プレス成形ねじ山ホースクランプは消耗品だが、当時のフェラーリ工場組付け品は鋼製・機械加工ねじ山・亜鉛ユニクロめっき仕上げ(イギリス製)で非常に品質が高く、きちんと点検しレストアすれば十分再使用に耐える。

レストアを終え再分類したナット/ワッシャ類。ナットの90%は本車新車装着のオリジナル品、残りもジャンクパーツから選別レストアした同仕様のものである。

シリコンホース入りの配線、ハイテンションコード、ゴムホースなどをパワートレーンに固定するためのクランプ類もすべてオリジナルをレストアし再使用した。写真中央上のものはシフトリンケージブーツを止めるバンドクランプ(レストア済状態)。

ガスケット類、排気系のジョイント、オイルシール、Oリング、銅ワッシャなどの消耗品は365GT/4 BB用オーバーホールキットとして市販されているものを異なる経路から複数入手し比較検討したが、内容は一長一短だったため選別/選択して使用した。写真は選別したもので、ひとつのキットの内容を表わすものではない。

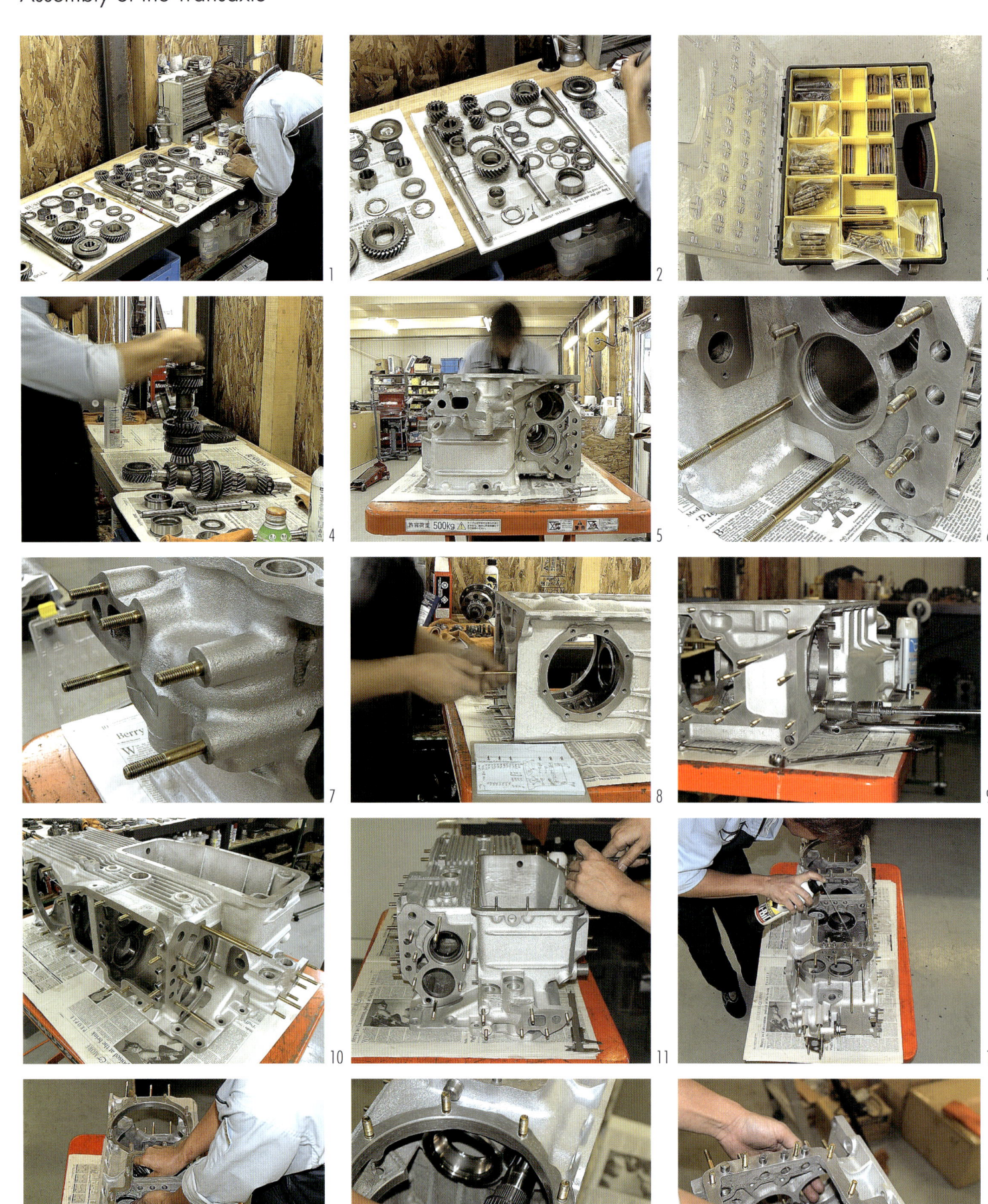

トランクアクスルの組み立て
Assembly of the Transaxle

121

エンジンの組み立て
Assembly of the Engine

123

Ferrari F102AB Specifications

ENGINE
Type F102A
Number of cylinders 12 at 180°Cylinder bore 81mm
Cylinder stroke 71mm
Total capacity 4391cc
Compression ratio 8.8 to 1
Maximum rpm 7000
Maximum horsepower(DIN) 344
Corresponding rpm 7200
Maximum torque 41.7kg
Corresponding rpm 3900

CRANKSHAFT
Number of main journals 7

PISTONS
Type Conical skirt section with 4 grooves

TIMING SYSTEM
Control via toothed belts

FUEL FEED
Electric pumps 2, CORONA
Carburetors 4, Triple-choke WEBER 401F3C

LUBRICATION
Pump Gear driven
Pressure regulating valve With adjustment spring
Lubrication pressure at 6000rpm, oil at 100° 6.5kg/cm^2
Engine oil capacity 12 ℓ Coolant capacity 22 ℓ

TRANSMISSION
Speed/Gears 5 forward, 1 reverse
Forward gears synchronizers Floating, on needle bearings
Lubrication Splash type
Transmission oil capacity 5.75 ℓ

CLUTCH
Type Dry, single plate
Clutch plate lining, outside diameter 241.3mm
Driven plate load 980kg
Pedal disengagement load 23-24kg

AIR CONDITIONER
System type Borletti
Compressor Aspera-Frigo HG 700 AP
System capacity 1.10kg

ALTERNATOR
Type MAGNETI-MARELLI GCA 113A-55A
Initial load velocity (alternator rpm) 1000
Maximum continuous velocity 12,000rpm

STARTER MOTOR
Type E 100-1.5/12 Var.1 F
Nominal power 1.5KW

IGNITION SYSTEM
Ignition distributor type MAGNETI-MARELLI S158A
Initial advance at engine 16°-18°at R1
Advance at 5000 engine rpm 36°-38°
Electronic system MAGNETI-MARELLI AEC 104 BK
Maximum operating frequency 800Hz
Ignition coil type MAGNETI-MARELLI BAE 202-B
Spark plugs type CHAMPION N63Y

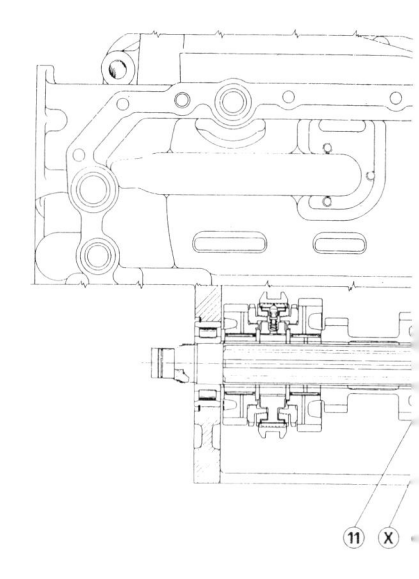

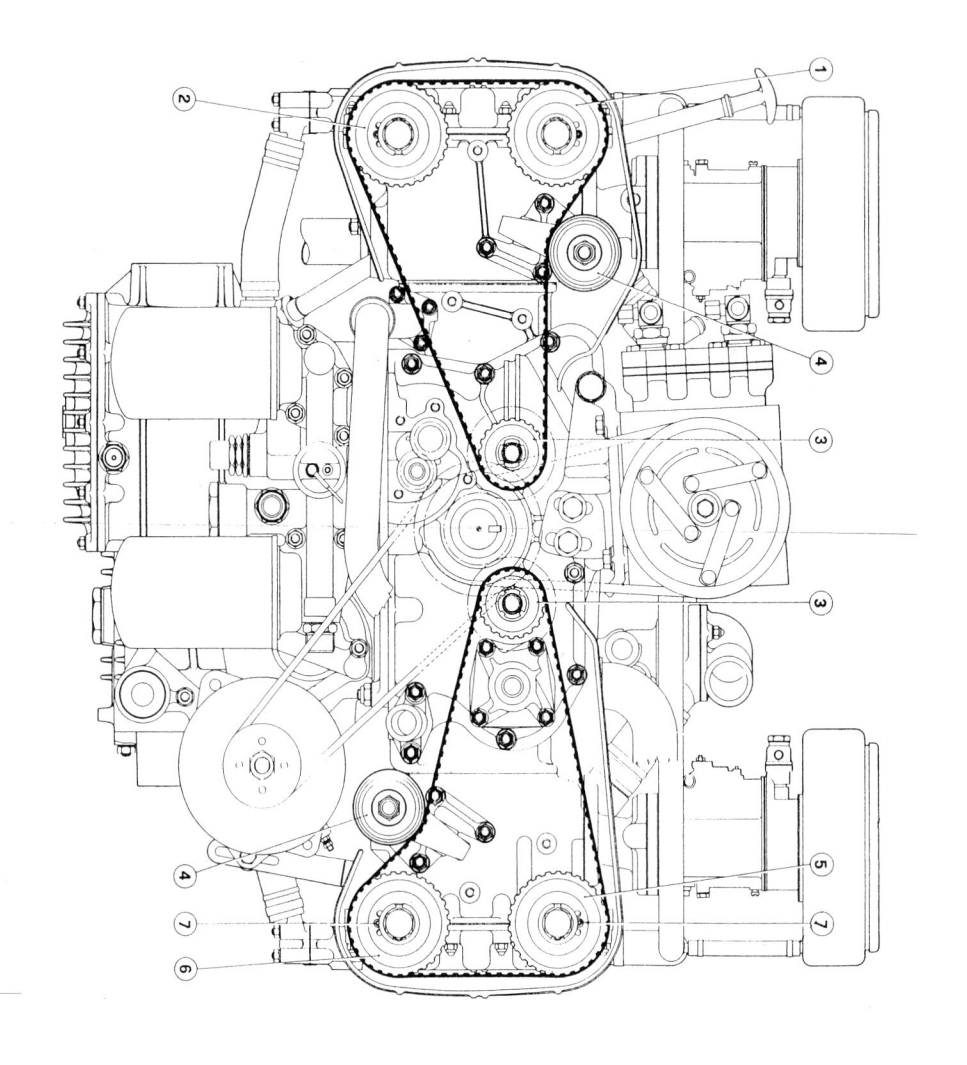

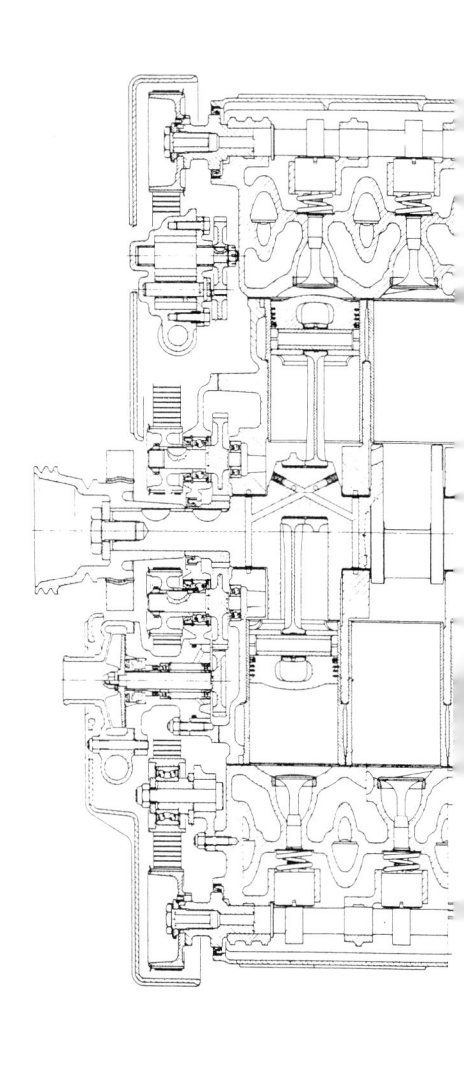

125

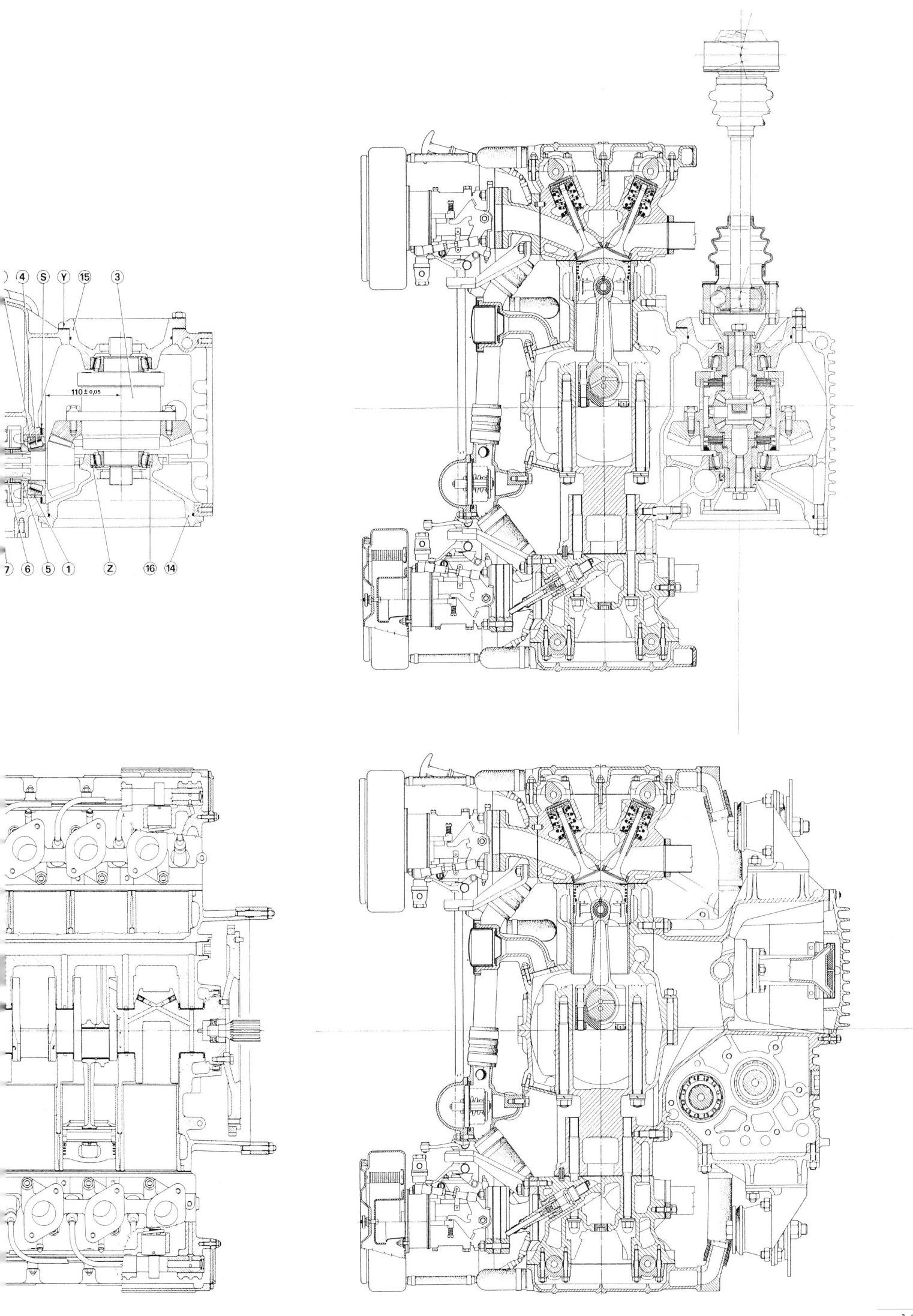

あとがき

◎ 小川 義文

　フェラーリの魅力がその超越した造型美にあるということは、だれもが認めるところである。しかし、フェラーリの本質的な魅力はエンジンにこそ宿っていると言っても過言ではない。フェラーリを評して「官能的なエンジン」の一語に尽きる、と私は思っている。空気を切り裂くような流線型の美しい車体も、その中に高性能なエンジンが収まっていなければ生まれなかっただろう。

　被写体となるのは、フェラーリの歴史に残る貴重な12気筒エンジンである。スタジオに運び込まれたクランクケース、クランクシャフト、ピストン、ヘッド、キャブレターなど、エンジンを構成しているそれぞれの部品の美しさに私の目が引き込まれていく。もはや部品としてではなく、美を表現するオブジェとして作られた作品のようだ。エンジンの中身がどうなっているのか、実はあまり知られていないフェラーリの核心部にレンズを向けることで、フェラーリの新たな美に出合うことができた。

　なぜ、フェラーリが高性能なのか、高級なのか。エンジンにも文化論が潜んでいる。異常とも言えるフェラーリの「エンジン」へのこだわりは、それがすなわちフェラーリの考える「高級性」の概念の重大な一要素を担っているのではないだろうか。

　この本には車体の写真が登場しない。365GT/4 BBの断片を見ることで、このクルマの疾走しているシーンを想像していただけたら、写真家としてこんなに嬉しいことはないと思う次第である。

◎ 福野礼一郎

　ソニーズフェラーリの古谷康一郎社長を始めソニーズのメカの皆さんの多大なる尽力、千数百点の品物をめっきしてくださった三和メッキ工業の皆さんの協力によってエンジンのレストアは完成した。ついに1枚のワッシャ、1本の割ピンも紛失せず納期をびしっと死守した三和メッキ工業さんの仕事っぷりにはまったく脱帽した。それに比べれば私はメモを取ったりブラストや塗装をしたり、座ってひとりやきもきしたりしていただけで、ほとんど何もしていない。

　すべてのパーツを梱包しスタジオに運び、床に並べて撮影するに際しては小川義文写真事務所の皆さんが総出で手伝ってくださった。とりわけ床に並べたパーツのひとつひとつを一辺のスキもなく一直線に整えてくださった小川事務所の佐藤俊幸さんの集中力は誠に驚嘆に値する。私といえば並べ方を考えてぼんやり眺めていただけだ。もとよりページ構成を考えたり図版や写真を選別したり原稿を書いたり写真説明を書いたりするのが当方の本業なのだからそれらもまったくどうというほどのことでもなかったのだが、それにしても拙文を一語一句正確に翻訳してくださった佐分利一さんの驚くべき忍耐力にはほとほと感服した。本書が国際版の体を成したのはまったく佐分利さんのおかげである。もちろんレストアから本作りに至るすべてにおいて(有)MPIの渡辺慎太郎社長は丁々発止の活躍で私を100％サポートしてくれた。

　というわけでレストアをするのも原稿を書くのも本を作るのもまったくのところそれぞれとっても簡単だったのだが、それら三つを同時にすべてやりとげるには文字通り死力を尽くす必要があったというのも事実である。だから私のことを馬鹿にしたり笑ったりしたい方はどうかレストアだけでなく原稿書きだけでなく本作りだけでもなく、レストアと原稿書きと本作り、三つともやってからにしていただきたいと思う。

Yoshifumi OGAWA
Born 1955 in Tokyo. Professional photographer.Recognized authority in automotive-related photography. Received many awards including theJapan Magazine Advertising Award. Active in commercial photos and magazine media fields.

Ray Ichiro FUKUNO
Born in Tokyo as the eldest son of an American of Japanese descent. Twenty-five years of professional experience as writer/editor of automotive magazines. The topmost commentator in Japan of automotive design and production technologies. In private life, an ardent enthusiast of European sports cars and high-performance cars. The Ferrari 365GT/4 BB described in this book is his seventh Ferrari after two 308s, 328, Testarossa, Daytona and 360 Spider. Published more than 20 literatures, but this is the first book with English text. Present domicile is in Tokyo.

Hajime SABURI
Born in New York, living in Tokyo. Worked 40 years in sales promotion, public relations and communications fields with the Japanese importer of the prestigious German motorcars produced by the manufacturer who invented the automobiles. Translated numerous books on cars, motor sports, etc.